Vauxhall & VX 4/90 FD series Owners Workshop Manual

by J H Haynes

Associate Member of the Guild of Motoring Writers

and D H Stead

Models covered:
Victor Saloon/Estate   1599 cc
Victor Saloon/Estate   1975 cc
VX 4/90 Saloon   1975 cc

ISBN 0 900550 53 8

© J H Haynes and Company Limited 1972   Z640/053

All rights reserved. No part of this book may be reproduced or transmitted in any form or by an means, electronic or mechanical, including photocopying, recording or by any information storage or retrieval system, without permission in writing from the copyright holder.

Printed in England (053 - 10A2)

HAYNES PUBLISHING GROUP
SPARKFORD YEOVIL SOMERSET ENGLAND
distributed in the USA by
HAYNES PUBLICATIONS INC
861 LAWRENCE DRIVE
NEWBURY PARK
CALIFORNIA, 91320
USA

Acknowledgements

Thanks are due to Vauxhall Motors Limited for their assistance in the supply of technical specifications and technical illustrations and to Autocar for the use of the cutaway drawing on the cover. Castrol Limited supplied the lubrication details and Champion Spark Plug Company, the spark plug photographs; our thanks goes to them.

The kind help of David Suiter must be specially acknowledged.

Invaluable assistance was given by Bill Kinchin in sorting out the text, and by Brian Horsfallin assisting with the photographs. Although every care has been taken to ensure the correctness of data used, it must be borne in mind that alterations and design changes can occur within the production run of a model without specific reclassification. No liability can be accepted for damage, loss or injury caused by errors in or omissions from the information given.

Photographic captions and cross references

The book is divided into twelve chapters. Each chapter is divided into numbered sections which are headed in **bold type** between horizontal lines. Each section consists of serially numbered paragraphs.

There are two types of illustration: (1) Figures which are numbered according to Chapter and sequence of occurrence in that Chapter and having an individual caption to each figure. (2) Photographs which have a reference number in the bottom left hand corner. All photographs apply to the chapter in which they occur so that the reference figures pinpoint the pertinent section and paragraph numbers.

Procedures, once described in the text, are not normally repeated. If it is necessary to refer to another chapter the reference will be given in chapter number and section number thus: Chapter 1/6.

If it is considered necessary to refer to a particular paragraph in another chapter the reference is eg 'Chapter 1/6:5'. Cross references given without use of the word 'Chapter' apply to sections and/or paragraphs in the same chapter, eg 'see Section 8' means also 'in this chapter'.

When the left or right hand side of a car is mentioned it is as if one was looking in the forward direction of travel.

VICTOR SUPER SALOON

VICTOR 2000 SL ESTATE CAR

Contents

Introduction

The Vauxhall Victor FD was a complete departure from the earlier range of Victor saloons and estates both in the engine and bodywork. The engine suddenly became more sophisticated offering an overhead camshaft configuration, and the bodywork took after the Viva HB being enlarged and made plump.

Although embodying some surprising modifications such as the completely new engine it is still a conventional car and therefore particularly suitable for home maintenance, almost in spite of itself.

This Owners Workshop Manual is intended for the owner of such a Victor who, having acquired his car either new or secondhand does not wish to spend a fortune keeping it in safe and economical condition. However, it does try to balance the time spent in repairing a part and the ease of its straight replacement together with the possible increase in cost. Such is the trend not to make component parts available individually but to supply complete replacement or exchange units, that it has not always been possible to actually dismantle and repair some parts. However, where it has been thought potentially economic to repair, it has been described in this manual. Many step by step dismantling and assembly sequences, often supported by photographic strip, have been given to this end. This range of cars has, however, been covered in total.

Safety is of paramount concern to the responsible owner who appreciates the hazards of increased traffic volume and motorway speeds. All the checks for safety are fully covered in this manual and the conscientious do-it-yourself maintenance man (or woman) will not regard these checks just as something to attend to only when MOT tests are due.

A totally neglected three year old vehicle is far more lethal than one ten times it age which is properly looked after.

For the more ambitious owner, this manual gives step by step details of all the other repairs and overhauls which we consider are within the capabilities of a practically minded person who is in possession of a reasonably comprehensive set of tools. With regard to the latter, this is one area where only good quality equipment will do. Borrowing of tools is discouraged except for certain special items which may only be used once in a blue moon. Certainly we would say that you should not be annoyed if someone should refuse to lend them. Appreciate how much they cost if lost or damaged - apart from the fact that keen owners regard their tools as particularly personal belongings.

Much of the work involved in looking after a car and carrying out repairs depends on accurate diagnosis in the first place. Where possible therefore, a methodical and progressive way of diagnosis is presented. The time that can be wasted in hopping from one possible source of trouble to another, suggested at random quite often by self-styled 'experts' must have been experienced by many people. It is best to say at the start, therefore, 'This could be one of several things - let's get the book out'.

Ordering spare parts

Buy genuine Vauxhall spares from a Vauxhall dealer direct or through a local garage. If you go to an authorised dealer the correctly fitting genuine parts can usually be supplied from stock which, of course, is a greatly added convenience.

Always have details of the car's serial number and engine number available when obtaining parts. If you can also take along the part to be renewed it is helpful. Modifications are continuously being made and many are not publicised. A storeman in a parts department is quite justified in saying that he cannot guarantee the correctness of a part unless the relevant numbers are available.

The position of the identification plates giving the vehicle numbers has changed since the model was first introduced.

First, the vehicle number plate was fixed to the left hand front door pillar. Then it moved to the left front wheel arch panel under the bonnet.

Latterly, the vehicle number appears on a plate on the top of the instrument panel at the left hand end. It can be read through the windscreen. Also on some cars (not necessarily all) a service parts identification plate is fitted in addition at the wheel arch panel location. This has six blocks of code numbers and letters referring, respectively, to the model, Destination, Job No, Paint Code, Trim Code and options.

Engine numbers are stamped on a machined pad at the rear of the block face next to the clutch bellhousings. In addition, there is a code letter stamped on the cylinder block at the front next to the distribution which tells you whether it is high or low compression (H or L).

On early engines an additional letter at the same place indicated the engine capacity 'S' being the 1599 cc and 'B' the 1975 cc.

Later on, these letters were cast into the block itself on the right hand side - the letter 'B' being replaced by 'L'.

The vehicle number is explained as follows:

eg 943691V325890

9 - Vauxhall
4 - Victor series
3 - 4 cylinder de luxe
69 - 4 door saloon (35 = 4 door estate)
1 - Model year (1971 - October 1970–September 1971)
V - Luton ('E' - Ellesmere Port, 'T' - Dunstable)
325890 - Serial number of chassis

The engine numbers (in the four cylinder OHC range) begin at 3000,001.

C. Engine number

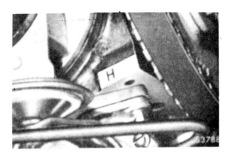

D. Engine compression ratio mark

E. Engine capacity mark (later models)

A. Vehicle number plate behind windscreeen (later models)

B. Service parts identification plate on wheel arch (later models)

Routine maintenance

The manufacturers base their own servicing operations on a time rather than mileage factor. They take 12000 miles per annum as an average to base this service plan. This system is very satisfactory as it enables both owner and service station to plan servicing in advance on a regular basis and confirm that deterioration of a vehicle's performance and safety is not necessarily connected with the number of miles covered. Where mileage is consistently and significantly in excess of the average the time intervals between services may be reduced in proportion.

By implication, the servicing cycle recommended by the manufacturers gives a 6000 mile interval between engine oil changes. Many owners prefer to change the oil more frequently particularly where much of the driving is in short runs or stop/start situations, where the engine either does not get many opportunities to warm up completely or operates constantly in heavy traffic. These conditions take far more out of an engine than steady runs along motorways in top gear.

The maintenance information given is not detailed in this section as the full information is given in the appropriate chapters of the book.

Weekly

COOLANT LEVEL IN RADIATOR
   1 inch (25 mm) below bottom edge of filler neck

ENGINE OIL LEVEL – DIPSTICK
   Level must be above 'Add oil' mark. Quantity required from 'Add oil' to 'Full' is 2.85 pints (1.62 litres).
BATTERY ELECTROLYTE LEVEL
   Should just cover the plate separators. Wipe away moisture or dirt from battery case exterior

TYRE PRESSURES
   Examine also tread depth and for signs of other damage

Safety check Service 'S'

BRAKES
   Master cylinder fluid level
   Hydraulic pipes and hoses inspection
   Wheel cylinder inspection
   Brake shoes - adjustment
   Handbrake lever setting

STEERING
   Tyre condition
   Front wheel hub bearings adjustment
   Track rods and ball joints - damage and/or wear

SUSPENSION
   Suspension arm upper and lower ball joints - wear
   Springs - level and unbroken

AUTOMATIC TRANSMISSION
   Fluid level correct

GENERAL
   Lights in order
   Exhaust system intact
   Windscreen wiper blades serviceable
   Seat belts and anchorage points in order

Service 'A'

BRAKES
   Examine linings and pads for wear. Renew if necessary and adjust

CLUTCH AND TRANSMISSION
   Check and adjust clutch lever free play

Oil level dipstick

Fan belt tension check

Gearbox oil level - check and top up
Rear axle oil level - check and top up

ENGINE
Renew oil and oil filter cartridge
Carburettor damper dashpot(s) (Stromberg carburettors only) -
check oil level and top up
Fuel pump - clean filter
Spark plugs - remove, clean and reset
Distributor contact points - adjust gap. Clean or renew if necessary
Valve clearances - check and adjust
Fan belt - check and adjust tension
Engine idling speed - adjust carburettor if necessary

Service 'B'

Carry out Service 'A' and add the following:

BRAKES
Disc brake servo air filter - renew

SUSPENSION
Grease upper and lower arm ball joints

AUTOMATIC TRANSMISSION
Clean all ventilation holes and slots around the torque converter
cover. Scrape all dirt accumulations from surrounding areas.

ENGINE
Spark plugs - renew
Carburettor air cleaner - renew paper element
Distributor - lubricate

Service 'C'

Carry out Service 'B' and add the following:

STEERING
Remove front wheel bearings, clean and repack with grease

BRAKES
Renew hydraulic fluid and cylinder seals

AUTOMATIC TRANSMISSION
Renew fluid
Renew oil pump suction screen
Adjust low band servo

Oil filter cartridge renewal

Front suspension arm ball joint grease nipples

Front brake shoe adjuster screws

Clutch pedal free play adjustment

RECOMMENDED LUBRICANTS

COMPONENT	TYPE OF LUBRICANT OR FLUID	CORRECT CASTROL PRODUCTS
ENGINE	Multi-grade engine oil 20W/50	Castrol GTX
GEARBOX/FINAL DRIVE	Gear oil SAE 90EP	Castrol Hypoy
FRONT WHEEL BEARINGS	Medium Grade multi-purpose grease...	Castrol LM Grease
FRONT SUSPENSION BALL JOINTS	Medium Grade Molybdenum Grease...	Castrol M53 Grease
DISTRIBUTOR AND GENERATOR BEARINGS	Engine or light oil	Castrol GTX or 'Everyman'
CARBURETTOR DASHPOT (STROMBERG)	Engine or light oil	Castrol GTX or 'Everyman'
UPPER CYLINDER LUBRICANT	Refined mineral oil	Castrollo
BRAKE AND CLUTCH MASTER CYLINDERS	Hydraulic fluid	Castrol/Girling Brake Fluid
ANTIFREEZE...	GLYCOL ANTIFREEZE	Castrol Antifreeze
CONTACT BREAKER CAM	Petroleum jelly (Vaseline)	
BATTERY TERMINALS	Petroleum jelly (Vaseline)	

Additionally Castrol GTX can be used to lubricate locks, hinges, cable linkages and latch mechanisms.

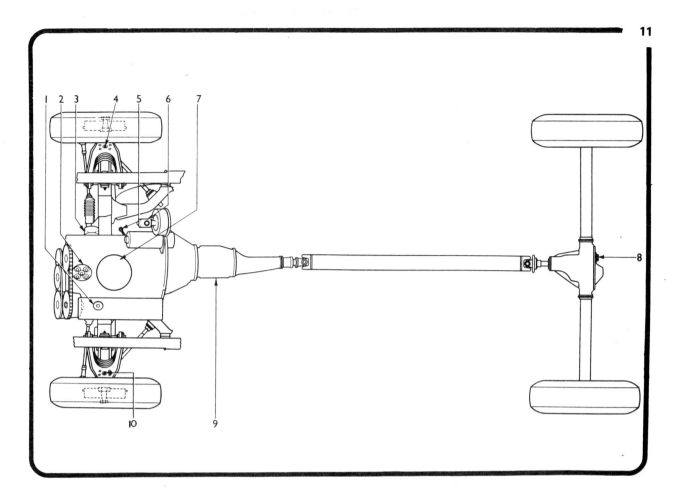

Engine Oil
Weekly
Check the oil level using the dipstick (5) and if necessary add sufficient Castrol GTX through the filler orifice (1) to bring the level up to the 'FULL' mark. 2.85 pints (1.62 litres) will raise the level from the 'ADD oil' to 'FULL' marks.
Service 'A'
When warm, undo the sump drain plug and drain the old oil. Renew the oil filter element (3). Replace the drain plug and refill with fresh Castrol GTX. Under abnormal conditions (city traffic, excess mileage, dusty or extreme temperature conditions) change the oil more frequently.
Capacity - dry:– 8.5 pints/4.83 litres
        - refill incl. filter:– 8 pints/4.55 litres

Gearbox Oil
Service 'A'
Remove the filler plug (9) and top up if necessary to the level of the plug orifice with Castrol Hypoy 90. Examine for any signs of leaks.
Capacity - 3 speed:– 2.1 pints/1.19 litres
        - 4 speed:– 2.4 pints/1.36 litres
      with overdrive:– 3.0 pints/1.17 litres

Automatic Transmission
Check the fluid level on the dipstick whilst the engine is running at normal working temperature. Top up as necessary with Castrol TQ 'Dexron' (R).
Service 'C' – Drain and refill.
Capacity refill:– 4.5 pints/2.56 litres

Rear Axle Oil
Service 'A'
Remove filler plug (8) and top up if necessary to the level of the plug orifice with Castrol Hypoy 90. Examine the casing for any signs of leakage.

Air Filter
Service 'B'
Renew paper element (7).

Front Suspension Arm Ball Joints
Service 'B'
Grease two nipples each side, top and bottom (4 and 10) with Castrol MS3 Grease.

Hydraulic Brake Master Cylinder Reservoir
Service 'S'
Clean cap and surrounding area (6) and after removing cap top up if necessary to ¼ inch (6 mm) below the lower edge of the filler neck. Use Castrol Girling Brake and Clutch Fluid Crimson.

Distributor
Service 'B'
Remove distributor cap and remove the two screws securing the rotor. Put a few drops of Castrol 'Everyman' or GTX through the hole marked oil and a drop on each of the two balance weight pivots. A smear of petroleum jelly (vaseline) should be put on the cam surfaces. Do not over lubricate.

Chapter 1 Engine

Contents

Specifications

Engine - General

Type...	4 cylinder in line inclined OHC	
	1599 cc (97.5 cu in)	1975 cc (120.5 cu in)
Bore	85.73 mm (3.375 ins)	95.25 mm (3.750 ins)
Stroke	69.24 mm (2.726 ins)	
Compression ratio - HC (Standard)	8.5:1	
- LC	7.3:1	
Compression pressure - HC	125 lbs/in^2	
LC	110 lbs/in^2	
Torque (gross)	96 lb ft at 2700 rpm	122 lb ft at 3300 rpm
bhp (gross)	80 bhp at 5500 rpm	108 bhp at 6000 rpm
Firing order..	1 3 4 2	
Oil pressure - hot	45–55 lbs in^2 at 3000 rpm	

Camshaft

Journal diameter - No 1 (front)	2.3735–2.3740 ins
No 2	2.3575–2.3580 ins
No 3	2.3425–2.3430 ins
No 4	2.3265–2.3270 ins
No 5	2.0605–2.0610 ins
Clearance in housing	.001–.0025 ins
End float	.001–.007 ins
Thrust washer thickness	.157–.160 ins

Auxiliary shaft

Journal diameter - front	1.749–1.750 ins
rear	1.686–1.687 ins
Clearance in bearings...	.001–.003 ins
Thrust washer thickness	.116–.118 ins
End float	.002–.008 ins

Crankshaft

Crank pin - diameter	1.9975—1.9985 ins
- bearing clearance	.001—.0032 ins
- fillet radius	.125 ins
- crank throw	1.30—1.365 ins
Main journals - diameter 1—4	2.4995—2.5005 ins
5 (rear)	2.500—2.5005 ins
bearing clearance 1—4	.0008—.0028 ins
5	.0008—.0025 ins
fillet radius	.125 ins
End float	.002—.010 ins
Maximum run-out	.0015 ins
Main bearing housing bores	2.6655—2.6660
Rear main journal (No 5) regrind length:	
.010 under	1.346—1.350 ins
.020 under	1.351—1.355 ins
.040 under	1.356—1.360 ins
Rear main bearing (No 5) width	
Standard	1.337—1.339 ins
.010 under	1.342—1.344 ins
.020 under	1.343—1.349 ins
.040 under	1.352—1.354 ins

Cylinder head and valves

Valve seating angle	45°
Valve seat width - inlet	.035—.060 ins
- exhaust	.055—.085 ins
Valve stem diameter - standard inlet	.341—.3417 ins
- standard exhaust	.3403—.3410 ins
Valve stem clearance in head - inlet	.0010—.0027 ins
- exhaust	.0017—.0034 ins
Valve seat angle	44°
Oversize valve stems available	.003, .006 and .012, .024
Valve head thickness - inlet	.025 in minimum
- exhaust	.035 in minimum
Maximum protrusion of valve stem above guide	1.13 ins
Valve springs free length - outer	1.64 ins
- inner	1.40 ins
Spring load - outer at 1.00 ins	139 lbs
- inner at .83 ins	72 lbs
Tappets - diameter	1.4365—1.437 ins
- clearance in housing	.001—.0015 ins
Valve clearances - hot - inlet	.007—.010 ins
exhaust (early) *	.010—.013 ins
exhaust (late)	.015—.018 ins

* Identified by a groove in the front end of the shaft between the block and the pulley

Pistons, piston rings and connecting rods

Piston clearance in bore 1599 cc engines	.0015 - .0017 ins
1975 cc engines	.00125—.00175 ins
Piston ring gaps in bore - top 1599 cc	.010 - .015 ins
- top 1975	.011—.016 ins
- centre	.010—.020 ins
Piston ring thickness - top and centre	.077—.078 ins
Piston ring in groove clearance - top	.0015—.0035 ins
- centre	.001—.003 ins
Connecting rod big end bearing housing bore	2.1460—2.1468 ins
Connecting rod big end bearing end float	.008—.014 ins
Gudgeon pins	semi-floating - interference fit in connecting rod eye

Torque Wrench Settings

	lb ft
Connecting rod cap bolts	47*
Main bearing cap bolts	83*
Flywheel bolts	48
Cylinder head bolts	83
Camshaft housing bolts	15

* Oiled threads - all others clean and dry

1 General description

The Series FD Victor was introduced in 1968 as a succession to the well proven line of FB, FC models.

A new engine was introduced with the new model, namely a 4 cylinder overhead camshaft design with an inclined cylinder block, externally mounted oil pump and the new feature for a British car, of a belt driven camshaft.

Overhead camshafts are normally associated with high performance sporting engines permitting, as they do, individual porting and large valves without a complex valve opening mechanism.

The toothed drive belt - which requires neither adjustment nor renewal in normal service is doubtless one of the features enabling this type of engine layout to be used in a family saloon of medium price. An auxiliary shaft, also driven by the timing belt from the crankshaft drives the distributor, fuel pump and oil pump. A feature here is the ability to remove the oil pump without taking the sump off.

The crankshaft runs in five main bearings of generous surface area and end float is controlled by a flanged shell in one of them.

Pistons are semi-floating on the gudgeon pins, the gudgeon pins being an interference fit in the small ends of the connecting rods.

The cast iron cylinder head has cross flow porting and the only unusual feature is an oil passage through it for lubricating oil to reach the camshaft. The valves are operated by inverted brackets each one of which is fitted with an adjustment screw to set valve clearances. Each screw has a wedge shaped flat machined in it which bears on the valve stem end. One rotation of the screw alters the clearance .003 inch, this being the minimum adjustment possible.

The camshaft and tappets both run in an alloy housing bolted above the cylinder head.

The auxiliary shaft is mounted in the block. It runs in two plain bearings. This shaft drives the distributor shaft via a skew gear and a slot in the end of the distributor shaft engages a torque on the oil pump shaft below it to drive that. The auxiliary shaft also incorporates an eccentric to drive the operating lever of the fuel pump. The shaft is held in position by the lip type oil seal, thrust from the distributor drive gear tending to keep it in the block. End float is controlled by a thrust washer.

The engine is mounted on two flexible supports - later versions are the shear type - one at each side at the front and the rear is held by the transmission unit support crossmember. Engine lubrication is pressurised. A mechanical pump draws oil from the sump and forces it through a full flow filter and then via an oil gallery to the main crankshaft bearings. Drillings in the crankshaft convey oil to the connecting rod bearings and thence up the connecting rod to a small orifice where it jets onto the cylinder wall. From the same gallery oil is also fed to the auxiliary shaft bearings and again up through the cylinder head to the camshaft housing. The camshaft housing has another gallery in it and opposite each tappet a small hole enables a spray of pressurised oil to lubricate the tappets and cams. The two end camshaft bearings are lubricated by oilways from this gallery. The others are lubricated by the spray jets. Oil that leaves the pressurised system at the bearings and oil jet outlets drains back to the sump under gravity.

2 Major operations possible with the engine installed

The following work may be carried out with the engine in the car (in addition to ancillaries):
1 Removal and replacement of camshaft and housing
2 Removal and replacement of the cylinder head
3 Removal and replacement of the front mountings
4 Removal of sump (after removing front suspension crossmember assembly)
5 Removal of flywheel (not recommended without availability of raised ramps or a pit).
6 Removal of crankshaft front oil seal.

3 Major operations requiring engine removal

1 Crankshaft and bearings removal
2 Pistons and connecting rods removal

4 Engine removal

1 The engine should only be lifted out after the gearbox has been taken off the bellhousing as described in Chapter 6.
2 With few exceptions it is simplest to lift out the engine with all the ancillaries (dynamo, distributor, carburettor) still attached.
3 The average do-it-yourself owner should be able to remove the engine fairly easily in about 3½ hours. It is essential to have a good hoist, and two strong axle stands if an inspection pit is not available. Engine removal will be much easier if you have someone to help you. Before beginning work it is worthwhile to get all the accumulated dirt cleaned off the engine unit at a service station which is equipped with steam or high pressure air and water cleaning equipment. It helps to make the job quicker, easier and, of course, much cleaner.
4 Remove the windscreen washer pipe from the bonnet jet connection and then mark the position of the upper hinge brackets, undo the bolts and lift the bonnet off. Help will be needed (photo).
5 Disconnect and remove the battery.
6 Remove the gearbox as described in Chapter 6 and then disconnect the clutch cable (Chapter 5).
7 Undo the radiator drain tap and drain the cooling system. Do this into containers to prevent mess and keep the coolant for re-use if it contains antifreeze.
8 Drain off the engine oil.
9 Disconnect the two heater hoses, one from the engine and the other from the junction with the lower radiator hose.
10 Disconnect the top and bottom radiator hoses from the engine, undo the two screws at each side of the radiator holding it to the body panel and lift it out complete with hoses. (Detail Chapter 2).
11 Disconnect the choke and throttle cables from the carburettor assembly. (Detail Chapter 3).
12 Disconnect the lead from the end of the starter motor.
13 Pull off the connections for the wires to the coil, oil pressure sender unit, and water temperature sender unit. These four leads are grouped together on the right hand side of the engine.
14 Pull off the connections to the generator at the front left of the engine.
15 Disconnect the earth strap which runs from the front right of the body frame (photo).
16 Pull off the four spark plug leads and the HT lead from the centre of the coil. Unclip the leads from the cam box cover, undo the distributor cap clips and remove the cap and leads together.
17 Undo the fuel pipe union at the carburettor and also remove the engine mounting bracket bolt that secures the clip holding the pipe to the side of the engine.
18 Above the starter motor mounting will be seen a blanked off hole in the casting. Use one of the bolts holding the blanking plate to fix a suitable lifting bracket.

Certain other makes of car have suitable brackets installed and it should be possible to get hold of one. This lifting bracket is important as there is nowhere else suitable to fix a sling if the engine is to be lifted easily at a reasonable angle. It is worthwhile making a bracket if necessary or fixing a suitable eye bolt in the hole (photo).
19 Sling the engine from this bracket to the front end of the exhaust manifold diagonally opposite. Do not worry about the heater ducting that overhangs the rear of the engine. This does not have to be moved (photo).
20 Depending on the type of mountings fitted remove the central vertical bolt and nut (early types) at each side or undo the nut securing the shear type (later) mounting to the front suspension crossmember. (Details in Section 7) (photo).

On early types the left hand mounting bolt head is somewhat obscured by the exhaust manifold. An open ended spanner can be

4.4 Removing the bonnet

4.15 Disconnecting the earth cable from the engine block

4.18 Fitting a lifting bracket to the right rear of the block

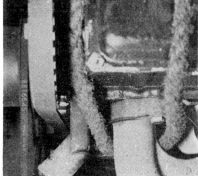
4.19 Engine slung round exhaust manifold at front

4.20 Removing the engine mounting bolt (RH)

4.21 Lifting the engine out

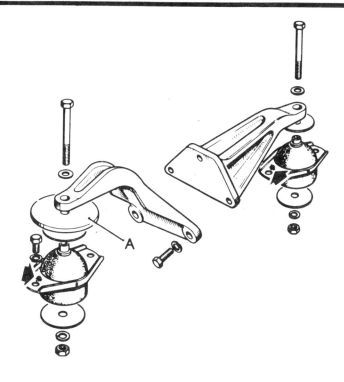
Fig.1.1. Engine mountings — early type
A. Heat shield above left, mounting arrows point to identifying colour spots for the mountings — left Yellow — right Blue

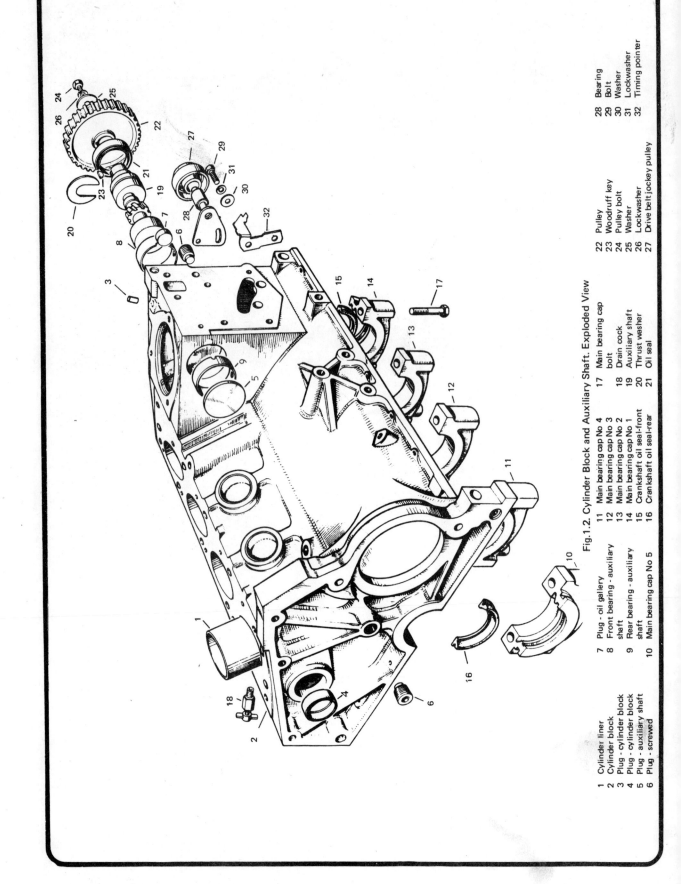

Fig.1.2. Cylinder Block and Auxiliary Shaft. Exploded View

1 Cylinder liner
2 Cylinder block
3 Plug - cylinder block
4 Plug - cylinder block
5 Plug - auxiliary shaft
6 Plug - screwed

7 Plug - oil gallery
8 Front bearing - auxiliary shaft
9 Rear bearing - auxiliary shaft
10 Main bearing cap No 5

11 Main bearing cap No 4
12 Main bearing cap No 3
13 Main bearing cap No 2
14 Main bearing cap No 1
15 Crankshaft oil seal-front
16 Crankshaft oil seal-rear

17 Main bearing cap bolt
18 Drain cock
19 Auxiliary shaft
20 Thrust washer
21 Oil seal

22 Pulley
23 Woodruff key
24 Pulley bolt
25 Washer
26 Lockwasher
27 Drive belt jockey pulley

28 Bearing
29 Bolt
30 Washer
31 Lockwasher
32 Timing pointer

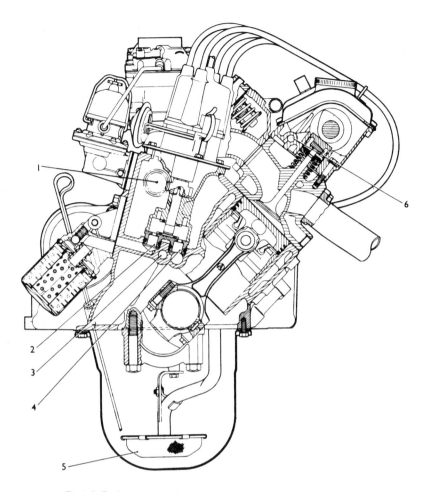

Fig.1.3. Engine cross section showing main features of lubrication system

1. Auxiliary shaft driving oil pump
   (via distributor shaft)
2. Pump outlet port
3. Main oil gallery in block
4. Pump inlet port
5. Strainer and suction pipe
5. Camshaft housing oil
   gallery

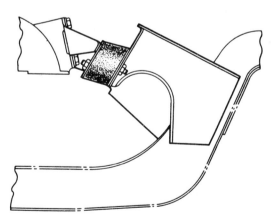

Fig.1.4. Engine Mountings - Shear type on later models. (N.B. Gearbox mountings changed at same time).

got on to it from the front whilst the nut is undone from the other end with a socket and extension.

21 Once the mounting has been released, take the weight of the engine on the hoist and bring it forward and upwards a little to get the mounting brackets clear. Then remove the right hand bracket from the engine. It will be necessary to swing the rear round in order to get the head clear of the heater duct. The engine can then be lifted up and brought out. Watch out that the heater valve control cable does not get caught up (photo).

22 Place the engine as soon as possible where you are going to work on it. Plenty of space is a great advantage. A free standing bench (rather than one against a wall) that you can work round is ideal.

5 Engine dismantling - general

1 Keen owners who dismantle a lot of engines will probably have a stand on which to put them but most will make do with a work bench which should be large enough to spread the inevitable bits and pieces and tools around on, and strong enough to support the engine weight. If the floor is the only possible place try and ensure that the engine rests on a hardwood platform or similar rather than concrete (or beaten earth!!).

2 Spend some time on cleaning the unit. If you have been wise this will have been done before the engine was removed, at a service bay. Good solvents such as 'Gunk' will help to 'float' off caked dirt/ grease under a water jet. Once the exterior is clean, dismantling may begin. As parts are removed clean them in petrol or paraffin (do not immerse parts with oilways in paraffin - clean them with a petrol soaked cloth and clear oilways with pipe cleaners. If an air line is available so much the better for final cleaning off. Paraffin, which could possibly remain in oilways would dilute the oil for initial lubrication after reassembly).

3 Where components are fitted with seals and gaskets it is always best to fit new ones - but do NOT throw the old ones away until you have the new ones to hand. A pattern is then available if they have to be made specially. Hang them on a convenient hook.

4 In general it is best to work from the top of the engine downwards. In any case support the engine firmly so that it does not topple over when you are undoing stubborn nuts and bolts.

5 Always place nuts and bolts back with their components or place of attachment if possible - it saves so much confusion later. Otherwise put them in small, separate pots or jars so that their groups are easily identified.

6 If you are lucky enough to have an area where parts can be laid out on sheets of paper do so - putting the nuts and bolts with them. If you are able to look at all the components in this way it helps to avoid missing something on reassembly because it is tucked away on a shelf or whatever.

7 Even though you may be dismantling the engine only partly - possibly with it still in the car - the principles still apply. It is appreciated that most people prefer to do engine repairs if possible with the engine in position. Consequently an indication will be given as to what is necessary to lead up to carrying out repairs on a particular component. Generally speaking the Victor engine is easy enough to get at as far as repairs and renewals of the ancillaries are concerned. When it comes to repair of the major engine components, however, it is only fair to say that repairs with the engine in position are more difficult than with it out.

6 Engine ancillaries - removal

1 If you are stripping the engine completely or preparing to install a reconditioned unit, all the ancillaries must be removed first. If you are going to obtain a reconditioned 'short' motor (block, crank-shaft, pistons and connecting rods) then obviously the cambox, cylinder head and associated parts will need retention for fitting to the new engine. It is advisable to check just what you will get with a reconditioned unit as changes are made from time to time.

2 The removal of all those items connected with fuel, ignition and charging systems are detailed in the respective chapters so for brevity they are merely listed here.

    Distributor
    Carburettor (can be removed together with inlet manifold).
    Generator
    Fuel pump
    Water pump
    Starter motor
    Thermostat

7 Engine mountings - removal and replacement

1 Mounting may be renewed with the engine in the car. On early models remove the vertical through bolts as described in Section 4, paragraph 20.

2 Place a wooden load spreader under the engine sump and jack up the engine just enough to take the weight of the brackets off the mounting. Then unbolt the brackets from the engine. On the left side access is possible from underneath. With the brackets removed the mountings can be taken out of the crossmember bracket. The mountings are different on each side - the left one is marked with a yellow paint spot and the right by blue (photo).

3 Replacement is a reversal of the removal procedure. Make sure the brackets are tightly bolted to the engine before letting them take the weight once more and ensure that the large heat shield disc is located above the left hand mounting but under the bracket before lowering (photo).

4 Engines fitted with the later shear type mountings should be first jacked up just enough to take the weight off the mountings. The bracket bolts and lower mounting nut are then removed and the bracket and mounting removed together. Fit a new mounting to the bracket and replace the bracket and mounting together. These later type mountings are interchangeable side for side.

5 With the early and later type front mountings different rear mountings are used. Details of these are given in Chapter 6.

8 Oil filter and adaptor - removal and replacement

1 The oil filter is a throwaway cartridge which is changed regularly under service procedures. The adaptor into which it screws is held to the block by three bolts. A gasket is used.

2 The adaptor may be removed for cleaning and checking of the spring loaded bypass valve. The bypass valve opens to permit oil to flow in the event that the filter should get blocked.

3 Always fit a new gasket when refitting the adaptor (photo).

4 Smear the filter element sealing ring with lubricant before fitting to prevent binding and removal difficulty later (photos).

9 Bellhousing and cover plate - removal and replacement

1 The bellhousing can be removed with the engine in the car but first the gearbox has to be removed and the engine disengaged from its mountings in order to get at the top two securing bolts on the left side. Unless a hoist or pit is available this operation is very difficult and it is recommended the engine be taken from the car first.

2 Remove all the bolts holding the bellhousing to the block and the lower cover plate to the bellhousing including those of the starter motor if not removed already. The housing will have the clutch actuating arm attached to it. Pull the housing off the dowel pegs. The clutch actuating arm can be pulled off the pivot pin - it is held by a spring clip.

3 Replacement is a reversal of this procedure.

4 Note that the bellhousing is never removed or replaced together with the gearbox.

7.2 Lifting mounting bracket away (RH)

7.3 Tightening bracket to engine before resting weight on engine

8.3 Replace oil filter adaptor bracket to block

8.4a Lubricating the oil filter cartridge sealing ring before replacement

8.4b Replacing the oil filter cartridge

11.2 Mark on timing belt to show direction of travel before removal

12.1 Levering off the crankshaft pulley

12.4a Fitting the crankshaft key

12.4b Fitting the crankshaft pulley (note how half the key engages each part of the pulley

13.12 Camshaft housing - the punch is indicating the fine oil spray orifice

15.13 Cleaning carbon from a valve. Power drill held in vice

19.2a Oil pump suction pipe securing bracket

10 Flywheel - removal, inspection and renovation

1 The flywheel is held to the rear of the crankshaft by five bolts and located by two dowel pegs. It can be removed with the engine in the car but the bellhousing has to come off first and this is not recommended for the reasons given in the last section.

2 If the engine is removed from the car take the flywheel off first after the bellhousing. Undo the bolts with a socket spanner and pull the flywheel off square. It is important not to damage the mating surfaces or the dowel pegs and holes.

3 The flywheel clutch friction surface should be shiny and unscored. Minor blemishes and scratches can be overlooked but deep grooves will probably cause clutch problems in time. Renewal may be advisable.

   If the starter ring gear teeth are badly worn the ring can be removed by first splitting it between two teeth with a chisel. Do not try and drive it off because it rests in a shallow groove. If you have never fitted a new ring gear yourself it is best to have it done for you. It needs heating to a temperature of 200ºC evenly in order to shrink fit it on the flywheel. The chamfers on the ring gear must face in the direction the flywheel normally rotates. On later models the chamfer is on one side of the teeth only and this must be towards the clutch side of the flywheel.

11 Drive belt for camshaft and auxiliary shaft - removal

1 The drive belt may be removed with the engine installed. On later models it will be necessary to remove the cover first and this, in turn, will involve removal of the fan and crankshaft V belt pulleys.

   The crankshaft pulley is held by a central bolt which can be undone with a socket. The V section is separate from the toothed section but located on the common crankshaft woodruff key. It should pull off easily. The fan pulley is held to the water pump shaft by the four bolts which also carry the fan blades.

2 Before removing the belt certain precautions should be taken, depending on the reasons for removing it, so as to minimise the risk of making mistakes on replacement, and, of course, to save time For all conditions mark the belt with a piece of chalk to indicate the direction of travel. This ensures that the wear pattern of the teeth stays the same and wear does not become excessive (photo).

3 In all situations other than complete engine dismantling, refer to the section on 'Valve timing and drive belt replacement' and set the pulleys in position before taking the belt off. In such situations do not move any pulleys (other than the one you may have to) until the belt is replaced.

   If any of the pulleys are to be removed from their shafts later, first slacken the centre retaining bolt before removing the belt. On 1599 cc HC engines independent movement of the camshaft and crankshaft with the belt off will not only lose the valve timing position but also cause valves to touch the crowns of pistons at TDC.

4 Slacken the bolts securing the belt jockey pulley mounting bracket. The belt may then be slid off the pulleys. Do not let it get kinked, damaged or contaminated. It is expensive. Normally it should last indefinitely and require no adjustment.

12 Crankshaft pulley, auxiliary shaft pulley and camshaft pulley - removal and replacement

1 All three pulleys are held onto their respective shafts in the same way - namely by a woodruff key in a parallel shaft. They should all pull off easily once the centre bolt is removed.

2 The centre bolt should be slackened before the drive belt is removed - and then the drive belt should be taken off as described in the previous section.

3 The crankshaft pulley is slightly different in that it is in three parts - the outer V belt section, the timing belt section and the inner flange.

4 The two belt sections each engage half of the Woodruff key and the flange locates in a hand on the back of the timing belt pulley (photos).

5 It should be remembered that if any one of the three shafts is moved when the belt is off, the timing must be reset before replacing the belt.

13 Camshaft housing, camshaft and tappets - removal and inspection

1 The operations described can be carried out with the engine installed.

2 The camshaft is removed together with the housing from the top of the cylinder head (ie you cannot move the camshaft with the housing fitted to the head).

3 Disconnect the leads from the spark plugs and then unclip them from the cambox cover.

4 Remove the timing belt as described in the previous section having first slackened the camshaft pulley bolt.

5 The camshaft housing is held to the head by ten bolts inside the housing. After removing the cover each bolt should be slackened a little at a time, evenly over the whole area until the valve springs held under tension are completely relaxed. Due to the narrow access to the bolt heads it will be found that a ½ inch drive socket set will be too big so unless you have a $3/8$ inch or ¼ inch drive set buy a tubular spanner to fit. The bolts are not very tight.

6 Having loosened all bolts lift them out. Before lifting the cam housing you should be aware that the tappets can all fall out and this must be prevented. As soon as the tappets are clear of the valves, therefore, tip the housing so that they will stay in their locations. When they are removed from the housing place them in a suitable container which marks clearly which position they are from.

7 To remove the camshaft first take off the pulley which is keyed to the shaft. Under no circumstances grip the pulley in a vice. If you forget to slacken the bolt use the timing belt to grip the pulley when removing it. Alternatively, grip the camshaft on an unmachined portion with a pair of self grips to hold it.

8 Remove the housing end cover from the rear. The thrust washer retaining bolt underneath is then undone and for this it is all right to clamp the nose of the camshaft in a vice with the jaws suitably covered with soft material.

9 The oil seal at the front end should now be prised out of the housing. Make sure you have a new one available as the old one will be no longer of any use.

10 The camshaft can be drawn out of the front of the housing. Take care not to catch the bearings with the cam lobes.

11 The bearing surfaces of the cam lobes and tappets should be flat and unpitted. If otherwise you may expect rapid wear to occur in the future. Badly worn cam lobes affect the opening of the valves and consequently engine performance.

   If lack of lubrication has occurred the tappets may have become badly worn in the housing bores. In any of these circumstances it will be necessary to renew the affected parts.

12 The camshaft housing has an oil gallery timing its full length with fine jet holes opposite each tappet bore. It is essential that this is perfectly clean. To clean the gallery properly unscrew the blanking plugs at each end and blow out the five jets and gallery with an air line. Do not try to enlarge the jet holes - they are of a particular size in order to maintain oil pressure and an adequate spray to the tappets and cams (photo).

13 Each tappet contains a screw with a wedge shaped flat on it for the purposes of adjusting the valve tappet clearances. Should these be damaged or need renewal for other reasons (see 'Valve clearance adjustment') they may be screwed out of the tappets using an Allen key.

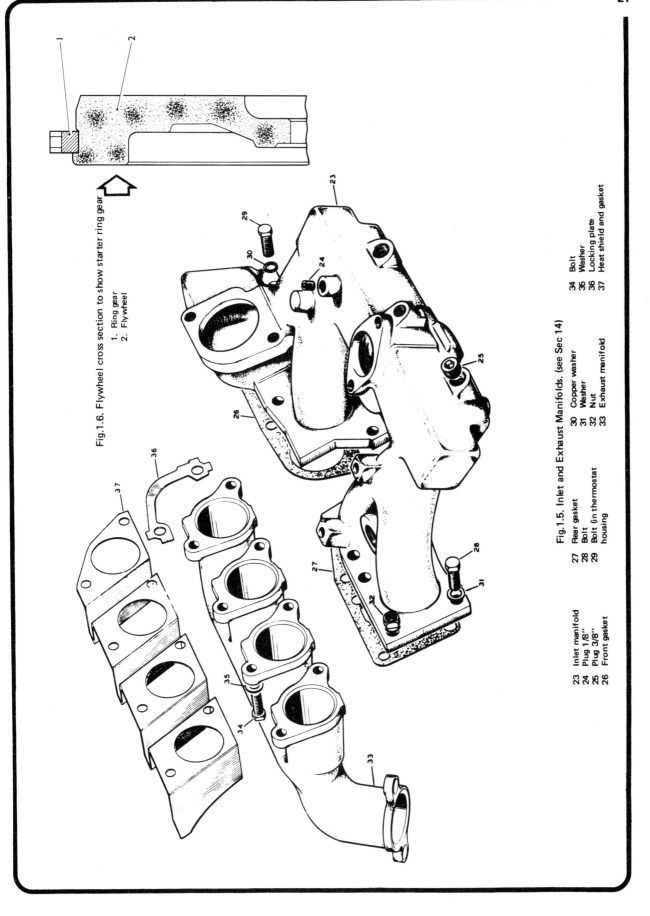

Fig.1.6. Flywheel cross section to show starter ring gear

1. Ring gear
2. Flywheel

Fig.1.5. Inlet and Exhaust Manifolds. (see Sec 14)

23	Inlet manifold	27	Rear gasket	30	Copper washer	34	Bolt
24	Plug 1/8"	28	Bolt	31	Washer	35	Washer
25	Plug 3/8"	29	Bolt (in thermostat	32	Nut	36	Locking plate
26	Front gasket		housing	33	Exhaust manifold	37	Heat shield and gasket

14 Inlet and exhaust manifolds - removal and replacement

Details of how to remove the exhaust and inlet manifolds are given in the next section dealing with cylinder head removal. The only difference is that if you are not removing the cylinder head it is not necessary to remove the camshaft housing first. Replacement is covered in Section 31 dealing with cylinder head replacement.

15 Cylinder head, valves and springs - removal, inspection and renovation

1 The cylinder head can be removed with the engine in the car. Remove the camshaft housing as described in the previous section, and drain the cooling system of about four pints.
2 Undo the exhaust pipe from the manifold by removing the two nuts with a socket and extension from underneath.
3 To get at all the cylinder head bolts the exhaust manifold has to be removed first. The exhaust manifold is secured by eight bolts each pair having a double tab lockwasher. Bend back the tabs and remove the bolts with a socket or tubular spanner. Lift off the manifold and the heat shield gasket behind it.
4 The inlet manifold may be removed before or after the head is removed. Note that one of the securing bolt heads is inside the thermostat housing. The housing cover and thermostat should first be removed (see Chapter 2) and the bolt taken out. Note the copper sealing washer under the head of the bolt. Undo the water pipe union into the manifold from the water pump.
5 The cylinder head bolts are tight and if the engine is out of the car it must be securely supported whilst they are slackened. Use only a good quality socket spanner for this job. Bolts should be slackened from the ends towards the centre - preferably in the reverse sequence of tightening as shown in Fig 1.19
6 Undo the bolt which holds the inlet elbow for the water pump to the front of the head.
7 The head is located on two small dowels to the block and should lift straight off. Tapping the sides will not do much good if it sticks and no form of lever should be forced between the head and block. A lever can be arranged across the lower front corner, however, where it projects over the block.
8 Even if the valves are not being removed it is best to remove all carbon deposits from the combustion chamber with a wire brush in a power drill. If no power drill is available scrape the carbon off with an old screwdriver.
9 To remove the valves from the cylinder head requires a special 'G' clamp spring compressor. This is positioned with the screw head on the head of the valve and the claw end over the valve spring collar. The screw is turned until the two split collars round the valve stem are freed and can be renewed. If the spring collar tends to stick so that the compressor cannot be tightened, tap the top of the spring (while the clamp is on) to free it.

Slacken off the compressor and the valve springs and collar will be released and can be lifted off. On later engines an oil seal cup is fitted round each valve guide shoulder and retained by a circlip. These should be renewed. Valves should be drawn out from the guides with care. Any tightness is probably caused by burring at the end of the stem so clean this up before drawing the valves through. The guides will not then be scored.
10 Valves, seats and guides should be examined in conjunction. Any valve which is cracked or burnt away at the edges must be discarded. Valves which are a slack fit in the guides should be discarded also if further rapid deterioration and poor seating are to be avoided. To decide whether a valve is a slack fit replace it in its bore and feel how much it rocks at the end. Then judge if this represents a gap of more than .003 inch between stem and bore.
11 If valves are obviously a very slack fit the remedy is to ream the guides out oversize to accept oversize valves. Valves are available in oversizes of .003, .006, .012 and .024 inch. Reaming should be done from the top of the head. Unless you have the proper reamers and

experience of their use you are strongly advised to have this work done by a specialist. It will not be possible to decide what oversize valves will be required until the guide bore oversize is established by reaming out.
12 Where a valve has deteriorated badly at the seat the corresponding seat in the cylinder head must be examined. Light pitting or scoring may be removed by grinding the valve into the seat with carborundum paste. If worse then the seat may need recutting with a special tool. Check again, if you do not have the correct tool it is best to have the work done by a specialist.
13 When grinding in valves to their seats all carbon must first of all be removed from the head and head end of the stem. This is effectively done by fitting the valve in a power drill chuck, clamping the drill in a vice and then scraping the carbon off the rotating valve with an old screwdriver. It is essential to protect the eyes with suitable goggles when doing this (photo).

New valves may also be ground into their seats but check first whether the ones you get have any special coating on them. The procedure for grinding in valves is as follows: Obtain a tin of carborundum paste which contains coarse and fine varieties and also a grinding tool consisting of a rubber suction cup on the end of a wooden handle. Smear a trace of coarse carborundum paste on the seat face and apply a suction grinder tool to the valve head. With a semi-rotary motion, grind the valve head to its seat, lifting the valve occasionally to redistribute the grinding paste. When a dull matt even surface finish is produced on both the valve seat and the valve, then wipe off the paste and repeat the process with fine carborundum paste, lifting and turning the valve to redistribute the paste as before. A light spring placed under the valve head will greatly ease this operation. When a smooth unbroken ring of light grey matt finish is produced, on both valve and valve seat faces, the grinding operation is complete.
14 After grinding, the thickness of the valve head (as indicated in Fig.1.10) should not be less than specified. Also the width of the seating should be not more than specified. If it is it means that the seating in the head may need recutting.
15 After the valve seats have been recut in the head the valve will naturally protrude further above the head. This protrusion should not exceed specification either (Fig.1.10). If you think of remedying this by grinding something off the end of the valve stem you could get into difficulties with valve clearances. It may be possible to fit valve seat inserts but the manufacturers do not recommend it. Being a relatively new engine, experience by specialist firms has not yet been built up on this feature.
16 When the grinding in process has finished all traces of carborundum paste must be removed. This is best done by flushing the head with paraffin and hosing out with water.
17 If the reason for removal of the head has been a blown gasket make sure that the surface is perfectly flat before it is refitted. This requires an accurate steel straight edge and a feeler gauge for checking. If there is any sign of warp over .003 inch it is worthwhile getting it machined flat.
18 Each valve has an inner and outer spring and these should, of course, not have any broken coils. The overall length of each spring must be no less than that specified and if it is it must be discarded. The normal practice is to renew all springs when some are defective.

16 Oil pump - removal and inspection

1 The oil pump may be removed after the distributor has been taken off as described in Chapter 4, and the fuel pump removed as described in Chapter 3.
2 To lift the pump out insert a suitable lever into the fuel pump lever hole and prise the pump upwards so as to draw the bottom of the pump out of the two ports in the block. Do not try and prise it by the upper flange which may bend or break.
3 Once the pump is clear it should be turned 90° clockwise so that it can be lifted out.

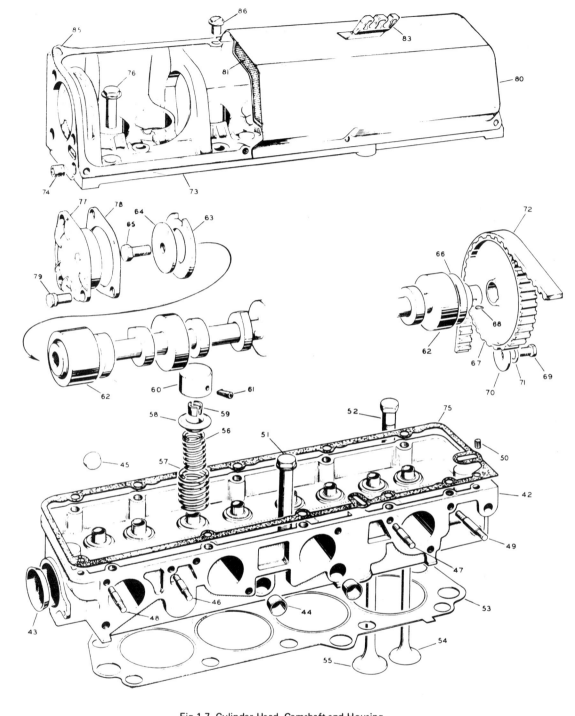

Fig.1.7. Cylinder Head, Camshaft and Housing

42	Cylinder head	51	Cylinder head bolt - long
43	Cup plug 1½''	52	Cylinder head bolt - short
44	Cup plug ¾''	53	Head gasket
45	Cup plug 5/8''	54	Exhaust valve
46	Stud - inlet manifold 1.5/16''	55	Inlet valve
47	Stud - inlet manifold 1.7/16''	56	Inner valve spring
48	Stud - inlet manifold 1.5/8''	57	Outer valve spring
49	Stud - inlet manifold 2.1/8''	58	Valve spring cap
50	Knurled dowel peg	59	Valve colletts
		60	Tappet
		61	Adjuster screw

62	Camshaft	75	Gasket
63	Camshaft thrust washer	76	Housing bolts
64	Retaining washer	77	Rear cover
65	Self locking bolt	78	Gasket
66	Oil seal	79	Cover bolt
67	Camshaft pulley	80	Housing cover
68	Woodruff key	81	Breather element
69	Pulley bolt		
70	Washer	83	Spark plug lead bracket
71	Lockwasher	85	Cover gasket
72	Drive belt	86	Cover screw and washer
73	Camshaft housing		
74	Oil gallery plug		

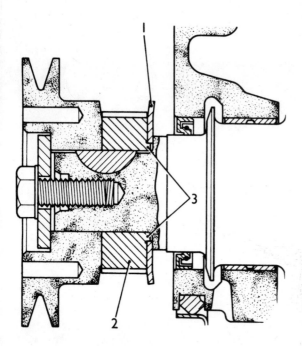

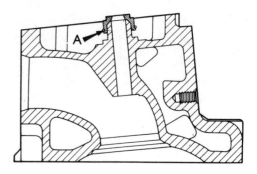

Fig.1.9. Valves

Later models have a valve stem seal fitted round the guide boss of the head and secured by a circlip 'A'.

Fig.1.8. Crankshaft pulley wheel assembly - cross section

1. Flange
2. Toothed pulley
3. Register for flange

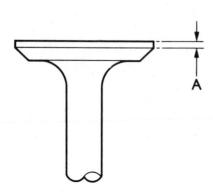

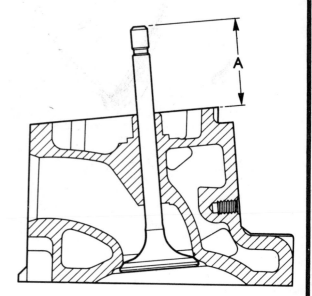

Fig.1.10. Valves

Left—Head thickness 'A' should not be less than .025 for inlet and .035 for exhaust.
Right—Valve stem protrusion through head not to be more than 1.13 ins.

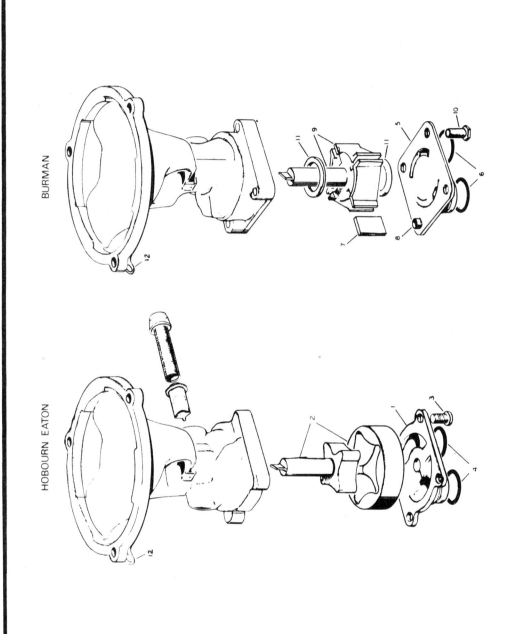

BURMAN

HOBOURN EATON

Fig.1.11. Oil Pumps

| 1 | Cover | 3 | Cover bolts | 5 | Cover plate | 7 | Rotor vanes | 9 | Rotor and shaft | 11 | Vane locating washer |
| 2 | Shaft and rotors assembly | 4 | 'O' rings | 6 | 'O' rings | 8 | Locating sleeve | 10 | Cover screw | 12 | Gasket |

4 Two types of pump are used - bi-rotor or vane type. To check the pump it is necessary to remove the bottom cover. Mark it first in relation to the main body and remove the four screws. Using a feeler gauge and straight edge the clearances between rotors and vanes, and the body housing them should be checked. On bi-rotor types the clearance between the tip of inner rotor and convex radius of outer rotor should not exceed .005 inch. The clearance between the outer rotor and the housing should not exceed .010 inch. End float of rotors is .005 inch maximum - measured with feeler blade and straight edge across the housing.

On vane type pumps the clearances between vanes and rotor, rotor and body (on the high point of the eccentric) and rotor end float should not exceed .005 inch. Tip clearance of the vanes opposite the high point of the rotor eccentric should not exceed .010 inch.

If any or all of the clearances are excessive and the shaft is a slack fit in the body then it is best to obtain a new pump.

After checking the pump make sure that both the upper and lower rotor centre rings are properly located in relation to the vanes in the vane type pump and that the radiused edges of the vanes face outwards. On rotor type pumps the outer rotor is assembled with the chamfered edge inwards. In the side of the pump body below the gear opening there is a small hole which delivers oil to lubricate the auxiliary gears. Make sure it is quite clear.

17 Auxiliary shaft - removal, inspection and renovation

1 The auxiliary shaft may be removed after removing the drive belt, the shaft pulley, distributor and fuel pump. Refer to the appropriate chapter and sections for details of their removal.
2 The shaft is held in position by the oil seal. The oil seal cannot be removed without damage to it so make sure a new one is available beforehand.
3 Prise it out with a suitable tool and avoid scratching the shaft or the bore in the housing.
4 The shaft complete with thrust washer will then come out.
5 If the shaft gear is damaged or badly worn calling for renewal of the shaft then the distributor drive gear should also be renewed.
6 Wear on the thrust washer will be indicated by grooves and this also calls for renewal.
7 End float should be as specified and if there is any noticeable play between the shaft and bearings new bearing shells should be fitted
8 The front and rear bearing shells can be drifted out although the rear one will come out with the block sealing plug.
9 When fitting new bearings see that the rear one has the offset hole and that the hole lines up with the passageway in the block.
10 The cut-out on the edge of the rear bearing should face the rear. Line up the hole for the front bearing with the cut-out facing the front.
11 Fit a new sealing plug at the rear using jointing compound to make it oil tight.

18 Sump - removal

1 To remove the sump means either lifting the engine out of the car or removing the front crossmember assembly.
2 If the engine is undergoing overhaul then, of course, it will be removed anyway.
3 If the problem is only leaking sump gaskets it is probably easiest to lower the front suspension. It is essential, however, to have proper stands to support the front of the car. Remove all the screws, marking the position of the one which holds the clutch cable clip. The sump can then be taken off.

19 Oil suction pipe and strainer - removal and replacement

1 The suction pipe and strainer can be removed when the sump is off.

2 It is held by a bolted clip to No 4 main bearing cap and a retaining plate held by a bolt at the elbow where the pipe goes into the block (photos).
3 With these removed the pipe can be pulled out.
4 Note the sealing ring round the pipe which is very important and should be renewed on replacement (photo).
5 Refitting is a straightforward reversal of these procedures.

20 Pistons, connecting rods and bearings - removal

1 To remove the pistons and connecting rods the engine should be removed from the car and the sump and cylinder head removed first as already described.
2 It is possible to make a preliminary examination of the state of the pistons relative to the bores with the engine in the car after removal of the cylinder head so bear this in mind where the inspection details are given in the next section.
3 Each connecting rod, bearing cap and piston is matched to each other and the cylinder, and must be replaced in the same position. Before removing anything mark each connecting rod near the cap with a light punch mark to indicate which cylinder it comes from. There is usually a makers number on the rod and cap so there should be no need to worry about mixing them up. If no numbers are apparent then mark the cap as well.
4 It is also important to ensure that the connecting rods and pistons go on the crankshaft the proper way round (the pistons are offset to the thrust side on the gudgeon pins). The best way to record this is by noting which side of the engine block the marks you have made or the existing numbers face. Provided the pistons are not being renewed then they can be arrowed with chalk on the crown pointing to the front but if they are separated from the connecting rods you still want to know which way the rods go.
5 Having made quite sure that positions are clear undo the connecting rod cap bolts with a socket spanner. A normal $^7/_{16}$ AF socket does not fit properly - a flank drive is needed - but an 11 mm metric socket is quite satisfactory.
6 Having removed the bearing caps the connecting rods and pistons may be pushed out through the top of the block.
7 The shell bearings may be slid round to remove them from the connecting rods and caps.
8 To separate the pistons from the connecting rods a great deal of pressure is needed to free the pins out of the small ends. This is not possible with anything other than a proper press and tools. Attempts with other methods will probably result in bent connecting rods or broken pistons. If new pistons are needed anyway it will need an experienced man to heat the connecting rods to fit the new gudgeon pins so the same man may as well take the old ones off.

21 Pistons, piston rings and cylinder bores - inspection and renovation

1 Examine the pistons for signs of damage on the crown and around the top edge. If any of the piston rings have broken there could be quite noticeable damage to the grooves, in which case the piston must be renewed. Deep scores in the piston walls also call for renewal. If the cylinders are being rebored new oversize pistons and rings will be needed anyway. If the cylinders do not need reboring and the pistons are in good condition only the rings need to be checked.
2 Unless new rings are to be fitted for certain, care has to be taken that rings are not broken on removal. Starting with the top ring first (all rings are to be removed from the top of the piston) ease one end out of its groove and place a thin piece of metal behind it.

Then move the metal strip carefully round behind the ring, at the same time nudging the ring upwards so that it rests on the surface of the piston above until the whole ring is clear and can be slid off. With the second and third rings which must also come off the top, arrange the strip of metal to carry them over the other grooves.

Note where each ring has come from (pierce a piece of paper with each ring showing 'top 1', 'middle 1' etc).

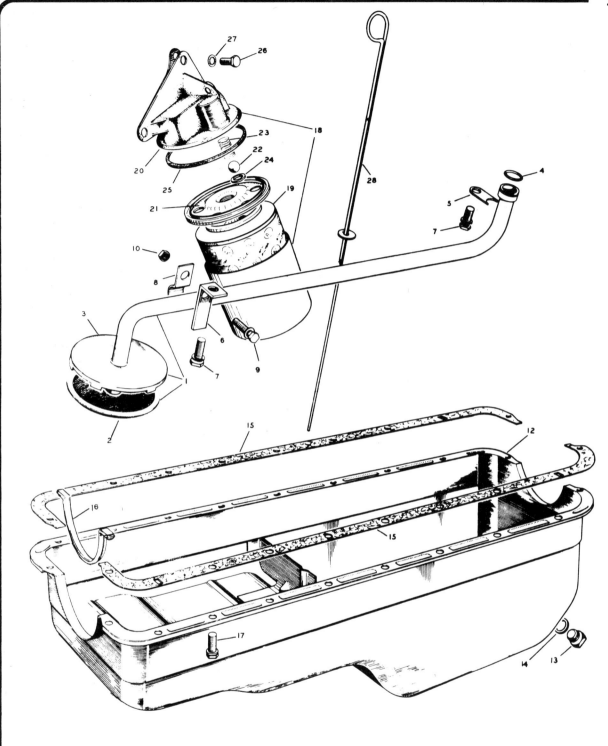

Fig.1.12. Sump, Oil Suction Pipe and Filter Assemblies

1	Screw and suction pipe assembly	7	Bolt	15	Gasket	22	Steel ball
2	Screen	8	Clamp plate	16	Seal	23	Spring
3	Cover	9	Clamp bolt	17	Screw and lockwasher	24	Sealing ring
4	'O' ring	10	Nut	18	Oil filter assembly	25	Gasket
5	Clamp plate	12	Sump	19	Filter element	26	Bolt
6	Support bracket	13	Drain plug	20	Adaptor head	27	Lockwasher
		14	Washer	21	Valve seat		

3 To check the existing rings, place them in the cylinder bore and press each one down in turn to the bottom of the stroke. In this case a distance of 2½ inches from the top of the cylinder will be satisfactory. Use an inverted piston to press them down square. With a feeler gauge measure the gap for each ring which should be as given in the specifications at the beginning of this Chapter. If the gap is too large, the rings will need renewal.

4 Check also that each ring gives a clearance in the piston groove according to specifications. If the gap is too great, new pistons and rings will be required if Vauxhall spares are used. However, independent specialist producers of pistons and rings can normally provide the rings required separately. If new Vauxhall pistons and rings are being obtained it will be necessary to have the ridge ground away from the top of each cylinder bore. If specialist oil control rings are being obtained from an independent supplier the ridge removal will not be necessary as the top rings will be stepped to provide the necessary clearance. If the top ring of a new set is not stepped it will hit the ridge made by the former ring and break.

5 If new pistons are obtained the rings will be included, so it must be emphasised that the top ring be stepped if fitted to an un-reground bore (or un-deridged bore).

6 The new rings should be placed in the bores and the gap checked. If an un-reground bore check the gap above the line of the ridge (photo). Any gaps which are too small should be increased by filing one end of the ring with a fine file. Be careful not to break the ring as they are brittle (and expensive). On no account make the gap less than specification. If the gap should close when under normal operating temperatures the ring will break.

7 The groove clearance of new rings in old pistons should be within the specified tolerances. If it is not enough, the rings could stick in the piston grooves causing loss of compression. The piston grooves in this case will need machining out to accept the new rings.

8 Before putting new rings onto an old piston clean out the grooves with a piece of old broken ring (photo).

9 Refit the new rings with care, in the same order as the old ones were removed. Note that some special oil control rings are supplied in three separate pieces (photo). The cylinder bores must be checked for ovality, scoring, scratching and pitting. Starting from the top, look for a ridge where the top piston ring reaches the limit of its upward travel. The depth of this ridge will give a good indication of the degree of wear and can be checked with the engine in the car and the cylinder head removed.

10 Measure the bore diameter across the block and just below any ridge. This can be done with an internal micrometer or a Mercer gauge. Compare this with the diameter of the bottom of the bore, which is not subject to wear. If no micrometer measuring instruments are available, use a piston from which the rings have been removed and measure the gap between it and the cylinder wall with a feeler gauge.

11 If the difference in bore diameters at top and bottom is .010 inch or more, then the cylinders need reboring. If less than .010 inch, then the fitting of new and special rings to the pistons can cure the trouble.

12 If the cylinders have already been bored out to their maximum it may be possible to have liners fitted. This situation will not often be encountered.

13 As mentioned in the previous section, new pistons should be fitted to the connecting rods by the firm which rebores the block.

22 Crankshaft - removal and inspection

1 With the engine removed from the car, remove the sump and oil suction pipe as described in Section 18. If the cylinder head is also removed so much the better as the engine can be stood firmly in an inverted position.

2 Remove the connecting rod bearing caps. This will already have been done if the pistons are removed.

3 Using a good quality socket wrench remove the two cap bolts from each of the five main bearing caps.

4 Lift off each cap carefully. Each one is marked with the bearing number.

5 The bearing cap shells will probably come off with the caps, in which case they can be removed by pushing them round from the end opposite the notch and lifting them out.

6 Grip the crankshaft firmly at each end and lift it out. Put it somewhere safe where it cannot fall. Remove the shell bearings from the inner housings noting that No 5 has a flange on each side. There is a two piece oil seal embedded in grooves of the crankcase and bearing cap of No 5 (rear) bearing. These should be levered out and the grooves properly cleaned. The circular oil seal on the front of the shaft should be pulled off.

7 Examine all the crankpins and main bearing journals for signs of scoring or scratches. If all surfaces are undamaged check next that all the bearing journals are round. This can be done with a micrometer or caliper gauge, taking readings across the diameter at 6 or 7 points for each journal. If you do not own or know how to use a micrometer, take the crankshaft to your local engineering works and ask them to 'mike it up' for you.

8 If the crankshaft is ridged or scored it must be reground. If the ovality exceeds .002 inch on measurement, but there are no signs of scoring or scratching on the srufaces, regrinding may still be necessary. It would be advisable to ask the advice of the engineering works to whom you entrust the work of regrinding in such instances.

23 Main and big end bearing shells - inspection and renewal

1 Big end bearing failure is normally indicated by a pronounced knocking from the crankcase and a slight drop in oil pressure. Main bearing failure is normally accompanied by vibration, which can be quite severe at high engine speeds, and a more significant drop in oil pressure.

2 The shell bearing surfaces should be matt grey in colour with no sign of pitting or scoring. If they are obviously in bad condition it is essential to examine the crankshaft before fitting new ones.

3 Replacement shell bearings are supplied in a series of thicknesses dependent on the degree of regrinding that the crankshaft requires, which is done in multiples of .010 inch. Thus depending on how much it is necessary to grind off, so bearing shells are supplied as '.010 inch undersize' and so on. The engineering works regrinding the crankshaft will normally supply the correct shells with the reground crank.

4 If an engine is removed for overhaul regularly it is worthwhile renewing big end bearings every 30000 miles as a matter of course and main bearings every 50000 miles. This will add many thousands of miles to the life of the engine before any regrinding of crankshafts is necessary. Make sure that bearing shells renewed are standard dimensions if the crankshaft has not been reground.

5 It is very important, if in doubt, to take the old bearing shells along if you want replacements of the same size. Some original crankshafts are .010 undersize on journals or crankpins and the appropriate bearings must be used.

24 Engine reassembly - general

1 To ensure maximum life with minimum trouble from a rebuilt engine, not only must everything be correctly assembled, but everything must be spotlessly clean, all the oilways must be clear, locking washers and spring washers must always be fitted where indicated and all bearing and other working surfaces must be thoroughly lubricated during assembly.

2 Before assembly begins renew any bolts or studs, the threads of which are in any way damaged, and whenever possible use new spring washers.

3 Apart from your normal tools, a supply of clean rag, an oil can filled with engine oil (an empty plastic detergent bottle thoroughly cleaned and washed out, will invariably do just as well), a new supply of assorted spring washers, a set of new gaskets, and a torque spanner should be collected together.

4 It is well worthwhile sitting down with a pencil and paper and listing all those items which you intend to renew and acquire all of

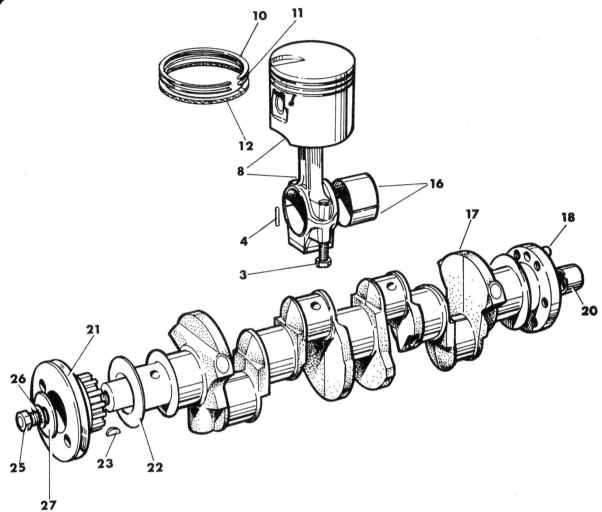

Fig.1.13. Crankshaft and Pistons

3	Big end bearing cap bolt	10	Top compression ring	17	Crankshaft	23	Woodruff key
4	Dowel pin	11	Lower compression ring	18	Dowel peg	25	Crankshaft pulley bolt
8	Piston and connecting rod	12	Oil control ring	20	Input shaft pilot bush	26	Lockwasher
		16	Big end shell bearings	21	Crankshaft pulley	27	Large plain washer
				22	Pulley flange		

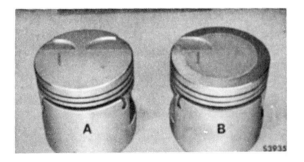

Fig.1.14. Pistons – Differences

Left   A. 1599 cc low compression
         B. 1599 cc high compression (Standard)
Right   A. 1975 cc low compression
         B. 1975 cc high compression (Standard)

them before beginning reassembly. If you have little experience of shopping around for parts you will appreciate that they cannot all be obtained quickly. Do not underestimate the cost either. Spare parts are relatively much more expensive now than they were a few years ago.

25 Pistons and connecting rods - replacement in cylinders

1 If the crankshaft has been removed, fit the pistons before replacing it. The pistons, complete with connecting rods and new shell bearings can be fitted to the cylinder bores in the following sequence:
2 With a wad of clean rag wipe the cylinder bores clean. If new rings are being fitted any surface oil 'glaze' on the walls should be removed by rubbing with a very fine abrasive. This can be a very fine (400 grade) 'wet and dry' paper as used for rubbing down paintwork. This enables new rings to bed into the cylinders properly which would otherwise be prevented or at least delayed for a long time. Make sure that all traces of abrasive are confined to the cylinder bores and are completely cleaned off before assembling the pistons into the cylinders. Then oil the pistons, rings, and cylinder bores generously with engine oil. Space the piston ring gaps equally around the piston (photo).
3 The pistons, complete with connecting rods, are fitted to their bores from above.
4 As each piston is inserted into its bore ensure that it is the correct piston/connecting rod assembly for that particular bore and that the connecting rod is the right way round, and that the front of the piston (which is marked) is towards the front of the engine.
5 The piston will only slide into the bore as far as the oil control ring. It is necessary to compress the piston rings into a clamp and to gently tap the piston into the cylinder bore with a wooden or plastic hammer. If a proper piston ring clamp is not available then a hose clip may be used (photo).
6 If new pistons and rings are being fitted to a rebored block the clearances are very small and care has to be taken to make sure that no part of a piston ring catches the edge of the bore before being pressed down. They are very brittle and easily broken. For this reason it is acceptable practice to chamfer the lip of the cylinder very slightly to provide a lead for the rings into the cylinder. The chamfer should be at an angle of 45º and should not be cut back more than .010 inch. If some form of hose clip is being used to compress the piston rings it may be found that the screw housing prevents the clip from lying exactly flush with the cylinder head. Here again watch carefully to ensure that no part of the ring slips from under the control of the clamp. Make sure also that the clamp is not gripping the piston tightly otherwise you will not be able to move it into the bore. (photo).
7 When all four assemblies have been inserted position the connecting rods so that they will not interfere with the crankshaft when it is replaced. Check that the connecting rod bearing shells are properly positioned with the notches engaging in their respective positions.

26 Crankshaft and seals - replacement

1 It is simpler to replace the pistons and connecting rods before the crankshaft. Ensure that the crankcase is thoroughly clean and that all oilways are clear. If possible blow the drillings out with compressed air.
2 It is best to take out the plug at each end of the main oil gallery in the cylinder block and so clean out the oilways to the crankshaft bearing housings. Replace the plugs using jointing compound to make an oil tight seal.
3 Treat the crankshaft in the same fashion and then inject engine oil into the crankshaft oilways.
4 Thoroughly clean the main bearing shell locations in the crankcase and carefully fit each half shell into the five locations.
5 The centre bearing shell has no oil groove and the No 5 bearing shell is flanged to control the crankshaft end float (photos).
6 New bearings may have over-thick flanges which will need reducing

in order to permit the crankshaft to be replaced and fitted with the correct amount of end float, which is from .002 inch to .010 inch. End float, which is the amount a crankshaft can move endways, is measured between the centre bearing upper shell flange and the bearing surface on the web of the crankshaft, with the crankshaft moved to one extreme of its end float travel.
7 It will be necessary to reduce the shell bearing flange thickness by rubbing it down evenly on an engineers flat bed covered with fine emery cloth. This is done progressively until a feeler blade of .002 inch thickness can be placed between the flange and the crankshaft web.
8 NOTE that at the back of each bearing is a tab which engages in locating grooves in either the crankcase or the main bearing cap housings.
9 If new bearings are being fitted, carefully clean away all traces of any protective grease or coating with which they may have been treated.
10 With the upper bearing shells securely in place, wipe the lower bearing cap housing and fit the five lower shell bearings to their caps ensuring that the right shell goes into the right cap.
   Check that the rear oil seal groove in the crankcase is completely free of old jointing compound and that the bearing cap faces throughout are similarly clean. Remove all traces of oil. When quite clean and dry apply 'Hylomar' jointing compound sparingly into the crankcase seal groove. Then fit the half of the seal into the groove firmly and with the ends protruding above the face of the crankcase (photo). Early engines were fitted with rubber composition seals and later models with braided fabric versions. Both are provided in the gasket set and either may be used. With the fabric seal make sure it is pressed fully into place - use a wooden hammer handle. The ends must be carefully trimmed to protrude no more than .020 inch and no frayed threads must be left to get trapped between the bearing cap and crankcase. Coat the seal with molybdenum paste or grease (Castrol MS3).
11 Thoroughly lubricate the main bearing shells with engine oil and lower the crankshaft carefully into position. Check the end float with a feeler gauge as described in paragraph 7.
12 Next fit the other half of the rear bearing oil seal into the groove in the cap, having first lightly smeared the groove with 'Hylomar' jointing compound. Take the same precautions as for the other half when using the braided fabric seal (photo).
13 Clean the bearing surface of the caps and position all the five shell bearings to them in the same way as was done for the others.
14 The front and rear main bearing caps need a trace of 'Hylomar' jointing compound across them to prevent oil leaks. It should be sparingly applied in the positions indicated in Fig 1.16 (photo).
15 Next lubricate all the journals with engine oil and fit the front and rear caps in position with the flat end faces flush with the ends of the crankcase (photo).
16 Place the other three caps in position the correct way round - as a guide the members should all be the same way (photos).
17 Replace the cap bolts in all bearings and nip them all up lightly. Turn the crankshaft to ensure it revolves freely and then start with No 1 and tighten the bolts of each cap to the correct torque of 83 lb ft (photo).
18 After tightening each cap turn the crankshaft by hand to ensure it is not binding. A reground crank may be a little stiff but it should be possible to turn it by hand without excess effort. If any bearing binds tight then something is wrong.
19 If the crank is a reground one check the journal diameters and bearing shell sizes. Do not hope that a very tight fit will ease up later after some running. It might - but 99 times out of 100 the bearing will bind and the surface 'pick up'. Then you will have to take everything apart once more.
20 The crankshaft front seal can be renewed if necessary without engine removal. All that is required is for the drive belt, fan belt and crankshaft pulley wheel to be removed.
21 Ideally the seal is removed by a special threaded tube puller which bites into the internal diameter. However, if care is taken it can be dug out with a sharp pointed tool. When this is done the shaft itself

19.2b Oil pump suction pipe securing plate

19.4 Oil pump suction pipe - 'O' ring seal

21.6 Checking a new ring gap above the ridge in an un-rebored cylinder

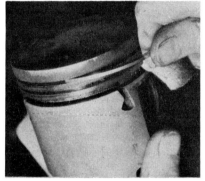

21.8 Cleaning out the ring groove in a piston with a piece of broken ring

21.9 Fitting a 3 part oil control ring in the bottom groove

25.2 Ring gaps spaced equally round the piston

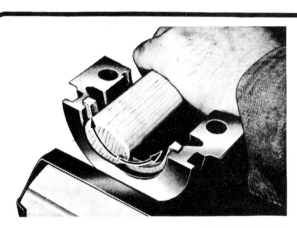

Fig.1.15. Crankshaft rear main bearing fabric seal. (later models). Using a hammer handle to press seal into groove.

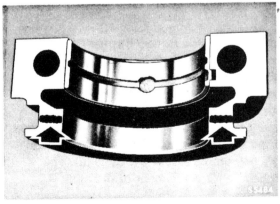

Fig.1.16. Crankshaft front and rear main bearing caps. Application of 'Hylomar' jointing compound (arrowed).

25.5 Clamping piston rings and putting the pistons and connecting rods into the cylinders

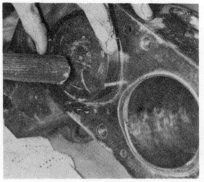
25.6 Tapping the piston into the bore

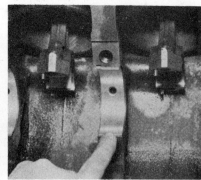
26.5a Main bearing showing plain centre shell No 3

26.5b Main bearing showing flanged rear shell No 5

26.10 Fit half the seal into the crankcase seal groove with the ends protruding above the face of the crankcase

26.11a Lubricate the bearing shells

26.11b Crankshaft ready to go into the bearings

26.11c Crankshaft in position

26.12 Fitting the other half of the rear bearing oil seal

26.14 Smearing jointing compound on the bearing caps

26.15 Lubricating the crankshaft journals

26.16a Replacing bearing caps

26.16b Note number on bearing cap

26.17 Tightening main bearing cap bolts with a torque wrench

26.22 Preparing the crankshaft front oil seal

26.23a Refitting the crankshaft front oil seal

26.23b Drifting the oil seal home

27.3a Fitting big end cap

27.3b Check the numbers match

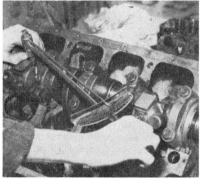

27.5 Tightening big end bearing bolts with a torque spanner

28.3 Fitting the sump end seals into the bearing cap grooves

28.4 Putting 'Bostik' 771 sealing compound onto the sump seal ends

28.5 Positioning the sump gasket

28.6a Fitting sump gasket and sump

must not be scored - neither should the seal housing.

22 When fitting a new seal first ensure that the housing is quite clean. Smear the seal lip with molybdenum paste or grease and the outer periphery with Hylomar sealing compound (photo).

23 Carefully drive it in squarely with a flat nosed punch or drift until it is flush with crankcase and bearing cap face (photo).

27 Connecting rods (big ends) - refitting to crankshaft

1 With the crankshaft replaced and all main bearing bolts tightened, the pistons replaced in the cylinders and shell bearings fitted in their rods with the locating tongues in their grooves, position the crankshaft so that the two centre or two end crankpins are conveniently placed for drawing the connecting rods up to them.

2 If not already done wipe the connecting rod bearing cap and back of the shell bearing clean, and fit the shell bearing in position ensuring that the locating tongue at the back of the bearing engages with the locating groove in the connecting rod cap.

3 Make sure the cap fits the correct rod by checking the numbers matching marks already made and see that the spring dowel pins are intact (photo).

4 Generously lubricate the shell bearing and offer up the connecting rod bearing cap to the connecting rod.

5 Fit the connecting rod bolts with oiled threads and tighten them down with a torque spanner to 47 lb ft (photo).

6 Rotate the crankshaft (it will be fairly stiff because of the drag of the piston rings in the bores - if very stiff slacken the bearing caps to ensure it is not due to a binding bearing) so that the other two crankpins are in position for the connecting rods and replace them in the same way.

7 Oil the cylinder bores generously for initial lubrication.

28 Sump - replacement

1 Before fitting the sump check that the oil pump suction pipe and strainer are correctly fitted (Section 19) and that all bearing cap bolts are tight.

2 The sump should have been thoroughly cleaned out and the flange mating surfaces of both the sump and crankcase perfectly cleaned free of all traces of old gasket. Check that the sump lies flat on the crankcase and that the flanges are not bent or damaged in any way.

3 Two specially shaped seals (included in the gasket set) are provided for the front and rear bearing caps. Ensure that the grooves and steps where the ends fit are perfectly clean and dry. Then apply a smear of 'Hylomar' jointing compound into the groove and onto the step where the ends fit and place the seals into the grooves (photo).

4 Place a blob of Bostik 771 compound on top of the ends of the seal as well (photo).

5 Put the cork sump gaskets in position on the crankcase so that the ends bed with the compound and overlap the end seals. If the sump is being replaced with the engine in the car it is a good idea to stick the cork gasket to the crankcase with grease to hold it in place. It is not recommended that jointing compound be used (photo).

6 Refit the sump without distrubing the position of the gaskets and replace all the set screws (remembering the clutch cable clip on the one you marked) and tighten them evenly. Do not overtighten (photos).

29 Flywheel - replacement

1 The flywheel is located on two dowel pegs and can only be fitted one way because the five bolt holes are not symmetrically arranged (photo).

2 Locate the flywheel on the dowels and tap it home square.

3 Replace the five bolts (there are no washers) and tighten them evenly to the correct torque of 48 lb ft on clean dry threads. The flywheel may be held with a screwdriver in the teeth wedged against the bell-housing dowel peg whilst the bolts are being tightened (photos).

30 Valves and springs - reassembly to cylinder head

1 The valves and head should all be thoroughly clean before reassembly. If the same valves are being refitted they should return to the same place. It is good practice to smear the stems with a molybdenum or graphite paste before inserting them in the guides (photo).

2 Fit new valve stem seals and clips (these may be fitted on early engines which did not have them originally) over the shoulders of the valve guide extension on the top of the head.

3 Replace the inner and outer coil springs and the retaining collar over them (photos).

4 Compress the springs using the tool until it is possible to fit the two split collars around the valve stem so that they engage the groove (photo).

5 Release the spring compressor whilst watching to ensure that the two collets do not slip out of the groove. When released tap the valve stem end with a mallet to 'bounce' it and ensure that everything is properly seated.

31 Cylinder head - replacement

1 Before replacing the cylinder head check that the oil passageway is clear. Early engines have a port flush with the block surface but later engines have either a hollow spring pin protruding .12 inch from the block with an 'O' ring round it; or a combined dowel and restrictor fitted with an even larger 'O' ring. If you have an early head which you wish to fit to a new half engine fitted with a dowel and restrictor then the oil passage hole in the head should be drilled out to $5/16$ inch to a depth of ½ inch. At the same time the two holes for the head locating pegs will also have to be drilled out with a $9/32$ inch drill to a depth of ½ inch. This is because with the restrictor, the locating pins fitted are larger so that they engage first when the head is replaced. Note that the camshaft housing may need modification also (see subsequent section). It is also possible to fit the hollow spring pin and 'O' ring to those early engines which may have had leakage difficulties from the oil transfer passage.

2 The surfaces of both cylinder block and head must be perfectly clean and dry.

3 Place the cylinder head gasket in position on the block making quite sure that it is the correct way up - it will be fairly obvious if it is not. The gaskets for 1599 cc and 1975 cc engines are different. The cylinder apertures for the larger engine are circular and there is an identifying tab (see Fig 1.18).

Do not use any seal or grease on the head gasket.

4 Place the cylinder head squarely in position, taking care not to damage the protruding pegs before it fits over them (photo).

5 Replace the ten cylinder head bolts and nip them all down lightly.

6 Cylinder head bolts are very tight and must be tightened down evenly and in the correct order as indicated in Fig 1.19. Tighten all bolts down first to a torque of 45 lb ft in the order shown and then go round again tightening to the final torque of 83 lb ft (photo).

7 The inlet and exhaust manifolds may be replaced next or after the camshaft housing if wished.

8 The exhaust manifold requires a combined heat shield and gasket. A used gasket may be re-used provided it is not damaged or burnt. Carefully clean off any carbon traces. The bolts are replaced with a lock tab to each pair and should be tightened up moderately. Do not overdo it, and break a bolt (photos).

9 Bend down a tab against a convenient flat on each bolt head.

10 The inlet manifold can be replaced with the carburettor fitted or otherwise. First of all make sure you fit the correct gaskets. On later 1975 cc engines with the Stromberg carburettor (not VX 4/90) a modified cylinder head is used. This has an additional water jacket and the rear inlet manifold gasket has an extra hole to match as shown in Fig 1.20 (photos).

11 Check that the manifold studs in the head are tight and before placing the gaskets in position smear sealing compound round the water jacket holes on both sides.

Fig.1.17. Cylinder head - Oil transfer passage from cylinder block fitted with spring pin (1) and 'O' ring (2). Dimension 'A' is .12 ins.

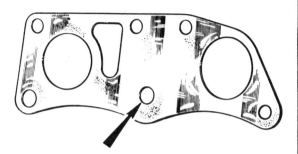

Fig.1.20. Inlet manifold gasket. Rear gasket with additional hole for 1975 cc engines fitted with Stromberg carburettor (not VX 4/90).

Fig.1.18. Cylinder head gaskets - Identification
    A. 1975 cc (note tab arrowed)
    B. 1599 cc.

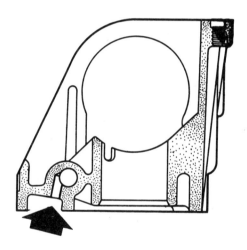

Fig.1.21. Camshaft housing - cross section showing oil gallery transfer orifice (arrowed)

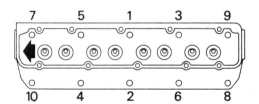

Fig.1.19. Cylinder head. Bolt tightening sequence. Arrow points to front.

28.6b Tightening down sump

29.1 Flywheel replacement

29.3a Tightening flywheel bolts

29.3b Holding the flywheel while tightening the bolts

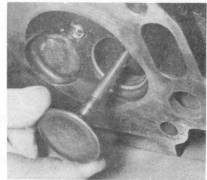

30.1 Fitting valve into guide

30.3a Replacing valve springs

30.3b Replacing valve upper collar

30.4 Compressing the valve springs and fitting the colletts

31.4 Replacing the cylinder head

31.6 Tightening cylinder head bolts

31.8a Replacing exhaust manifold

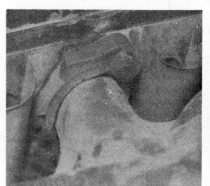

31.8b Lock tabs and bolts on the exhaust manifold

31.10a Inlet manifold replacement showing two different gaskets

31.10b Tightening of the securing bolt in the thermostat housing

32.5a Lubricating camshaft bearings before reassembly

32.5b Inserting the camshaft into its bearings

32.6 Camshaft thrust washer fitted with cut-out upwards

32.7 Replacing the camshaft washer and bolt

32.8 Tightening the camshaft bolt using a self-grip wrench to hold the camshaft

32.9 Fitting camshaft rear end cover. Note lug (arrowed) which engages in thrust washer cut-out

32.10a Fitting a camshaft front oil seal

32.10b Tapping home the camshaft front oil seal

32.11 Replacing tappets in camshaft housing

33.2 Fitting camshaft housing gasket to cylinder head

12 Replace the bolts and the nuts - all of which have lockwashers and tighten them evenly. The bolt which fits inside the thermostat aperture should have a new copper washer under the head. Do not forget to reconnect the water pipe from the pump.

32 Camshaft, camshaft housing and tappets - reassembly

1 The camshaft must be fitted into the housing before fitting the housing to the head.
2 Smear all the bearing surfaces of the camshaft with an oil treated with graphite or molybdenum disulphide.
3 To check the end float, before fitting the shaft into the housing fit the thrust washer, retaining washer and original securing bolt to the rear end and check the gap between the two washers.
4 If you are fitting an early type camshaft housing to a later type cylinder head (see Section 31) with a dowel/restrictor fitted in the oil transfer port it will be necessary to bore out the corresponding port in the camshaft housing to $3/16$ inch. The depth of the hole should be no more than .74 inch below the housing bottom face (Fig 1.21).
5 Lubricate the bearings and then insert the camshaft into the housing from the front (photos).
6 Fit the thrust washer so that the cut-out faces upwards where it it will engage with the lug in the cover (photo).
7 The retaining bolt is locked with a nylon insert and a new one should be used. If not, use a proprietary locking compound on the bolt threads (photo).
8 Grip the camshaft with self-grips whilst tightening the bolt (photo).
9 Using a new gasket refit the end cover so that the lug engages in the thrust washer cut-out and tighten the securing bolts (photo).
10 Fit a new oil seal in the front end of the housing. Smear the inner lip with molybdenum paste or grease and fit it facing inwards. Tap it home square (photos)
11 Lubricate the tappet bores in the housing and replace the tappets into the same locations from which they came. If you have removed the tappet adjusting screws for any reason they should be screwed in first so that the flat section faces the open end of the tappet and is approximately central across the tappet diameter. If any of the tappets look like dropping out easily under gravity use a smear of grease to hold them in position (photo).

33 Camshaft housing assembly - replacement

1 Make sure the cylinder head bolts are all correctly tightened down.
2 Place a new gasket in position on the cylinder head noting that the hole for the oil transfer passage should line up (photo).
3 With 1599 cc HC engines make sure that the crankshaft pulley timing mark is set approximately 90º BTDC to ensure valve to piston crown clearance (all pistons are halfway down the cylinders in this position).
4 Place the camshaft housing assembly in position without letting the tappets fall out of their locations in the process. Engage it over the dowels at each end of the head, and ensure the gasket position is not disturbed (photo).
5 The assembly will not seat right down yet because some valves will be opposite cams in the open position. Replace all the mounting bolts and using a pattern similar to that of tightening the cylinder head, tighten them all evenly a little at a time to the correct torque of 15 lb ft (photo).
6 Replace the pulley wheel over the key and fit the washer and bolt. The bolts may be tightened fully later after the belt has been replaced.

34 Auxiliary shaft - replacement

1 The drive belt and pulley, fuel pump and distributor must be removed before the shaft can be refitted.
2 Lubricate the bearings with oil (treated with graphite or molybdenum disulphide) and place the shaft with the 'U' shaped thrust

washer located in the shaft groove into position in the block. The small notch in the thrust washer should engage the dowel peg in the housing (photo).
3 Lubricate the oil seal lip with molybdenum paste or grease and place it over the shaft open side first (photo).
4 Carefully tap the seal squarely into position until it stops up against the thrust washer.
5 Fit the pulley over the key and replace the washer and bolt. The bolt can be tightened after the belt is replaced (photo).

35 Oil pump - replacement

1 The oil pump may be refitted with the auxiliary shaft in position or not.
2 Fit new 'O' rings into the grooves around ports in the bottom cover and oil the ports in the cylinder block where they will press in. It is important that the 'O' rings are not dragged out of position when the pump is pushed into position (photo).
3 Place a new gasket in position on the block (photo).
4 If the auxiliary shaft is installed hold the pump so that the opening in the body (for the gear of the auxiliary shaft) is 90º clockwise from the gear position. Put the pump into the housing and turn it anticlockwise 90º to line up the ports at the bottom (photo).
5 Do not press the flange of the pump body to push it down into position. Use a tube or socket of some sort in the centre of the body in order to tap it down (photo).
6 The pump is finally secured by the same bolts that hold the distributor in position.

36 Drive belt replacement and valve timing

1 The drive belt controls the valve timing and it is imperative to get it fitted in exactly the correct tooth.
2 Before running the drive belt for any reason other than when an engine is undergoing a complete overhaul the crankshaft pulley timing mark must be set at 90º BTDC on HC 1599 cc engines. In this position all the pistons are halfway down the cylinders and there is no chance of them fouling the valves when the camshaft pulley is independently turned.
3 When replacing the belt the crankshaft pulley should first be positioned, as for removal.
4 The auxiliary shaft and camshaft should then be turned so that their timing marks and the shaft centre lines line in a straight line, the timing marks being at the ends of the line.
5 The camshaft pulley mark is a round depression on the front face and the auxiliary pulley mark is a V notch on the front face. Ignore the circular mark on the rear of the auxiliary shaft pulley.
6 Use a straight edge to line up the marks and centres (photo).
7 Next turn the crankshaft clockwise (use a spanner on the pulley bolt) until the timing mark in the front face of the flange is lined up with the TDC pointer (the upper one). If a belt cover is fitted it will be necessary to replace this temporarily as the timing marks are moulded on its front face.
8 Without disturbing the position of the pulleys, fit the drive belt with the chalked arrow pointing in the direction of movement. There should be very little slack apparent between the auxiliary and camshaft pulleys and camshaft and crankshaft pulleys when the teeth are engaged. There will be more between the crankshaft and auxiliary shaft pulleys as this is where the jockey pulley goes (photo).
9 Position and lock the jockey pulley to give moderate tension (photo). Then rotate the crankshaft once more and stop at TDC again. This will automatically put the correct tension on the section of belt between the camshaft and crankshaft pulleys because the greatest valve spring drag will be applied to the camshaft in this position. (If you inadvertently overshoot the TDC position go round again. Do not reverse!).

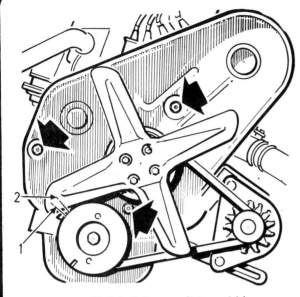

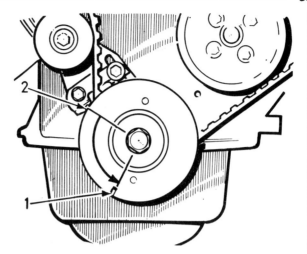

Fig.1.22. Drive belt cover - (later models)

Note securing points (arrowed) and ignition timing marks. (1 and 2).

Fig.1.23. Drive belt replacement. Positioning crankshaft pulley timing mark (1) 90° before T.D.C. pointer (2) to ensure valve/ piston clearance.

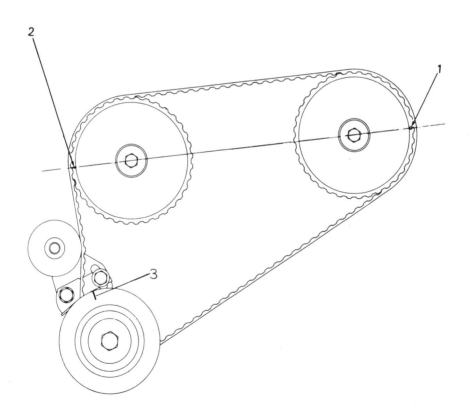

Fig.1.24. Camshaft drive belt. Alignment of camshaft pulley timing mark '1' and auxiliary shaft pulley mark '2' with crankshaft pulley mark '3' at T.D.C.

33.4 Placing the camshaft housing assembly into position

33.5 Tightening the camshaft housing bolts to the cylinder head

33.6 Replacing the camshaft pulley and locking bolt

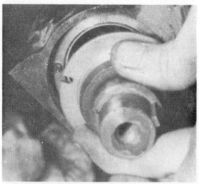

34.2 Putting the auxiliary shaft together with the thrust washer into the block. Note notch which engages the peg in the bearing housing

34.3 Placing the auxiliary shaft retainer/oil seal in position

34.5 Replacing the auxiliary shaft pulley

35.2 Oil pump showing oil port 'O' rings in position

35.3 Placing oil pump gasket in position

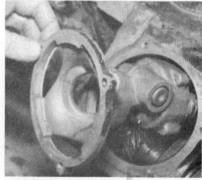

35.4 Putting the oil pump into position

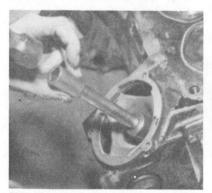

35.5 Tapping the oil pump down onto its seating using a socket and extension

36.6 Lining up the camshaft and auxiliary shaft timing marks with a straight edge

36.8 Fitting the timing belt (it is not yet round the crankshaft pulley)

36.9 Adjusting the drive belt jockey pulley

37.6 Turning the tappet with a screwdriver in the notch

37.7 Measuring tappet clearance with a feeler blade

37.9 Turning the tappet clearance adjusting screw with a hexagonal section key

37.11a Fitting a new gasket to the camshaft housing cover

37.11b Fitting the camshaft housing

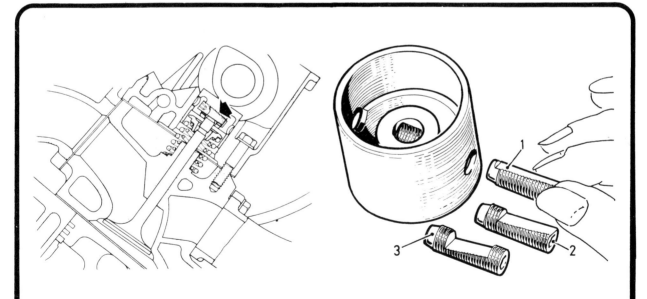

Fig.1.25. Cylinder head/camshaft housing.
Cross section to show position of valve clearance adjusting screw relative to tappet and valve stem.

Fig.1.26. Valve clearance adjustment. 3 types of adjusting screw.

1. Standard
2. 1st undersize (inadequate gap obtainable with standard screw)
3. 2nd undersize (inadequate gap obtainable with 1st undersize)

10 The rest of the belt tension is adjusted by movement of the jockey pulley. A 10 lb load applied midway between the auxiliary and camshaft pulleys should deflect the belt .30 inch. It is important to remember that this tension must be checked only when the tension between camshaft and crankshaft pulleys has been set and left as described in the previous paragraph.

11 A belt set too tight will whine. A slack belt wears out quickly.

12 Tighten all pulley bolts.

37 Valve tappet clearances - adjustment

1 In order that the valves open the correct amount and to provide tolerance for thermal expansion the gap between the face of the cam and the tappet (which fits over the end of the valve stem) must be correctly set.

2 The clearances may be set with the engine in the car after removal of the camshaft housing cover.

3 Each tappet contains a screw running laterally across it with a tapered flat in the screw which bears on the end of the valve stem. The movement of the screw in or out alters the relative distance between the end of the valve stem and the tappet face.

4 Access to the end of the adjusting screw is through a hole in the side of the tappet. This hole must be aligned with the cut-out part of the housing by revolving the tappet. There are holes in the tappet at both ends of the screw and the one which has the socket head is indicated by a small notch in the top edge of the tappet.

4 In order to identify the valve clearance requirement, early engines with the smaller clearances can be recognised by a groove in the front end of the camshaft behind the pulley.

5 Valve clearances are set when the valve is fully closed - that is when the tappet is bearing on the lowest point of the cam - this position is easy to see - the highest point of the cam is directly opposite.

6 Turn the tappet with a screwdriver in the notch in the top edge until the screw opening is visible (photo).

7 Measure the gap with a feeler blade. If the engine has not been run because of overhaul and is therefore cold the gap initially should be .003 inch less than specified (photo).

8 Having measured the gap accurately adjustment is necessary if it is not within the given range (which is inclusive).

9 The adjusting screw must be turned one complete revolution clockwise or anticlockwise to decrease or increase the gap respectively by .003 inch (photo). A measured gap of .006 inch will therefore be increased to .009 inch if the adjusting screw is given one complete anticlockwise turn.

If a measured gap of .005 inch occurred on a cold engine one would decide whether .008 inch (+.003) fell within the range and adjust as necessary.

10 Once the cold clearances have been set they must be checked and adjusted again if necessary, when the engine is hot.

11 Refit the camshaft housing cover carefully - and preferably with a new gasket. As the gasket curves it is important to ensure that it is not dislodged during replacement (photos).

38 Engine - final reassembly of the major overhaul

1 The ancillary components which were removed as listed in Section 6 (Engine ancillaries - removal) should be replaced as far as possible before putting the engine back in the car. Accessibility will be far better. One particular point to take care over is the fitting of the water pump inlet elbow short hose. Make sure the joining surfaces are clean and the hose is in good condition.

It may be worthwhile replacing the manufacturers wire type hose clips with the more positive worm screw drive type.

39 Engine - replacement in car

1 Replacement of the engine is a reversal of the removal procedure. A little trouble in getting the engine properly slung so that it takes up a suspended attitude similar to its final position will pay off when it comes to getting it set easily on the front engine mountings.

2 Refit the gearbox propeller shaft as described in the appropriate chapters. Do not forget to connect the exhaust pipe to the manifold.

3 It is likely that the engine will be initially stiff to turn if new bearings and rings have been fitted and it will save a lot of irritation if the battery is well charged. After a rebore the stiffness may be more than the battery can cope with so be prepared to link another up in parallel with jumper leads.

4 The following final check list should ensure that the engine starts safely and with the minimum of delay:

a) Fuel lines to pump and carburettor - connected and tightened.
b) Water hoses connected and clipped.
c) Radiator and engine drain taps closed.
d) Cooling system replenished.
e) Sump drain plug fitted and tight.
f) Oil in engine
g) Oil in gearbox and level plug tight.
h) LT wires connected to distributor and coil.
j) Oil pressure and water temperature sender units screwed in tight and leads connected.
k) Spark plugs tight.
l) Tappet clearances set correctly
m) HT leads connected securely to distributor, spark plugs and coil.
n) Rotor arm replaced in distributor.
o) Choke and throttle cables connected.
p) Braided earthing cable, engine to frame reconnected.
q) Starter motor lead connected.
r) Fan belt fitted and correctly tensioned.
s) Generator leads connected.
t) Battery charged and leads connected to clean terminals.

5 Once the engine has started set the throttle stop screw to a fast tickover and let it run until fully warmed up - five minutes at least. Watch it all the time and keep an eye open for water or oil leaks.

Fault Finding Chart - Engine

NOTE: When investigating starting and uneven running faults do not be tempted into a snap diagnosis. Start from the beginning of the check procedure and follow it through. It will take less time in the long run. Poor performance from an engine in terms of power and economy is not normally diagnosed quickly. In any event the ignition and fuel systems must be checked first before assuming any further investigation needs to be made.

Symptom	Reason/s	Remedy
Engine will not turn over when starter switch is operated	Flat battery Bad battery connections Bad connections at solenoid switch and/or starter motor	Check that battery is fully charged and that all connections are clean and tight.
	Starter motor jammed	Turn the square headed end of the starter motor shaft with a spanner to free it. Where a pre-engaged starter is fitted rock the car back and forth with a gear engaged. If this does not free pinion remove starter.
	Defective solenoid	Bridge the main terminals of the solenoid switch with a piece of heavy duty cable in order to operate the starter.
	Starter motor defective	Remove and overhaul starter motor.
Engine turns over normally but fails to fire and run	No spark at plugs	Check ignition system according to procedures given in Chapter 4.
	No fuel reaching engine	Check fuel system according to procedures given in Chapter 3.
	Too much fuel reaching the engine (flooding)	Check the fuel system as above.
Engine starts but runs unevenly and misfires	Ignition and/or fuel system faults	Check the ignition and fuel systems as though the engine had failed to start.
	Incorrect valve clearances	Check and reset clearances.
	Burnt out valves Blown cylinder head gasket	Remove cylinder head and examine and overhaul as necessary.
	Worn out piston rings Worn cylinder bores	Remove cylinder head and examine pistons and cylinder bores. Overhaul as necessary.
Lack of power	Ignition and/or fuel system faults	Check the ignition and fuel systems for correct ignition timing and carburettor settings.
	Incorrect valve clearances	Check and reset the clearances.
	Burnt out valves Blown cylinder head gasket	Remove cylinder head and examine and overhaul as necessary.
	Worn out piston rings Worn cylinder bores	Remove cylinder head and examine pistons and cylinder bores. Overhaul as necessary.
Excessive oil consumption	Oil leaks from crankshaft front and rear oil seals camshaft oil seal, auxiliary shaft oil seal, cambox gasket, oil filter, sump gasket or drain plug	Identify source of leak and renew seal as appropriate.
	Worn piston rings or cylinder bores resulting in oil being burnt by engine, smoky exhaust is an indication	Fit new rings or rebore cylinders and fit new pistons, depending on degree of wear.
	Worn valve guides and/or defective valve stem seals	Remove cylinder heads and recondition valve stem bores and valves and seals as necessary.
Excessive mechanical noise from engine	Wrong valve to rocker clearances	Adjust valve clearances.
	Worn crankshaft bearings Worn cylinders (piston slap).	Inspect and overhaul where necessary.
Unusual vibration	Fan blade broken off	Break off another fan blade to balance fan until renewal is possible.
	Broken engine/gearbox mounting	Renew mounting.
	Misfiring on one or more cylinders	Check ignition system.

Chapter 2 Cooling system

Contents

Specifications

Type of system	Pressurised, pump assisted circulation with thermostat temperature control
Capacity	
with heater	13.5 pints
without heater...	12.4 pints
Radiator	
leak test pressure	20 lb/in^2
filler cap valve opening pressure	13½–17½ lb/in^2
Fan belt	V pulley drive Tension set to .36 ins (9 mm) midway between pump and generator pulleys (53 lb linear tension).

Thermostat	AC	Western Thomson
Starts to open at	80–84ºC	85º–89ºC
Fully open at	98ºC	99º–102ºC
Opening distance (minimum)	.48 in (12 mm)	.51 in (13 mm)

1 General description

The engine cooling water is circulated by a thermosyphon, water pump assisted system, and the coolant is pressurised. This is both to prevent the loss of water down the overflow pipe with the radiator cap in position and to prevent premature boiling in adverse conditions.

The radiator cap is, in effect, a safety valve designed to lift at a pressure of 13½–17½ lbs sq inch which means that the coolant can reach a temperature above 212ºF (100ºC) before it lifts the cap. It then boils off, steam escaping down the overflow pipe. When the temperature/pressure decreases the cap reseats until the temperature/pressure builds up again. In addition there is a vacuum valve in the cap which permits air to enter the system when it cools down, Fig 2.1

It is therefore important to check that the radiator cap fitted is of the correct specification (the relief pressure is stamped on the top) and in good condition, and that the spring behind the sealing washer has not weakened. Most garages have a device in which radiator caps can be tested.

The system functions in the following fashion: Cold water in the bottom of the radiator circulates up the lower radiator hose to the water pump where it is pushed round the water passages in the cylinder block, helping to keep the cylinder bores and pistons cool.

The water then travels up into the cylinder head and circulates round the combustion spaces and valve seats absorbing more heat, and then when the engine is at its proper operating temperature, travels out of the cylinder head, past the open thermostat into the upper radiator hose and so into the radiator head tank.

The water travels down the radiator where it is cooled by the inrush of cold air through the radiator core, which is created by both the fan and the motion of the car. The water, now cold, reaches the bottom of the radiator, whereupon the cycle is repeated.

When the engine is cold the thermostat (a valve which opens and closes according to the temperature of the water) maintains the circulation of the same water in the engine, excluding that in the radiator.

The cooling system comprises the radiator, top and bottom water hoses, heater hoses (if heater/demister fitted) the impeller water pump (mounted on the front of the engine it carries the fan blades and is driven by the fan belt), the thermostat and two drain taps.

Only when the correct minimum operating temperature has been reached, as shown in the specification, does the thermostat begin to open, allowing water to return to the radiator.

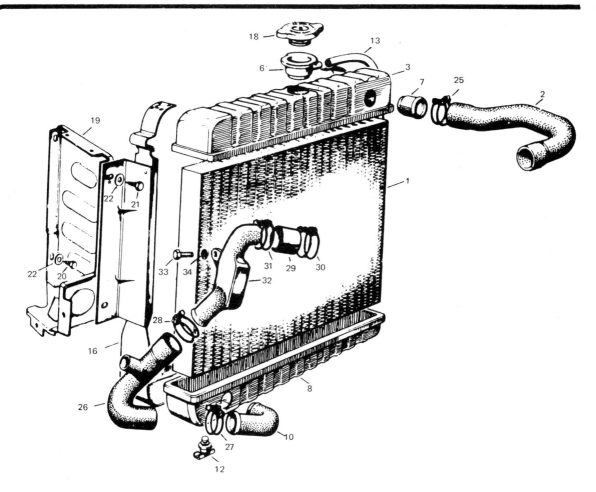

Fig 2.1 RADIATOR AND FITTINGS

1 Radiator core	13 Overflow pipe	24 Inlet hose	31 Hose clip
3 Top tank	16 Assembly strap	25 Hose clip	32 Inlet elbow
6 Filler neck	18 Filler cap	26 Outlet hose	33 Bolt
7 Inlet pipe	19 Support bracket	27 Hose clip	34 Lockwasher
8 Bottom tank	20 Self tap screws	28 Hose clip	
10 Outlet pipe	21 Self tap screws	29 Hose - pump to elbow	
12 Drain tap	22 Plain washer	30 Hose clip	

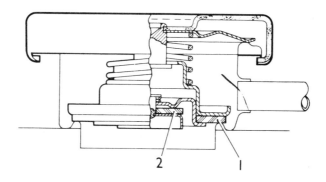

Fig 2.2 RADIATOR PRESSURE/FILLER CAP
1 Pressure valve seating   2 Vacuum valve seating

2 Cooling system - draining

1 With the car on level ground drain the system as follows:

2 If the engine is cold remove the filler cap from the radiator by turning the cap anticlockwise. If the engine is hot having just been run, then turn the filler cap very slightly until the pressure in the system has had time to disperse. Use a rag over the cap to protect your hand from escaping steam. If, with the engine very hot, the cap is released suddenly, the drop in pressure can result in the water boiling. With the pressure released the cap can be removed.

3 If antifreeze is in the radiator drain it into a clean bucket or bowl for re-use.

4 Open the two drain taps. The radiator drain tap is on the bottom radiator tank, and the engine drain tap is halfway down the rear left hand side of the cylinder block.

5 When the water has finished running, probe the drain tap orifices with a short piece of wire to dislodge any particles of rust or sediment which may be blocking the taps and preventing all the water draining out.

NOTE: Opening only the radiator tap will not drain the cylinder block.

3 Cooling system - flushing

1 With time the cooling system will gradually lose its efficiency as the radiator becomes choked with rust scales, deposits from the water and other sediment. To clean the system out, remove the radiator cap and the drain tap and leave a hose running in the radiator cap orifice for ten to fifteen minutes.

2 In very bad cases the radiator should be reverse flushed. This can be done with the radiator in position. A hose must be arranged to feed water into the lower radiator outlet pipe. Water, under pressure, is then forced up through the radiator and out of the header tank filler orifice.

3 The hose is removed and placed in the filler orifice and the radiator washed out in the usual fashion.

4 Cooling system - filling

1 Close the two drain taps.

2 Fill the system slowly to ensure that air locks are minimised.

3 Do not fill the system higher than within ½ inch of the filler orifice. Overfilling will merely result in wastage, which is especially to be avoided when antifreeze is in use.

4 Only use antifreeze mixture with an ethylene glycol base. Vauxhall also use an anti-corrosion inhibitor - adding $1/8$ pint each month for the first six months is recommended. Thereafter it should be added each time the coolant is changed. If the inhibitor is used it is strongly recommended that Vauxhall antifreeze is also used to prevent possible chemical incompatibility.

5 Replace the filler cap and turn it firmly clockwise to lock it in position.

5 Radiator removal, inspection, cleaning and replacement

1 Drain the cooling system as described in Section 12.

2 Undo the clip which holds the top water hose to the thermostat outlet and pull it off (photo).

3 Remove the hose from the heater (if fitted) where it joins the main bottom radiator hose (photo), and disconnect the hose from the elbow fitted to the front of the block.

4 Remove the screws securing each side of the radiator to the body panels and lift it out complete with hoses (photos). On later models with GM automatic transmission the oil cooler is housed in the bottom of the radiator. When disconnecting the oil pipes they must be protected against dirt entering. The fluid level in the transmission must be checked after replacement.

5 Clean out the inside of the radiator by flushing as described in Section 3. When the radiator is out of the car it is well worthwhile to invert it for reverse flushing. Clean the exterior of the radiator by hosing down the matrix (honeycomb cooling material) with a strong water jet to clear away embedded dirt and insects which will impede the air flow.

6 If it is thought that the radiator may be partially blocked, a good proprietary chemical product such as 'Radflush' should be used to clear it.

9 Inspect the radiator hoses for cracks, internal or external perishing, and damage caused by the securing clips. Replace the hoses as necessary. Examine the radiator hose securing clips and renew them if they are rusted or distorted. The drain taps should be renewed if leaking, but ensure the leak is not caused by a faulty washer behind the tap. If the tap is suspected try a new washer first to see if this clears the trouble.

10 Replacement is a straightforward reversal of the removal procedure.

6 Thermostat removal, testing and replacement

1 To remove the thermostat, partially drain the cooling system (four pints is enough), loosen the upper radiator hose at the thermostat elbow end and pull it off the elbow.

2 Unscrew the two set bolts and spring washers from the thermostat housing and lift the housing and gasket away.

3 Remove the thermostat and suspend it by a piece of string in a saucepan of cold water together with a thermometer. Neither the thermostat nor the thermometer should touch the bottom of the saucepan, to ensure a false reading is not given.

4 Heat the water, stirring it gently with the thermometer to ensure temperature uniformity, and note when the thermostat begins to open. The temperature at which this should happen is given in the specification, and see also Fig 2.4.

5 Discard the thermostat if it opens too early. Continue heating the water until the thermostat is fully open. Then let it cool down naturally. If the thermostat will not open fully in boiling water, or does not close down as the water cools, then it must be exchanged for a new one.

6 If the thermostat is stuck open when cold, this will be apparent when removing it from the housing.

7 Replacing the thermostat is a reversal of the removal procedure. Remember to use a new paper gasket between the thermostat housing elbow and the thermostat (photo).

7 Water pump - removal and replacement

1 Partially drain the cooling system as described in Section 2.

2 Undo the clips which hold the hoses to the water pump and pull the hoses off. This involves removing the top hose first, followed by the elbow bolted to the front of the block (photos).

3 Remove the fan belt and the fan blades followed by the drive belt cover if fitted (photo). On later models with an eight-bladed fan the radiator will need removal also.

4 Undo the four bolts which hold the pump body to the cylinder block. Lift the water pump away and remove the gasket.

5 Replacement is a straightforward reversal of the removal sequence (photo). NOTE: The fan belt tension must be correct when all is reassembled. If the belt is too tight undue strain will be placed on the water pump and dynamo bearings, and if the belt is too loose it will slip and wear rapidly as well as giving rise to low electrical output from the dynamo.

8 Water pump - dismantling and reassembly

1 Before dismantling check the economics of spares availability and cost against a complete new unit. To renew the bearing and shaft

5.2 Unclipping the radiator hose

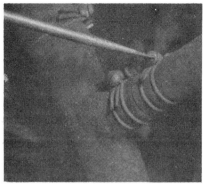

5.3 Disconnecting the heater hose from the bottom radiator hose

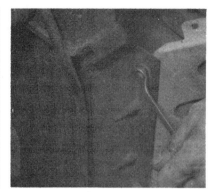

5.4a Unbolting the radiator

5.4b Lifting the radiator out

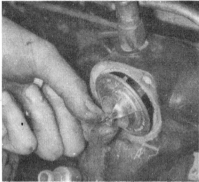

6.7a Replacing the thermostat

6.7b Replacing the thermostat cover

6.7c Tightening down the thermostat cover

7.2a Removing the elbow from the water pump inlet

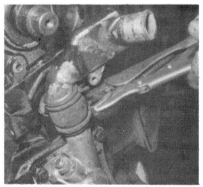

7.2b Removing the hose from the water pump inlet

7.3a Unbolting the fan blades and pulley

7.3b Removing the fan and pulley

7.5 Refitting the water pump

assembly or to replace the seal and thrust washer it is necessary to use a proper puller as the pump is held together by press fit.

2 First pull off the pump impeller and then lift out the retaining clip which engages the bearing in the body of the housing.

3 The shaft and bearing can be driven out of the body.

4 The seal assembly can be removed from the pump body. When fitting a new one make sure that the two halves are correctly assembled - the groove in the thrust face piece engaging in the pin in the outer seal sleeve.

5 The outer rim of the seal should be smeared with rubber grease (Castrol/Girling Red).

6 If the bearing/shaft assembly is being renewed draw off the pulley flange.

7 Reassembly is a reversal of the dismantling procedure, bearing in mind that a way has to be found of pressing the rotor and pulley flanges into position accurately.

9 Antifreeze coolant solution

1 Where temperatures are likely to drop below freezing point the coolant system must be adequately protected by the addition of antifreeze. Even if you keep the engine warm at night it is possible for water to freeze in the radiator with the engine running in very cold conditions - particularly if the engine cooling is being adequately dealt with by the heater radiator. The thermostat stays closed and the radiator water does not circulate.

2 It is best to drain the coolant completely and flush out the system first.

3 The table below gives the details of the antifreeze percentage to be used (on the basis of the cooling system capacity of 13½ pints):

%	Quantity (pints)	Complete protection
25	3½	−11ºC
35	4¾	−19ºC
45	6	−29ºC

4 Mix the required quantity of antifreeze with four pints of water and fill the system. Top up with water and then run the engine up to normal temperature with the heater turned on.

10 Fan belt - removal replacement and adjustment

1 If the fan belt is worn or has stretched unduly it should be replaced. The most usual reason for replacement is breakage in service

and every wise motorist will carry a spare.

2 Even though the belt may have broken and fallen off, go through the removal routine which is first of all to loosen the two generator pivot bolts and the nut on the adjusting link (brace). Take off the old belt.

3 Put a new belt over the pulleys.

4 The dynamo must now be used as a tensioner in effect, by pulling it away from the engine and locking it in the required position (photo). This can call for some sustained effort unless the pivot bolts are slackened only a little so that the dynamo is quite stiff to move. A lever between the dynamo and block can help. When an alternator is fitted care must be taken to avoid applying pressure to the rear end cover or it may break. Always tighten the front lug securing bolts first.

5 The tension of the belt midway between the generator and water pump pulleys should allow a deflection of .4 inch under a 10 lb load (thumb pressure). If in doubt it is better to be a little slack than tight. Only slipping will occur if it is too slack. If too tight, damage can be caused by excessive strain on the pulley bearings.

6 When the adjustment is right tighten all the generator mounting bolts.

7 With a new belt, check the tension 250 miles after fitting.

8 Periodic checking of the belt tension is necessary and there is no hard and fast rule as to the most suitable interval, because fan belts do not necessarily stretch or wear to a pre-determined schedule. Assuming most owners check their own oil and water regularly it is suggested as a good habit to check the fan belt tension every time the bonnet goes up. It takes only a second.

11 Water temperature warning indicator

1 The warning light or gauge - whichever may be fitted - is operated by a heat sensitive switch which is screwed into the water jacket round the intake manifold.

2 Normally the gauge should stay out of the red sector, or the warning lamp stay out when normal engine temperature is being maintained and the ignition is switched on.

3 Either instrument can be tested by removing the lead from the temperature sender unit and touching the lead to earth (photo).

4 If then the indicator lamp lights or gauge goes into the red when the ignition is switched on the sender unit is faulty and must be renewed.

5 If there is still no reaction from the indicator then there is an electrical fault (fuse, wiring or indicator unit).

10.4 Tightening the fan belt

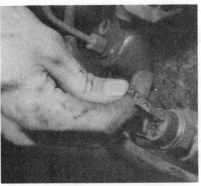

11.3 Detaching the lead from the water temperature sender switch in the inlet manifold

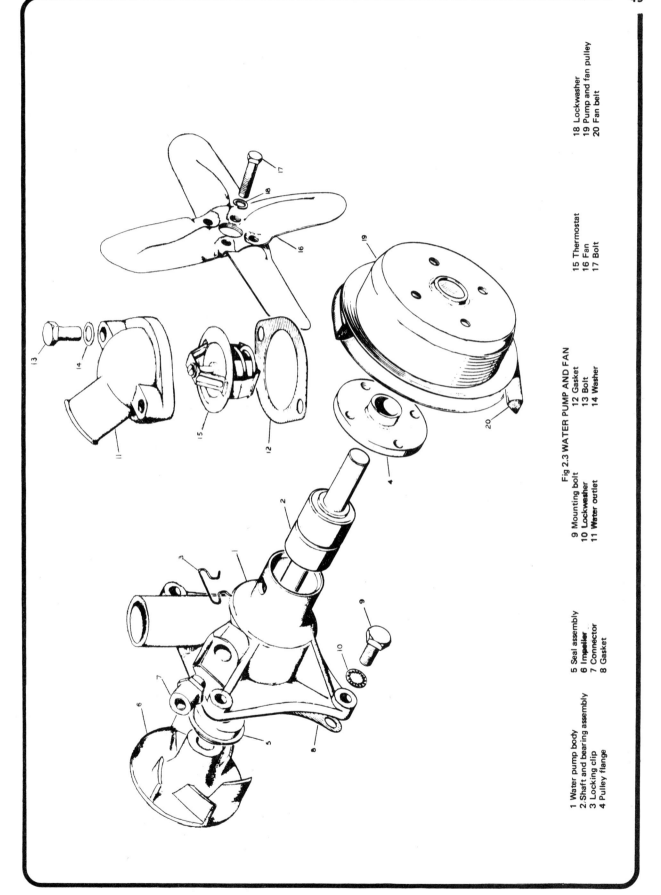

Fig 2.3 WATER PUMP AND FAN

1 Water pump body
2 Shaft and bearing assembly
3 Locking clip
4 Pulley flange

5 Seal assembly
6 Impeller
7 Connector
8 Gasket

9 Mounting bolt
10 Lockwasher
11 Water outlet

12 Gasket
13 Bolt
14 Washer

15 Thermostat
16 Fan
17 Bolt

18 Lockwasher
19 Pump and fan pulley
20 Fan belt

Fault Finding Chart - Cooling System

Symptom	Reason/s	Remedy
Loss of coolant	Leak in system	Examine all hoses, hose connections, drain taps and the radiator and heater for signs of leakage first when the engine is cold, then when hot and under pressure. Tighten clips, renew hoses and repair radiator as necessary.
	Defective radiator pressure cap	Examine cap for defective seal or spring and renew if necessary.
	Overheating causing rapid evaporation due to excessive pressure in system forcing vapour past radiator cap	Check reasons for overheating.
	Blown cylinder head gasket causing excess pressure in cooling system forcing coolant past radiator cap overflow	Remove cylinder head for examination.
	Cracked block or head due to freezing	Strip engine and examine. Repair as required.
Overheating	Insufficient coolant in system	Top up.
	Water pump not turning properly due to slack fan belt	Tighten fan belt.
	Kinked or collapsed water hoses causing restriction to circulation of coolant	Renew hose as required.
	Faulty thermostat (not opening properly)	Fit new thermostat.
	Engine out of tune	Check ignition setting and carburettor adjustments.
	Blocked radiator either internally or externally	Flush out cooling system and clean out cooling fins externally.
	Cylinder head gaskets blown forcing coolant out of system	Remove head and renew gasket.
	New engine not run-in	Adjust engine speed until run-in.
Engine running too cool	Missing or faulty thermostat	Fit new thermostat.

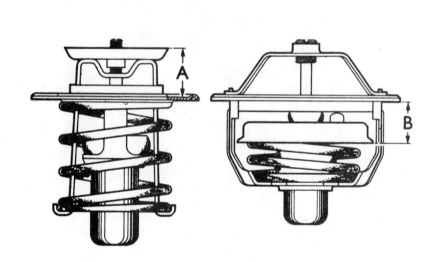

Fig 2.4 THERMOSTATS
Fully open position is either 'A' - .51 inch Western Thomson or 'B' - .48 inch (AC)

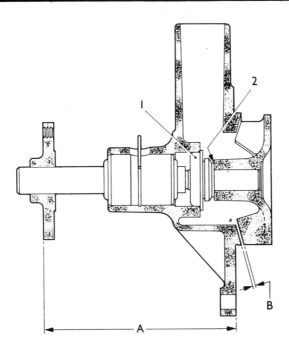

Fig 2.5 WATER PUMP — CROSS SECTION (EARLY TYPE 4 BLADE FAN) (See Section 8)
2 Thrust face   A = 4.44 inches   B = 0.03—0.05 inch

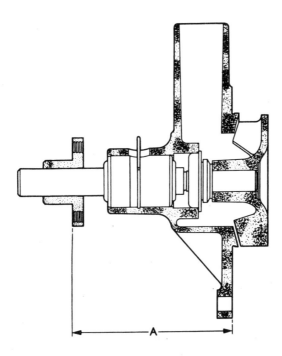

Fig 2.6 WATER PUMP — CROSS SECTION (LATER TYPE 8 BLADE FAN) (See Section 8)
A = 3.78 inches

Chapter 3 Fuel system and carburation

Contents

Specifications

Fuel pump

Make and type	AC FG
Delivery pressure	2—3½ lb/in^2
Diaphragm spring load when compressed to .64 inch	8—8½ lb

Carburettors - 1599 cc and 1975 cc standard engines

Make	Zenith 36 IV
Type...	Fixed choke
Identification number	3139 (1599 cç)
	3140 (1975 cc)
	3141 (1975 cc automatic)
Main jet...	100
Compensating jet - 1599 cc	125
- 1975 cc	145
Idling jet	50
Pump jet..	55
Part throttle air bleed screw	None
Needle valve	1.75 mm
Needle valve washer thickness	2 mm
High altitude settings for jets	
Main jet 5—7000 ft	97
7—10000 ft	95
10—15000 ft	92
Compensating jet - 1599 cc	
5—7000 ft	122
7—15000 ft	120
Compensating jet - 1975 cc	
5—7000 ft	142
7—15000 ft	140

Modifications were made later in connection with modifications to the distributor. For a time the ignition setting was changed to 18ºBTDC
It then reverted to 9º BTDC. The corresponding changes to the carburettor are listed below. This applies only to 1599 cc engines.

	18º BTDC	9º BTDC (reverted)
Identification No	3203	3326
Main jet...	90	90
Compensating jet	130	125
Idling jet	45	50
Pump jet	55	50
Part throttle air bleed screw	—	2.8 mm
High altitude jet settings - Main jet 5—7000 ft	87	87
7—10000 ft...	85	85
10—15000 ft	80	80

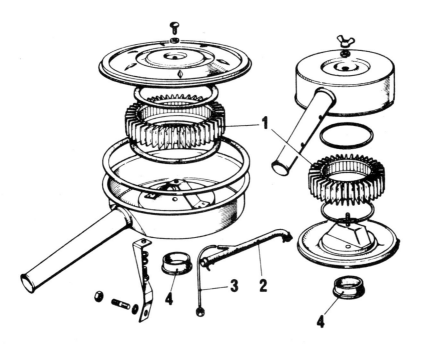

Fig 3.1 AIR CLEANER ASSEMBLIES — LEFT - 1975 cc AND RIGHT - 1599 cc

1 Paper elements
2 Crankcase ventilation hose
3 Crankcase ventilation pipe (high manifold depression)
4 Rubber mounting sleeve

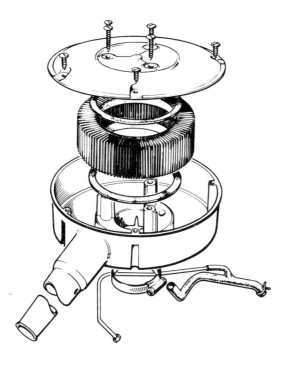

Fig 3.2 Air cleaner assembly - 1599 cc engines - later type

Compensating jet

5—7000 ft	127	122
7—15000 ft...	125	120

1975 cc engines - later versions (not VX 4/90)

Make	Zenith/Stromberg 175 CD—2S
Type...	Variable choke side-draught
Identification Number	3269
Metering needle standard	2 AM
High altitude needle	
5—7000 ft	1 AT
7—10000 ft	1 AU
10—15000 ft	1 AV
Float level	15.5—16.5 mm above main body face with carburettor inverted and needle valve seated
Air valve spring colour	Blue
Needle valve	1.75 mm
Needle valve washer	1.6 mm thick
Engine idle speed	700—750 rpm

1975 cc engines - Automatic transmission

Make	Zenith/Stromberg 175 CD 2ST
	Similar to 175 CD 2S fitted with a hot water controlled automatic cold start device instead of a manual operation

1975 cc engines - Exhaust emission controlled version

Make	Zenith/Stromberg 175 CD 2SETV
	Similar to 175 CD 2ST but fitted with a biased metering needle permanently in contact with one side of the jet orifice.
Identification Number	3355
	3354 (automatic)
Metering needle	B2 AP
Float level	16—16.5 mm above main body face with carburettor inverted and needle valve seated
Auto cold start device needle - manual	J7
- automatic...	JK
Fast idle cam	B or B2
Fast idle cam setting (initial)	B2 - .002—.008 in
	B - .022—.028 in
Engine idle speed	700—750 rpm

1975 cc engines - VX 4/90

Make	Twin Zenith/Stromberg 175 CD—2S
Type...	Variable choke side-draught
Identification number - manual transmission - early	3295 *
- late...	3438
- automatic transmission	3312 *
Standard metering needle - No 3295	1AS
- No 3438	1BJ
High altitude metering needles	
5—7000 ft	1BB
7—10000 ft...	1BC
10—15000 ft	1BD
Air valve spring colour	Red
Engine idling speed	725—775 rpm

* Manual LHD 3297
   Auto LHD 3313

NOTE: Later models are fitted with two 175 CD—2ST carburettors for automatic transmissions

Identification No	3439
Fast idle cam	A6 (.035 in setting)
Cold start needle	K

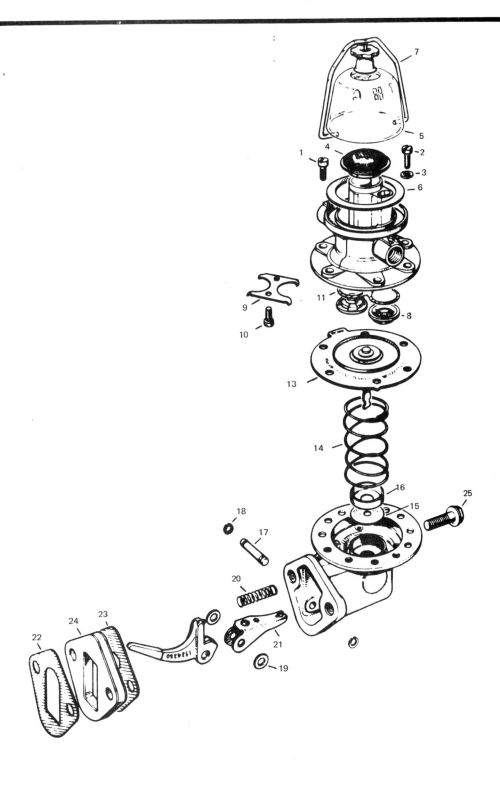

Fig 3.3 FUEL PUMP — COMPONENTS

1 Upper cover screw	7 Securing stirrup	14 Spring	20 Spring
2 Upper cover screw	8 Valve	15 Oil seal	21 Link
3 Lockwasher	9 Valve retainer	16 Oil seal retainer	22 Gasket - engine pad
4 Filter screen	10 Retainer screw	17 Rocker arm pin	23 Gasket - fuel pump
5 Filter bowl	11 Valve gasket	18 Pin clip	24 Insulator
6 Gasket	13 Diaphragm	19 Spacer washer	25 Mounting bolt

1 General description

A mechanically operated diaphragm type pump draws petrol from the fuel tank and delivers it to the carburettor. The level of petrol in the carburettor is controlled by a float operated needle valve. Petrol flows through until the float shuts off this needle valve causing the pump to 'freewheel' under the back pressure. When the petrol level drops, the needle valve opens and petrol is ready to flow again.

Fuel is drawn into the cylinders during the suction stroke by air passing through the carburettor and inlet manifold. The air is carefully filtered before it enters the fuel system to eliminate undesirable contents.

2 Air filter elements - removal and servicing

1 A variety of types is fitted. For those with paper elements the cover of the filter element housing should be removed and the element taken out at the required interval (see Routine maintenance). If no loose dust deposits are released by tapping it do not try cleaning it with fluids or air jets.

2 In industrial or dusty atmospheres paper elements will need changing more often than otherwise. Although an interval is recommended for filter changing there is no way of telling whether it is necessary. If a filter is choked then one may expect fuel consumption to rise due to the restricted air inflow. Do not run an engine without a filter.

3 Gauze elements which are washable are slightly less efficient but more predictable and one can see when they need cleaning. Do not forget that engines tuned on either paper or gauze elements need carburettor recalibration if changed from one to the other.

4 Air cleaner assemblies are mounted on the carburettor using a brace to hold them in position on some models. Others retain them with a hose clip round the mounting flange (photos). It is not necessary to remove the unit to change the element. The top cover can be removed separately.

3 Zenith 36 IV carburettors - description

1 Early models of the Victor, both with 1599 cc and 1975 cc engines are fitted with the Zenith fixed choke downdraught carburettor. It is fitted with an accelerator pump and incorporates an economy unit to correct fuel mixture at certain intermediate engine speeds. The principle of operation is as follows: At full throttle opening with the choke flap open, the depression (low pressure) in the choke tube draws a fuel/air mixture from the main discharge beak.

The fuel/air mixture has been emulsified in the emulsion tube below the discharge beak. The fuel has reached the emulsion tube, via the reserve well, from the main jet in the float chamber.

When the engine is cold and the choke flap is closed the throttle flap is automatically slightly opened a pre-determined amount.

The choke tube depression draws principally on the discharge beak and therefore a very rich mixture reaches the engine, as air from the main air inlet has been closed off.

At idling speed, with the throttle shut, there is no depression at the main discharge beak. It is now concentrated at the idling discharge orifice on the engine side of the throttle flap. Fuel from the main reserve well is drawn via the pilot jet to this orifice, taking the requisite amount of air for the mixture through the pilot air bleed bypass orifice. The volume of the mixture supplied is controlled by the idling mixture control screw.

As soon as the throttle is opened further, the bypass orifice is then also subject to depression, so instead of feeding air in one direction to the idling discharge orifice, it now delivers fuel/air mixture in the other direction until the throttle is open sufficiently for the main discharge beak to take over.

The economy unit augments the fuel flow from the main jet automatically through the economy jet when the choke tube depres-

Fig 3.4 ZENITH 36IV CARBURETTOR – COMPONENTS
1 Economiser cover screw
2 Spring washer
3 Economiser valve cover
4 Spring
5 Gasket
6 Diaphragm
7 Cover screw
8 Cover screw
9 Float chamber cover
10 Gasket
11 Pump lever nut
12 Washer
13 Pump lever
14 Retaining ring
15 Float pivot
16 Float
17 Main jet
18 Compensating jet
19 Needle seating washer
20 Needle and seating
21 Volume control screw
22 Spring
23 Main body
24 Throttle flap
25 Throttle return spring
26 Throttle fixing screw
27 Throttle spindle
28 Locating lever
29 Floating lever
30 Washer
31 Throttle stop
33 Throttle lever
34 Nut
35 Lockwasher
36 Throttle stop screw
37 Spring
40 Pump link
41 Interconnection link
44 Emulsion block screw
45 Spring washer
46 Sealing ring
47 Emulsion block
48 Pump jet
49 Plug
50 Pump discharge valve
51 Valve ball circlip
52 Ball
53 Slow running jet
54 Pump piston
55 Choke control mounting bracket
56 Screw
57 Clip
58 Pump link pin
59 Washer
60 Pump spindle
61 Spacer washer
62 Choke spindle
63 Return spring
64 Circlip
65 Swivel screw
66 Choke control lever
67 Lever spring
68 Spindle washer
69 Choke flap
70 Screw
71 Insulator
72 Gasket
73 Mounting stud
74 Mounting nut

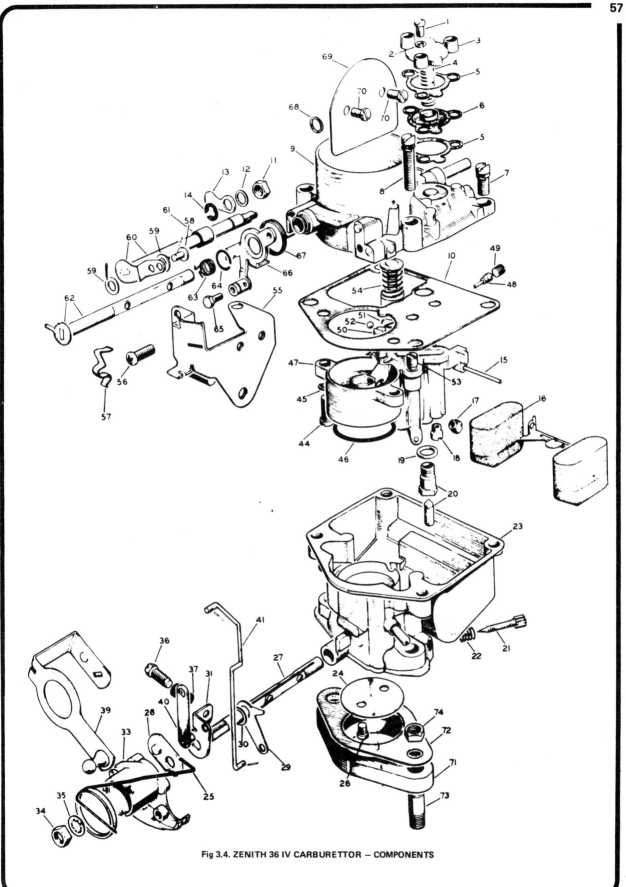

Fig 3.4. ZENITH 36 IV CARBURETTOR – COMPONENTS

sion is low. At cruising speeds, when the depression is high, a diaphragm operated valve shuts off the economy jet.

There is also an accelerator pump which delivers a metered jet of neat fuel into the choke tube whenever the accelerator pedal is operated quickly. This gives the richer mixture necessary for rapid acceleration. The fuel is drawn from the float chamber into the pump chamber via a non-return valve at the bottom of the float chamber. When the pump is operated quickly (ie sudden accelerator pedal operation) the pump release valve is forced shut under pressure and the fuel passes through the injector. If the pump is operated slowly, the pressure is insufficient to close the release valve, so fuel passes through it back to the float chamber rather than out of the injector.

4 Zenith 36 IV carburettor - removal, dismantling, reassembly and replacement

1 Most of the carburettor is incorporated in the top cover so do not take the carburettor off the car unless you have to. Remove the air cleaner assembly.

2 Undo the choke cable clamp screw and disconnect the choke cable clip (photos).

3 Slacken the throttle cable outer clamp/adjusting screw (photo).

4 Remove the throttle spindle return spring and unhook the cable nipple from the lever (photo).

5 Pull off the fuel feed pipe and the vacuum pipe.

6 Undo the two retaining nuts and lift the carburettor off together with the gaskets and insulator block.

7 To remove the top cover disconnect the pump linkage and choke control rod. Undo the four screws and lift the cover off carefully to avoid damaging the gasket. Take care also not to bend or damage the floats which are attached to the cover.

8 To get to the jets and accelerator pump the emulsion block must be removed from the underside of the cover. First draw out the pin on which the floats pivot and lift out the needle valve.

9 Unscrew the needle valve seat. Undo the two screws holding the emulsion block to the cover.

10 When releasing the emulsion block take care to prevent the accelerator pump and spring dropping out.

11 The economy device is held on the top cover by three screws. When these are released the cover, diaphragm and spring may be lifted out. See that the diaphragm is intact.

12 Reassembly starts with the refitting of the emulsion block to the cover. See first that the non-return ball and retaining clip of the accelerator pump are in position (Fig 3.6).

13 Fit a new gasket and ensure that the accelerator pump lever is positioned correctly (Fig 3.7)

14 Examine the needle valve for any signs of ridging on the bevelled face and renew both the needle and the seat if in doubt.

15 Refit the floats and spindle and, holding the cover upside down, measure the distance from the bottom of the floats to the face of the cover gaskets (Fig 3.8). It should be 1.20–1.24 inch (31-32 mm). Make adjustments by carefully bending the float arm centre tag which contacts the needle. This setting is important.

16 Before replacing the cover to the body check that the sealing ring around the choke tube is in good order (Fig 3.9). A bad seal will result in fuel leaking from the float chamber.

17 Reconnect the accelerator pump linkage noting that the pin should always be fitted to the upper hole in the pump lever.

18 The choke control rod is not provided with any obvious adjustment. With the choke flap held shut there should be a .040 inch gap (1 mm—No 61 drill) down the side of the throttle flap. Bend the control rod if necessary to get this setting (Fig 3.11).

19 The choke flap spindle return spring should engage the first notch on the lever (Fig 3.10).

20 When refitting the carburettor to the inlet manifold use two new gaskets one each side of the heat insulator (Fig 3.12).

21 Later models of the 1599 cc engine are fitted with a 'corrector bar' across the inlet manifold intake (Fig 3.15). This was apparently a hasty modification to counteract some design imbalance between the manifold volume and the carburettor choke tube diameter. Make sure you put the article back in position so that it is clamped firmly by the carburettor. Do not drop it inside the manifold!

22 When reconnecting the throttle cable and return spring locate the return spring correctly (Fig 3.13).

23 It is important that the outer cable of the throttle is adjusted so that when the accelerator pedal is down as far as it will go the throttle flap is just fully open. The throttle should not open fully before the pedal is right down otherwise further pressure will impart a very severe strain on the throttle spindle (Fig 3.5).

24 Make sure that the choke cable operates correctly also and that the outer sleeve is clipped far enough back to allow full travel of the choke spindle lever.

5 Zenith 36 IV carburettor - adjustment

1 If it is known that the reason for adjustment is something more than just slow running then check the setting as described in the previous section on assembly.

2 Slow running adjustment is carried out by the throttle stop screw and volume control screw together (Fig 3.16).

3 First get the engine up to running temperature and set the volume control screw 1¼ turns out from closed. Then set the throttle stop screw so that the engine runs fast enough not to stall. Adjust the volume control screw one way or the other so the engine speed increases and then reduce speed using the throttle stop screw. Keep doing this in stages until the tickover speed (650–700 rpm) is even.

4 With automatic transmission the adjustment is made with drive or reverse engaged and the handbrake on. Adjust to smoothest idling speed with minimum creep when the handbrake is released.

6 Stromberg 175 CD–2S carburettor - description

Later models of the 1975 cc engined Victor are fitted with the Stromberg carburettor. It has a single horizontal variable choke and is quite different in principle of operation to the fixed choked Zenith. The air intake is choked by cylindrical air valve which moves vertically.

To the base of the air valve a tapered needle is fitted which runs in and out of a jet orifice through which fuel is drawn from the float chamber which is underneath the main body. Suction from the engine inlet manifold passes through a hole in the base of the air valve to the suction chamber. This suction acts on the diaphragm, to which the air valve and metering needle are attached, and raises them. This increases the air flow through the choke tube and the fuel flow through the jet as the tapered needle withdraws. As the air valve rises to the concentration of suction through the valve hole is reduced and the valve reaches a point of equilibrium, balanced against throttle opening and air valve height.

Sudden acceleration demands would apparently cause the air valve to rise sharply, thus tending to weaken the mixture. In fact the rise of the valve is damped by an oil controlled piston. Thus when the throttle is opened suddenly the initial suction is concentrated at the fuel jet and the quantity of air let through to reduce the mixture richness to normal occurs slightly later as the piston rises. The taper of the metering needle is obviously the main controlling feature of the carburettor's performance and this controls the fuel/air mixture at all heights of the valve. At the same time the height of the air valve is nicely balanced, according to throttle opening, in conjunction with the metering needle. The jet itself is adjustable by raising or lowering, thus altering the position of the jet orifice in relation to the taper of the needle.

For cold starts there is a device mounted on the side consisting of a rotating disc with a number of holes drilled in it. When the disc is moved by the control lever a passageway is opened up. Depending on the number of holes uncovered so the flow is restricted. The fuel from the float chamber can then be drawn direct into the choke tube supplementing that from the main jet.

2.4a Releasing the air cleaner clamp screw

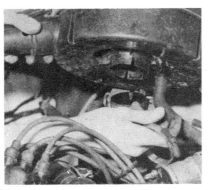

2.4b Removing the air cleaner

4.2a Disconnecting the choke cable

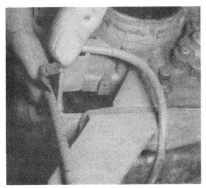

4.2b Disconnecting the choke cable outer clip

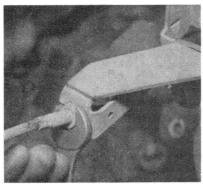

4.3 Slackening throttle cable threaded sleeve adjuster screw

4.4 Throttle cable disconnected from operating lever

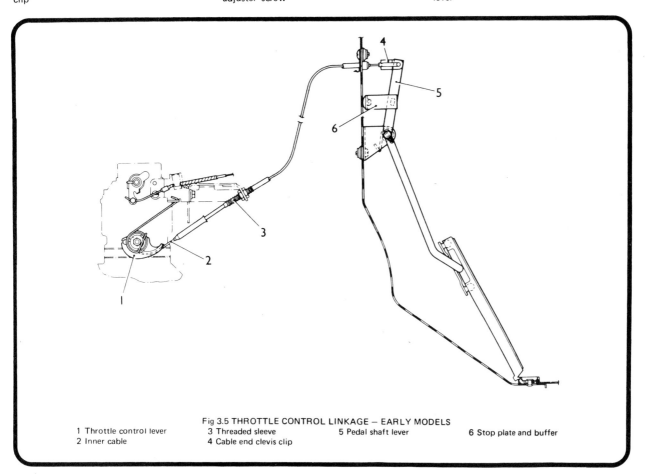

Fig 3.5 THROTTLE CONTROL LINKAGE — EARLY MODELS

1 Throttle control lever
2 Inner cable
3 Threaded sleeve
4 Cable end clevis clip
5 Pedal shaft lever
6 Stop plate and buffer

Fig 3.6 ZENITH 36 IV CARBURETTOR
Location of accelerator pump inlet ball (2) and locating clip (1)
in the emulsion block

Fig 3.7 ZENITH 36 IV CARBURETTOR
Location of accelerator pump lever (A) on assembly

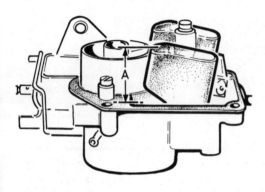

Fig 3.8 ZENITH 36 IV CARBURETTOR
Float level height - A = 1.20–1.24 ins (31–32 mm)

Fig 3.9 ZENITH 36 IV CARBURETTOR
Sealing ring (arrowed) for between float chamber and cover

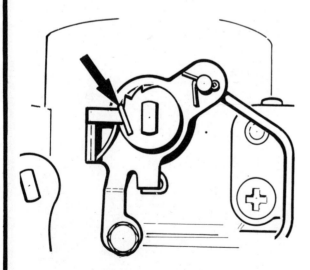

Fig 3.10 ZENITH 36 IV CARBURETTOR
Position of choke flap spindle return spring (arrowed

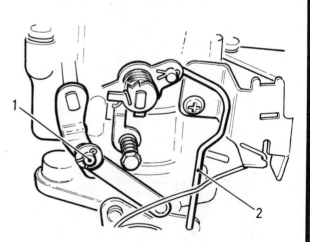

Fig 3.11 ZENITH 36 IV CARBURETTOR
1 Pump lever link pin   2 Choke control rod

Fig 3.12 ZENITH 36 IV CARBURETTOR
Heat insulator and gaskets (arrowed)

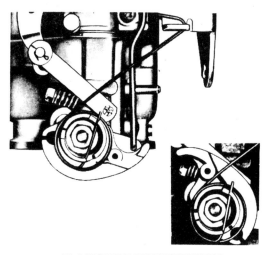

Fig 3.13 ZENITH 36 IV CARBURETTOR
Throttle lever return spring position - (inset LHD)

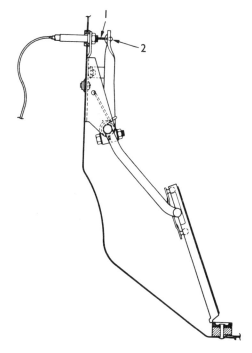

Fig.3.14. Accelerator pedal linkage - cross section
1. Cable
2. Cable end nipple

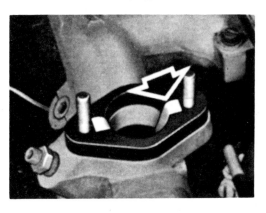

Fig 3.15 ZENITH 36 IV CARBURETTOR
Corrector bar fitted in later 1599 cc engine inlet manifolds

Fig 3.16 ZENITH 36 IV CARBURETTOR
1 Volume control screw   2 Throttle stop screw

Fig 3.17 STROMBERG 175 CD–2S CARBURETTOR
Slackening the jet bush retainer

7 Stromberg 175 CD—2S carburettor - adjustment

1 As there is no separate idling jet, the mixture for all conditions is supplied by the main jet and variable choke. Thus the strength of the mixture throughout the range depends on the height of the jet in the carburettor body and when the idling mixture is correct, the mixture will be correct throughout the range. A knurled screw at the base of the carburettor increases or decreases the strength of the mixture. Turning the screw clockwise raises the jet and weakens the mixture. Turning the screw anticlockwise enriches the mixture. The idling speed is controlled by the throttle stop screw.

2 To adjust a Stromberg carburettor from scratch it is assumed that the fast idle cam has already been correctly set as described in the reassembly procedure. Run the engine until it is at its normal working temperature and then remove the air cleaner. Insert a .002 inch feeler gauge between the air valve and carubrettor body and screw in the jet adjusting screw until it touches the air valve. The feeler should now be withdrawn and the adjuster unscrewed two complete revolutions. This will give an approximate setting. Start the engine and adjust the throttle stop screw so that the engine runs fairly slowly and smoothly (about 750 rpm) without vibrating excessively on its mountings. To get the engine to run smoothly at this speed it may be necessary to turn the jet adjuster nut a small amount in either direction.

3 To test if the correct setting has been found, lift the air valve piston $1/32$ inch with the lifting pin. On later versions this pin is left out so the air valve must be lifted with a screwdriver. This is a very small amount and care should be taken to lift the piston only fractionally. If the engine speed increases and stays so then the mixture is too rich. If it hesitates or stalls it is too weak. Re-adjust the jet adjusting nut and recheck. All is correct when the engine speed rises momentarily and then drops when the air valve is lifted the specified $1/32$ inch. Make sure that the air valve damper is correctly filled with engine oil. With the plunger and air filter removed, the level should be ¼ inch below the top of the air valve guide. Lift the air valve with a finger through the air intake during the topping up operation.

4 Replace the air cleaner.

8 Stromberg 175 CD—2S carburettor - float chamber fuel level setting

1 Take off the air cleaner and then remove the carburettor from the engine.

2 Slacken the jet bush retainer and undo the screws which hold the float chamber to the base of the carburettor. Remove the float chamber.

3 Turn the carburettor body upside down and accurately measure the highest point of the floats which should be 15.5—16.5 mm above the flange normally adjacent to the float chamber (see Fig 3.19). During this operation ensure that the needle is against its seating. To reset the level, carefully bend the tag which bears against the end of the needle.

4 Re-centre the jet after replacing the float chamber (Section 6).

9 Stromberg 175 CD—2S carburettor - dismantling and reassembly

1 Take off the air cleaner, disconnect the choke and accelerator controls at the carburettor, also the vacuum advance and retard pipe, and undo the nuts and spring washers holding the carburettor in place. Remove the carburettor.

2 With the carburettor on the bench, undo and remove the damper cap and plunger. Then undo the screws which hold the suction chamber cover in place and lift off the cover.

3 The air valve complete with needle and diaphragm is then lifted out. Handle the assembly with the greatest of care as it is very easy to knock the needle out of true.

4 The bottom of the float chamber is removed by undoing the five screws and washers which hold it in place. Take out the pin and

Fig 3.18 STROMBERG 175 CD—2S CARBURETTOR — COMPONENTS

 1 Suction chamber cover screw
 2 Damper assembly
 3 Retaining ring
 4 Piston
 5 'E' clip
 6 Washer
 7 Diaphragm
 8 Diaphragm retaining plate
 9 Screw
10 Retaining ring
11 Air valve spring
12 Jet
13 Jet spring
14 'O' ring
15 Jet bush
16 Washer
17 Jet retainer
18 'O' ring
20 Jet adjuster
21 'O' ring
22 Air valve lifting pin
23 Pin spring
24 Clip
25 Needle
26 Retaining screw
27 Throttle spindle
28 Throttle flap
29 Screw
30 Return spring
31 Fast idle lever
32 Throttle lever
33 Lockwasher
34 Nut
35 Throttle stop screw
36 Spring
37 Fast idle screw
38 Locknut
39 Cold start device
40 Screw
41 Lockwasher
42 Control cable bracket
43 Clip
44 Screw
48 Float chamber
49 Gasket
50 Cover screw
51 Cover screw
52 Float
53 Float pivot pin
54 Needle valve
55 Washer
57 Insulator
58 Gasket
59 Mounting stud
60 Mounting nut
61 Gasket - air filter

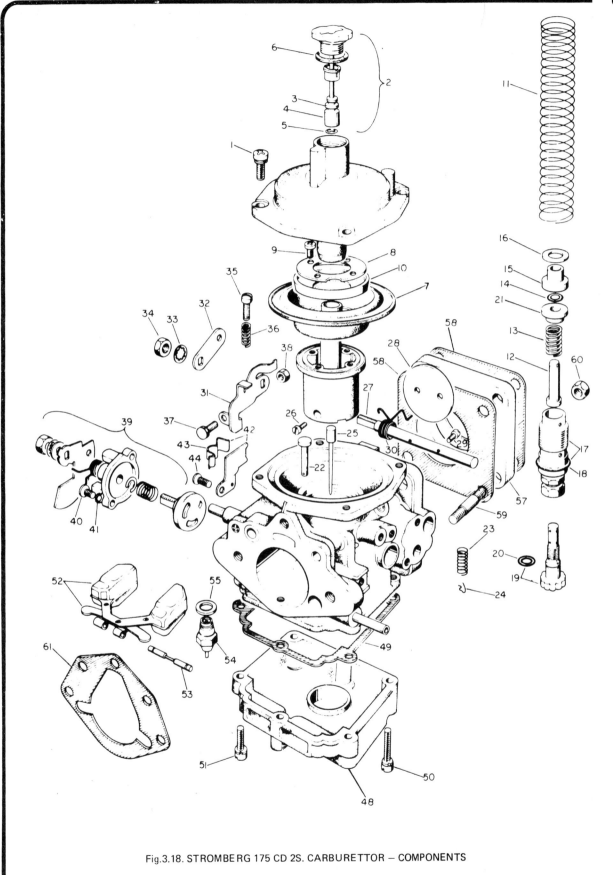

Fig.3.18. STROMBERG 175 CD 2S. CARBURETTOR – COMPONENTS

remove the float assembly from the main body.

5 If wished, the needle may be removed from the air valve by undoing the grub screw in the side of the piston.

6 To remove the diaphragm from the piston, simply undo the four screws and washers which hold the diaphragm retaining ring in place.

7 The jet and associated parts are removed after the jet locking nut has been undone.

8 The cold start device can be removed from the side of the main body after undoing the two securing screws.

9 Some later versions are fitted with a temperature compensation. This alters the amount of air which can bypass the main air valve. It is controlled by a tapered plug operated by a bi-metal strip (Fig 3.20). Heat transferred to the carburettor body acts on the strip and makes fine adjustments to the air bleed. Do not tamper with it.

10 On reassembly there are several points which should be noted particularly. The first is that if fitting a new needle to the piston ensure it has the same markings as the old one stamped on it, and fit it so that the needle shoulder is perfectly flush with the base of the piston. This can be done by placing a metal ruler across the base of the valve and pulling the needle out until it abuts the ruler.

11 Thoroughly clean the piston and its cylinder in paraffin.

12 Refit the jet and associated parts, lift the piston and tighten the jet assembly.

13 Turn the mixture adjusting nut clockwise until the tip of the jet just stands proud into the choke tube. Now loosen the jet bush retainer about one turn so as to free the bush.

14 Allow the piston to fall. As it descends the needle will enter the orifice and automatically centralise it. With the needle still in the orifice tighten the jet assembly slowly, frequently raising and dropping the piston ¼ inch to ensure the orifice bush has not moved. Finally check that the piston drops freely without hesitation and hits the bridge with a soft click.

15 Make sure that the holes in the diaphragm line up with the screw holes in the piston and retaining ring, and that the diaphragm is correctly positioned with the upper and lower tongues engaged in the slots in piston and body. Reassembly is otherwise a straightforward reversal of the dismantling sequence.

16 The cold start device can be set to operate in two positions. The two-position stop can be set to control the maximum amount to which the unit may rotate. With the cross-pin in the slot the device may rotate to its full extent, but this is not usually needed unless the temperature drops below −18°C. The fast idle cam operates against the throttle lever via an adjusting screw which may be set to ensure a suitably fast idling speed under cold start situations (Fig 3.21).

17 To adjust the fast idle, the cold start cam must be set correctly in relation to the throttle flap. To do this put the cold start setting pin in the normal (vertical) position and press the cam against the end of the pin. Then move the adjusting screw on the throttle control lever against the cam until there is a .8 mm (.032 in) gap between the throttle flap and the body (Fig 3.21).

18 The throttle control linkage is modified to suit the carburettor (Fig 3.22).

10 Twin Stromberg 175 CD−2S carburettors VX 4/90

1 Each of the carburettors is the same as already described except that the cold start device is fitted to the front one only and it is connected by a pipe to the other.

2 Unless the carburettors have been significantly disturbed they should not be fiddled with. The balance of the two is important for performance and fuel consumption and adjustment is a procedure which must be followed through from the beginning. Random adjustments to one or the other are useless.

3 Assuming both carburettors are in good condition, and the jet of each is centralised properly certain basic settings can be made if either of the carburettors has been disturbed or some other cause has resulted in noticeable imbalance.

4 Disconnect the battery (the starter solenoid is very close to the air cleaner).

5 Remove the nuts holding the air cleaner to the carburettors (Fig 3.23). (The air cleaner element requires the removal of the unit for renewal) (Fig 3.24).

6 Set both jets as described in the previous section.

7 Detach the throttle cable and slacken the rear throttle spindle coupling clamp so that both throttle flaps can prove independently. Back off the throttle stop screw on each carburettor until each throttle flap is just fully closed (Fig 3.25). Turn each stop screw an exactly equal amount so that the throttles are open enough to enable the engine to start and run at a fast tickover.

8 Ideally an air flow balancer would be used at this juncture to check that the flow of air through each carburettor was the same. Some people maintain they can detect differences by using a piece of flexible tube held in the air intake and noting the difference in the pitch of the 'hiss' of the air being drawn in. If you are one of these, then alter the throttle stop screws until you are satisfied that the air flow is balanced. If not then clamp up the throttle spindle coupling now in the knowledge that any difference in throttle flap opening is only fractional.

9 Back one of the throttle stop screws right off and use the other to bring the idling speed down to 700−750 rpm.

10 Both carburettor jets may now be adjusted **equally** in order to smooth out any roughness at the idling speed. If, as a result of adjusting the jets the idling speed increases or decreases then start all over again setting the throttle stop screws to give a higher or lower tickover speed as appropriate whilst still maintaining the balanced air flow.

11 It must be emphasised that carburettor balancing is only a part of the proper tuning of the whole engine. The VX 4/90, being a high performance engine, it is only possible to tune the carburettors properly when you know that cylinder compression, valves, and the ignition system are in a first class condition.

11 Stromberg 175 CD−2ST carburettor

1 The 175 CD−2ST carburettor is fitted to 1975 cc engined automatic transmission models. It is the same as the 175 CD−2S except that a hot water controlled automatic cold start device is fitted.

This device is controlled by the temperature of the engine coolant. A bi-metal spring thermostat controls a tapered needle which regulates fuel flowing into a mixing chamber. In addition a pushrod and piston controlled by inlet manifold vacuum override the action of the thermostat under certain engine speed conditions.

2 It is not recommended that this item is tampered with but in the event of the owner deciding to investigate because of malfunction the following points should be noted on reassembly.

3 When replacing the fast idle cam and thermostat lever the lever peg should engage in the taper needle slot and the spade in the flat in the vacuum kick rod (Fig 3.26).

4 The interconnecting spring should be fitted so that the inner end goes over the long arm of the thermostat lever and the other end hooks into the hole in the fast idle cam afterwards (Fig 3.27).

5 The clearance between the fast idle screw and cam (on the base circle) should be .030 inch for type B cam and .010 inch for type B2 when the thermostat lever is rotated fully anticlockwise. The fast idle screw can be adjusted as required and re-secured using 'Loctite' (AA Grade) (Fig 3.28).

6 When fitting the water jacket and cover make sure that the square loop on the thermostat spring engages the peg on the thermostat lever.

7 Correct positioning of the thermostat after assembly is indicated by line up marks on the housing and rims. No variations should be made (Fig 3.29).

8 The only adjustment after assembly is to the idling screw which is set when the engine has reached normal running temperature.

Adjustment should never be made to the fast idle screw except as described in paragraph 5 (Fig 3.28).

9 If the fast idle cam should stick in the open position for some reason it can be moved back manually. Remove the plug in the housing and insert a piece of $3/16$ inch rod and push it back (Fig 3.30).

Fig 3.19 STROMBERG 175 CD—2S CARBURETTOR
Float level setting. A = 15½—16½ mm

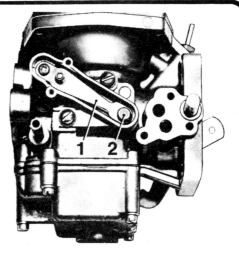

Fig 3.20 STROMBERG 175 CD—2S CARBURETTOR
Temperature compensation (cover removed)
1 Bi-metal strip   2 Tapered plug

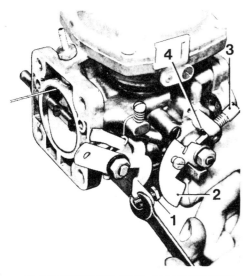

Fig 3.21 STROMBERG 175 CD—2S CARBURETTOR
Fast idle setting

1 Stop screw
2 Fast idle cam
3 Cold start stop pin
4 Stop pin cross piece in vertical position

NOTE: .8 mm drill used to set throttle flap gap

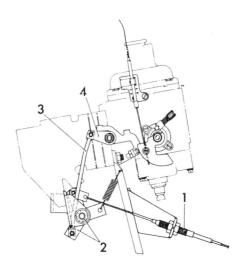

Fig 3.22 STROMBERG 175 CD—2S CARBURETTOR
Throttle control linkage
1 Threaded sleeve   3 Link
2 Relay lever and shaft   4 Throttle lever

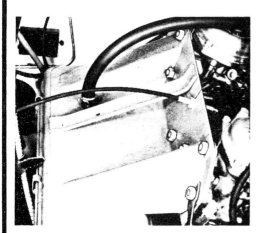

Fig 3.23 V X 4/90 — TWIN STROMBERGS
Air cleaner fixing

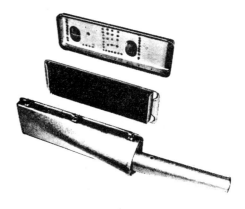

Fig 3.24 V X 4/9 — TWIN STROMBERGS
Air cleaner components

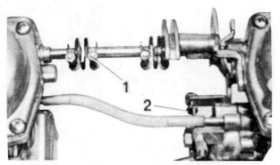

Fig 3.25 VX 4/90 TWIN STROMBERGS
1 Throttle coupling clamp bolt   2 Stop screw

Fig 3.26 STROMBERG 175 CD—2ST CARBURETTOR
Automatic cold start device
1 Thermostat lever peg   3 Vacuum kick rod
2 Thermostat lever spade

Fig 3.27 STROMBERG 175 CD—2ST CARBURETTOR
Automatic cold start device
Arrow shows spring hooked over thermostat lever

Fig 3.28 STROMBERG 175 CD—2ST CARBURETTOR
Automatic cold start device
Plunger to cam clearance (A)

Fig 3.29 STROMBERG 175 CD—2ST CARBURETTOR
Automatic cold start device
Housing, insulator and body line up marks

Fig 3.30 STROMBERG 175 CD—2ST CARBURETTOR
1 Idling speed adjusting screw   adjusted independently)
2 Fast idle screw (not to be

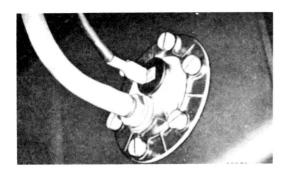

Fig 3.31 FUEL TANK
Outlet pipe and gauge sender unit assembly

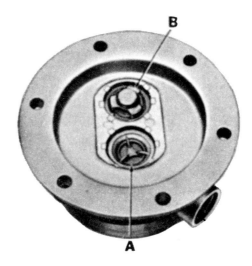

Fig 3.32 FUEL PUMP
Valves secured by staking

A   Outlet valve   B   Inlet valve

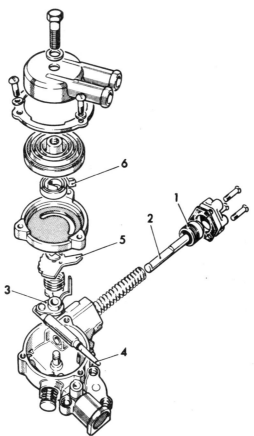

Fig 3.33 STROMBERG 175 CD—2ST CARBURETTOR
Automatic cold start device

1 Vacuum piston   3 Thermostat lever   5 Fast idle cam   6 Bi-metal spring thermostat
2 Vacuum kick rod   4 Tapered fuel needle

12 Fuel tank - removal and replacement

1 Remove the battery from the car as a safety measure, also ensure there are no open flames in the vicinity. DO NOT smoke during removal and replacement of the tank.
2 The tank outlet pipe is on the front of the tank and should be disconnected by pulling off the flexible pipe connection. Detach also the tank gauge sender unit wire from the same place (Fig 3.31). If the tank is to be drained this should be done now by attaching a longer piece of pipe to the outlet and syphoning the contents out.
3 The tank is held to the floor of the luggage compartment by bolts, with stiffener plates at each side.
4 The filler pipe is connected with hose clips to the tank inlet and need not be removed when taking the tank from the car.
5 Replacement is a reversal of the removal procedure but the flange should be sealed with a suitable compound to prevent water coming up into the luggage compartment.
6 Repairs to the fuel tank to stop leaks are best carried out using resin adhesives and hardeners as supplied in most accessory shops. In cases of repairs being done to large holes, fibre glass mats or perforated zinc sheet may be required to give area support. If any soldering, welding or brazing is contemplated, the tank must be steamed out to remove any traces of petroleum vapour. It is dangerous to use naked flames on a fuel tank without this, even though it may have been lying empty for a considerable period.

13 Fuel pump - removal

1 Disconnect the fuel lines (photo).
2 Remove the two bolts holding the pump to the block and lift it away.
3 Recover the insulator block and gaskets.

14 Fuel pump - dismantling

1 Undo the knurled screw holding the glass bowl in position and lift off the filter screen (see Fig 3.3).
2 Mark the relationship between centre and base sections of the pump body and then remove the five securing screws and lift off the centre section.
3 To release the diaphragm, depress the centre and turn it 90°. This will release the diaphragm pull rod from the stirrup in the operating link. Lift out the seal and seal retainer.
4 Do not remove the rocker arm and pivot pin from the body base unless there are signs of excessive wear - in which case it would probably be more economical to obtain an exchange pump.
5 To remove the valve assemblies from the body centre, undo the retaining plate screws and lift out each valve and the gasket behind them.

15 Fuel pump - inspection, reassembly and replacement

1 Examine the diaphragm for signs of splitting or cracking and renew it if in any doubt.
2 If the valves are suspected of malfunctioning, replace them.
3 The filter screen should be intact with no signs of enlarged holes or broken strands.
4 Renew the oil seal.
5 Clean up the recesses where the valves have been staked into the body to ensure that when replaced the valves will seat neatly.
6 To refit the valves fit a new gasket first and then locate each valve the correct way up. The inlet valve has its spring facing the bottom of the pump. Later models have the valves staked in position and these are not easily removed and replaced. Each one must lie perfectly flat and be staked securely with a flat nosed punch around the edge in six places (Fig 3.32).

7 To refit the diaphragm first put a new oil seal followed by the retainer into the body base. Put the diaphragm pull rod through the seal and the groove in the rocker arm link. Then turn the diaphragm anticlockwise 90° so that it lines up with the screw holes and the lug on the body aligns with the tab on the diaphragm.
8 Move the rocker arm until the diaphragm is level with the body flanges and hold the arm in this position. Reassemble the two halves of the pump ensuring that the previously made marks on the flanges are adjacent to each other.
9 Insert the five screws and lockwashers and tighten them down finger tight.
10 Move the rocker arm up and down several times to centralise the diaphragm, and then with the arm held down, tighten the screws securely in a diagonal sequence.
11 Replace the gauze filter in position. Fit the cover sealing ring, glass bowl and securing stirrup. Tighten the nut with the fingers only.
12 Fuel pump replacement is a straightforward reversal of the removal procedure. However, note the following points:

a) The fuel pump should be assembled to the engine block with new gaskets - one each side of the insulator block (photo).
b) Ensure that the pump operating arm is resting on the camshaft, and not under it (photo).
c) Do not overtighten the pump retaining bolts.
d) Test that the pump is working, by disconnecting the pipe feed at the carburettor, holding a container under it and getting someone to turn the engine. The fuel should spurt out in intermittent jets.

16 Fuel gauge sender unit - fault finding

1 The sender unit is mounted on the front face of the tank and incorporates the outlet pipe (Fig 3.31).
   If the fuel gauge does not work correctly the fault is either in the sender unit in the fuel tank, the gauge in the instrument panel or the wiring.
2 To check the sender unit first disconnect the wire from the unit at the connector on the tank. With the ignition on, the gauge should read 'full'. With the same lead connected to earth the gauge should read 'empty'. If BOTH of these situations are correct then the fault (if any) lies in the sender unit.
3 If the gauge does not read full with the wire disconnected from the sender unit, the wire should then also be disconnected from the gauge unit (having removed the instrument panel as described in Chapter 10). If the gauge now reads 'full' then the fault lies in the wire from the gauge to the sender unit.
4 If not, the gauge is faulty and should be replaced. (For details see Chapter 10).
5 With the wire disconnected from the sender unit and earthed, if the gauge reads anything other than empty, check the rest of the circuit as described in Chapter 10.
6 To remove the unit first make sure that the level of fuel in the tank is below the lower edge of the units mounting flange.
7 Disconnect the fuel outlet pipe and sender wire and remove the six mounting screws. Take care not to bend the wire or float when drawing it from the tank. Similarly the fuel pipe must not be bent otherwise its position in relation to the bottom of the tank will be upset.
8 Replacement is a straightforward reversal of this procedure. Fit a new gasket and locate the flange so that the blade terminal is directly above the fuel outlet pipe.

17 Exhaust system

1 Two types of system are fitted depending on whether or not a single or two branch manifold is fitted.
2 The single branch system comprises a front pipe, intermediate pipe with silencer, and a rear pipe with resonator (Fig 3.34).
3 The twin branch system comprises two front pipes, the rear

13.1 Undoing fuel pump unions

15.12a Preparing to replace fuel pump using new gaskets

15.12b Replacing fuel pump to engine block

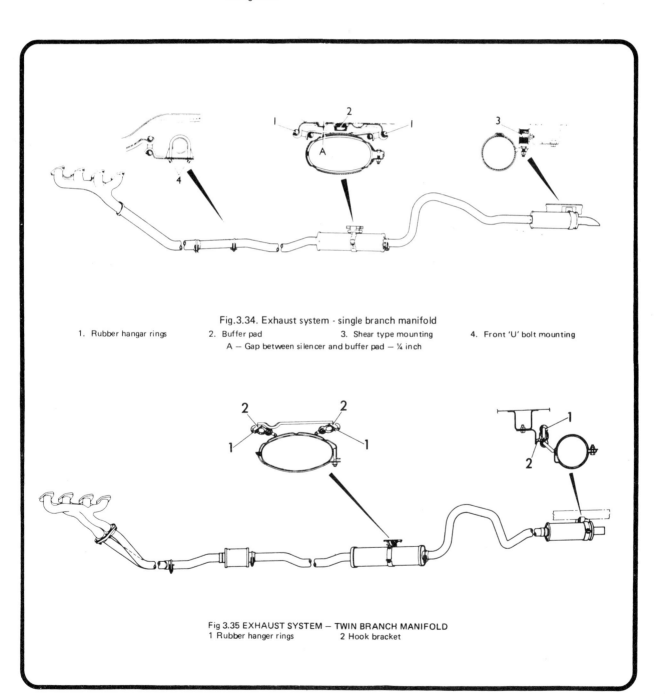

Fig.3.34. Exhaust system - single branch manifold

1. Rubber hangar rings   2. Buffer pad   3. Shear type mounting   4. Front 'U' bolt mounting

A — Gap between silencer and buffer pad — ¼ inch

Fig 3.35 EXHAUST SYSTEM — TWIN BRANCH MANIFOLD

1 Rubber hanger rings   2 Hook bracket

section with resonator, intermediate pipe with silencer and rear pipe with another resonator.

4   If any section of the system needs renewing it is safest to disconnect the front pipe from the manifold and then unhook all the hanger rings (and unbolt the rear mounting where fitted) so that the complete assembly may be worked on away from the car. Otherwise damage can be caused to other sections when separating them. Cut off the old clamps rather than try and undo them.

5   Fit the new sections but do not clamp them up until the whole system is once again slung underneath and the attitudes of the pipes corrected.

6   On single branch systems the centre silencer support bracket has a rubber buffer and the clearance between the silencer strap and buffer should be ¼ inch. This can be altered by rotating the forward U bolt on the pipe (Fig 3.34, Item 4) to suit.

7   Tighten all clamps firmly but not so much that they squeeze the pipes.

Fault Finding Chart - Fuel System and Carburation

Unsatisfactory engine performance and excessive fuel consumption are not necessarily the fault of the fuel system or carburettor. In fact they more commonly occur as a result of ignition and timing faults. Before acting on the following it is necessary to check the ignition system first. Even though a fault may lie in the fuel system it will be difficult to trace unless the ignition is correct The faults below, therefore, assume that this has been attended to first (where appropriate). It is also assumed that the engine is not significantly worn.

Symptom	Reason/s	Remedy
Smell of petrol when engine is stopped	Leaking fuel lines or unions	Repair or renew as necessary.
	Leaking fuel tank	Fill fuel tank to capacity and examine carefully at seams, unions and filler pipe connections. Repair as necessary.
Smell of petrol when engine is idling	Leaking fuel line unions between pump and carburettor	Check line and unions and tighten or repair.
	Overflow of fuel from float chamber due to wrong level setting, ineffective needle valve or punctured float	Check fuel level setting and condition of float and needle valve, and renew if necessary.
Excessive fuel consumption for reasons not covered by leaks or float chamber faults	Worn jets (Zenith)	Renew jets.
	Over-rich jet setting (Stromberg)	Adjust jet.
	Sticking strangler flap (Zenith)	Check correct movement of strangler flap.
Difficult starting, uneven running, lack of power, cutting out	One or more jets blocked or restricted	Dismantle and clean out float chamber and jets.
	Float chamber fuel level too low or needle valve sticking	Dismantle and check fuel level and needle valve.
	Fuel pump not delivering sufficient fuel	Check pump delivery and clean or repair as required.
	Air valve piston not operating correctly (Stromberg)	Dismantle and examine. Clean and repair as required.

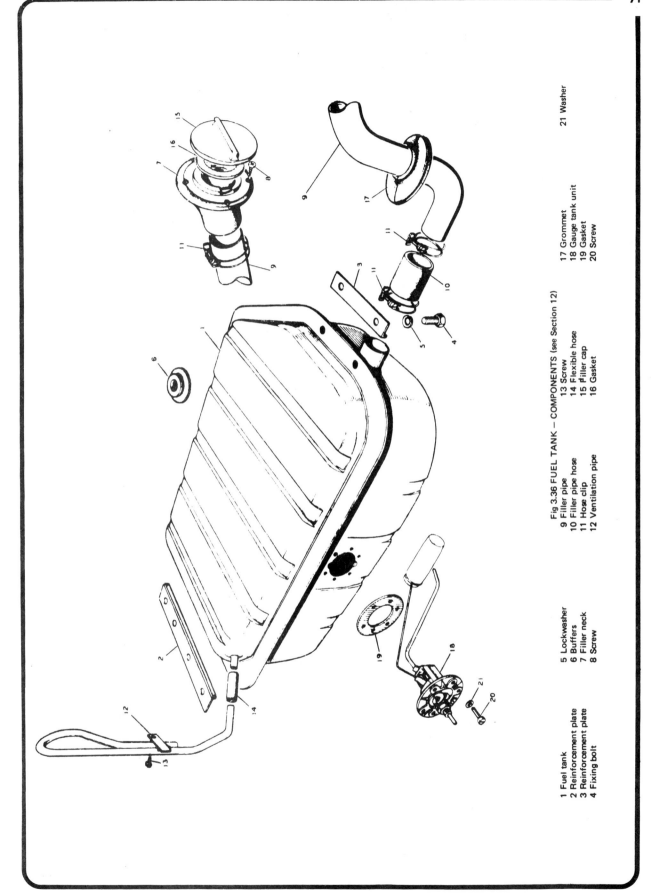

Fig 3.36 FUEL TANK – COMPONENTS (see Section 12)

1 Fuel tank	5 Lockwasher
2 Reinforcement plate	6 Buffers
3 Reinforcement plate	7 Filler neck
4 Fixing bolt	8 Screw

9 Filler pipe	13 Screw
10 Filler pipe hose	14 Flexible hose
11 Hose clip	15 Filler cap
12 Ventilation pipe	16 Gasket

17 Grommet	21 Washer
18 Gauge tank unit	
19 Gasket	
20 Screw	

Chapter 4 Ignition system

Contents

Specifications

Spark plugs

Standard	AC 42TS
High speed	AC 41T
Electrode gap	.030 normal 76-77
	.026 during running in

Coil

Make	Delco-Remy
Type...	Oil-filled, LT resistor in circuit bypassed for additional starting voltage
Coil feed resistance	2 ohms

Distributor

Make	Delco-Remy D300
Rotation	Anticlockwise
Firing sequence	1 3 4 2
Contact points gap - new	.022 in
- used	.020 in S1
Contact arm spring tension	22–26 ozs
Cam dwell angle	35–37°
Mainshaft clearance in bushes	.0001–.0011
Mainshaft end float	.085–.175 in

Ignition timing ... ...

A limited number of 1599 cc engines have a static advance of 18°
BTDC. To identify these check the distributor and carburettor type
numbers as specified

Static advance ... ... 9° BTDC

Vacuum advance (early models) ... ...

Vacuum Hg	Distributor degrees
5	0
7	0–2
9	2–4
11+	4–5½

Vacuum advance (later models - distributor part No 7953734
and 7953732 ... ...

4½	0
6	½–2½
8	3½–5½
10+	6½–8½

Centrifugal advance (early 1599 cc and 1975 cc (LC) engines)
Cut in speed 375/525 rpm ... ...

Distributor rpm	Distributor degrees
400	0–½
600	1–3
800	3½–5½
1000	6–8
1200	8½–10½
1400	11–13
1600+	13½–15½

Centrifugal advance (later 1599 cc models) (with distributor part No 7953734)	Distributor rpm	Distributor degrees
Cut in speed 360–500 rpm...	400	0–½
	600	3–6
	800	8–10½
	1000	9½–11½
	1200	10½–12½
	1400	11–13
	1600	12–14
	1800	13–15
	2000	14–15½
	2200	15–16½
	2400	15½–17½
	2500+	16–18

Centrifugal advance (1975 cc HC engines (including VX 4/90)		
Cut in speed 290–475 rpm...	400	0–1½
	600	1–3½
	800	3½–5½
	1000	5½–7½
	1200	6½–8½
	1400	7½–9½
	1600	8½–10½
	1800	9–11
	2000+	10–12

Centrifugal advance (later 1975 cc LC engines (distributor part No 7953732)		
Cut in speed 360–500 rpm...	400	0–½
	600	2–4½
	800	5½–8
	1000	8½–10½
	1200	9½–11½
	1400	10–12
	1600	11–13
	1800	12–14
	2000	12½–14½
	2200	13½–15½
	2400	14–16
	2500+	14½–16½

1975 cc engines - Exhaust emission control (Part No 9553779)
Vacuum advance mechanism omitted
Centrifugal advance

Cut in speed	600	2–4½
	800	5½–8½
	1000	8½–11
	1200	9½–11½
	1400	10–12
	1600	11–13
	1800	12–14
	2000	12½–14½
	2200	13½–15½
	2400	14–16
	2600+	14½–16½

Details of numbers and colour codes on mainshafts, cams and centrifugal advance weights	1599 cc		1975 cc	
	HC (Std)	LC	HC (Std)	LC
Mainshaft No (early)	36	36	26	36
Mainshaft No (later)	786	786	*	795
Cam No (early)	20	20	22	20
Cam No (later)	35	35	*	33
Advance weights (early)	—	—	53	—
Advance weights (later)	843	843	*	53
Advance weight springs colour (early)...	Orange/Green	Orange/Green	Orange/blue	Orange/Green
Advance weight springs colour	Red	Red	*	Red

* No change except for a limited Number which were the same as the LC version

Torque wrench setting

Spark plugs...	12 lb/ft

1 General description

In order that the engine can run correctly it is necessary for an electrical spark to ignite the fuel/air mixture in the combustion chamber at exactly the right moment in relation to engine speed and load. The ignition system is based on feeding low tension voltage from the battery to the coil where it is converted to high tension voltage. The high tension voltage is powerful enough to jump the sparking plug gap in the cylinders many times a second under high compression pressures, providing that the system is in good condition and that all adjustments are correct.

The ignition system is divided into two circuits. The low tension circuit and the high tension circuit.

The low tension (sometimes known as the primary) circuit consists of the battery, lead to the control box, lead to the ignition switch, lead from the ignition switch to the low tension or primary coil windings (terminal SW), and the lead from the low tension coil windings (coil terminal CB) to the contact breaker points and condenser in the distributor.

The high tension circuit consists of the high tension or secondary coil windings, the heavy ignition lead from the centre of the coil to the centre of the distributor cap, the rotor arm, and the spark plug leads and spark plugs.

The system functions in the following manner: High tension voltage is generated in the coil by the interruption of the low tension circuit. The interruption is effected by the opening of the contact breaker points in this low tension circuit.

High tension voltage is fed via the carbon brush in the centre of the distributor cap to the rotor arm of the distributor.

The rotor arm revolves anticlockwise at half engine speed inside the distributor cap, and each time it comes in line with one of the four metal segments in the cap, which are connected to the spark plug leads, the opening and closing of the contact breaker points causes the high tension voltage to build up, jump the gap from the rotor arm to the appropriate metal segment and so via the spark plug lead to the spark plug, where it finally jumps the spark plug gap before going to earth.

The ignition is advanced and retarded automatically, to ensure the spark occurs at just the right instant for the particular load at the prevailing engine speed.

The ignition advance is controlled both mechanically and by a vacuum operated system. The mechanical governor mechanism comprises two weights, which move out from the distributor shaft as the engine speed rises, due to centrifugal force. As they move outwards they rotate the cam relative to the distributor shaft, and so advance the spark. The weights are held in position by two light springs and it is the tension of the springs which is largely responsible for correct spark advancement.

The vacuum control consists of a diaphragm, one side of which is connected via a small bore tube to the carburettor, which varies with engine speed and throttle opening, causes the diaphragm to move, so moving the contact breaker plate, and advancing or retarding the spark. A fine degree of control is achieved by a spring in the vacuum assembly.

2 Distributor rotor - removal and replacement

1 Having removed the distributor cap by undoing the two spring clips, remove the rotor by undoing the two securing screws in the top.
2 Lift off the rotor.
3 It will be seen that on the underside of the rotor there are two locating pegs. One is round and the other square. These must fit into the corresponding holes in the mainshaft and cam assembly when the rotor is replaced.
4 The contact spring on the rotor should not be bent or damaged in any way. The height of the spring should be set 1.38—1.44 inch (35—37 mm) above the base of the rotor (Fig 4.2).

5 Tighten the screws firmly on replacement but not overtight.

3 Contact breaker points - adjustment

1 To adjust the contact breaker points to the correct gap, first pull off the two clips securing the distributor cap to the distributor body, and lift away the cap. Clean the cap inside and out with a dry cloth. It is unlikely that the four segments will be badly burned or scored, but if they are, the cap will have to be renewed.
2 Check the carbon brush located in the top of the cap to make sure that it is not broken or missing.
3 Access to the contact points is better if the rotor is removed.
4 Gently prise the contact breaker points open to examine the condition of their faces. If they are rough, pitted or dirty, it will be necessary to remove them for resurfacing, or for replacement points to be fitted.
5 Presuming the points are satisfactory, or that they have been cleaned and replaced, measure the gap between the points by turning the engine over until the contact breaker arm is on the peak of one of the four cam lobes.
6 A .020 inch feeler gauge should now just fit between the points (.022 inch with new points).
7 If the gap varies from this amount, slacken the two securing screws.
8 Adjust the contact gap by inserting a screwdriver in the slot in the fixed plate and levering it. It is best to do this with the securing screws holding the plate enough to prevent inadvertent movement (Fig 4.3).
9 Always check the gap again after tightening the screws. Sometimes the final tightening moves the points from their original setting.

4 Contact breaker points - removal and replacement

1 Remove the distributor cap.
2 Remove the rotor arm. Do not pull it by the contact spring.
3 Remove the contact points holding screws.
4 Ease the end of the moving contact spring out of the insulator (Fig 4.4).
5 Lift the complete contact set assembly off the pivot pin of the mounting plate.
6 If the condition of the points is not too bad they can be reconditioned by rubbing the contacts clean with fine emery cloth or a fine carborundum stone. It is important that the faces are rubbed flat and parallel to each other so that there will be complete face to face contact when the points are closed. One of the points will be pitted and the other will have deposits on it.
7 It is necessary to remove completely the built-up deposits, but not necessary to rub the pitted point right down to the stage where all the pitting has disappeared, although obviously if this is done it will prolong the time before the operation of refacing the points has to be repeated.
8 Thoroughly clean the points before refitting them. Locate the fixed contact plate over the base of the pivot pin and then fix the moving contact into position so that the end of the spring fits over the centre boss of the nylon lug. Replace the fixing screws. Press in the condenser and coil lead tags to the nylon lug behind the spring (Fig 4.4).
9 Adjust the gap as described in Section 3.

5 Condenser - removal, testing and replacement

1 The purpose of the condenser (sometimes known as capacitor) is to ensure that when the contact breaker points open there is no sparking across them which would waste voltage and cause rapid deterioration of the points.
2 The condenser is fitted in parallel with the contact breaker points. If it develops a short circuit, it will cause ignition failure as the points

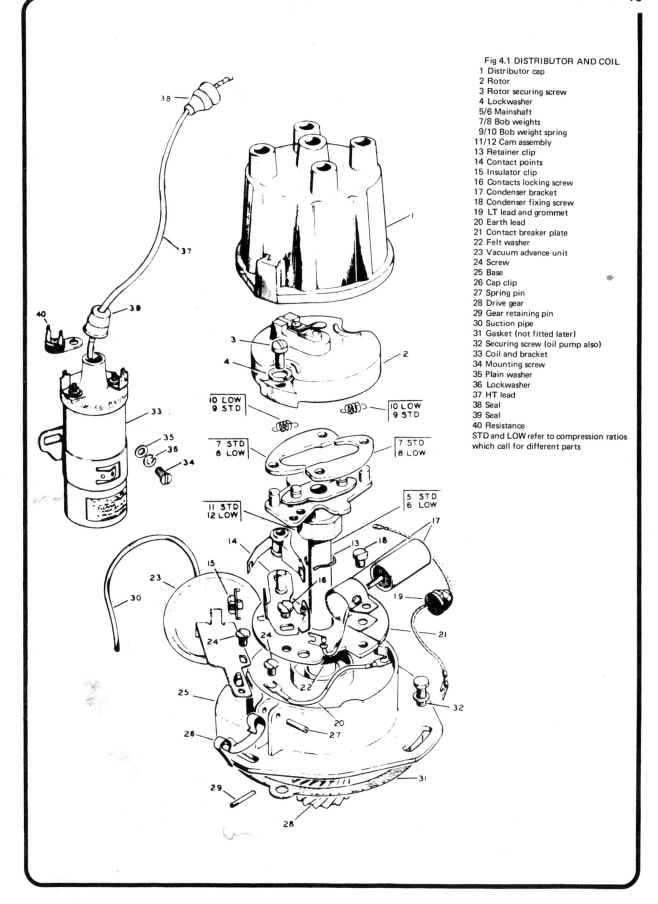

Fig 4.1 DISTRIBUTOR AND COIL
1 Distributor cap
2 Rotor
3 Rotor securing screw
4 Lockwasher
5/6 Mainshaft
7/8 Bob weights
9/10 Bob weight spring
11/12 Cam assembly
13 Retainer clip
14 Contact points
15 Insulator clip
16 Contacts locking screw
17 Condenser bracket
18 Condenser fixing screw
19 LT lead and grommet
20 Earth lead
21 Contact breaker plate
22 Felt washer
23 Vacuum advance unit
24 Screw
25 Base
26 Cap clip
27 Spring pin
28 Drive gear
29 Gear retaining pin
30 Suction pipe
31 Gasket (not fitted later)
32 Securing screw (oil pump also)
33 Coil and bracket
34 Mounting screw
35 Plain washer
36 Lockwasher
37 HT lead
38 Seal
39 Seal
40 Resistance
STD and LOW refer to compression ratios
which call for different parts

will be prevented from interrupting the low tension circuit.

3 If the engine becomes very difficult to start or begins to misfire whilst running and the breaker points show signs of excessive burning, then the condition of the condenser must be suspect. A further test can be made by separating the points by hand with the ignition switched on. If this is accompanied by a bright spark at the contact points it is indicative that the condenser has failed.

4 Without special test equipment the only sure way to diagnose condenser trouble is to replace a suspected unit with a new one and note if there is any improvement.

5 To remove the condenser from the distributor, remove the distributor cap and the rotor arm.

6 Pull out the condenser lead clip from the nylon insulator where it fits behind the spring (Fig 4.4).

7 Undo the mounting bracket screw and remove the condenser.

8 Replacement is simply a reversal of the removal process. Take particular care that the condenser wire cannot short circuit against any portion of the breaker plate.

6 Distributor - removal and replacement

1 To remove the distributor complete with cap from the engine, begin by pulling the plug lead terminals off the four spark plugs. Free the HT lead from the coil.

2 Pull off the vacuum advance.

3 Disconnect the low tension wire from the coil.

4 It is not possible to remove and replace the distributor without having to reset the ignition timing. Removal and replacement therefore is dealt with under the 'Ignition timing' section.

5 The distributor is held in place by three bolts through slotted holes in the base flange. When the bolts are removed the distributor can be lifted straight out.

6 Replacement of the distributor must follow the procedure as described under 'Ignition timing'.

7 Distributor - dismantling and reassembly

1 Before deciding to dismantle the distributor bear in mind the following:

a) Shaft bushes, if worn, are not supplied separately (by Vauxhall). A complete base assembly must be acquired.

b) With the exception of the rotor and contact points other parts may not be readily obtainable. It is very important to be quite sure of the type of distributor fitted before changing weights, springs or mainshaft cam. The specifications at the beginning of the Chapter indicate the types there are.

c) If the distributor is seriously worn it may be more satisfactory in the long run to change the whole unit.

2 Begin dismantling by removing the rotor, condenser and contact breaker points as previously described.

3 The contact breaker points mounting plate may be detached after removing the circlip at the top end of the mainshaft (Fig 4.6).

4 To remove the mainshaft involves driving out the spring pin which holds the gear to the shaft - use a flat nosed punch (Fig 4.5).

5 If items are being replaced take care to note the numbers stamped on them which identify the type for each engine. The specifications give details but these should be checked with parts supplier.

6 Some later mainshafts were revised and incorporated an oil return scroll at the upper end. They also had a wider slot in the end which drives the oil pump and in such instances the oil pump drive shaft should be changed to suit (Fig 4.9).

7 When reassembling the distributor make sure the felt oil retainer engages properly in the slot in the main base before installing the circuit breaker plate (Fig 4.7).

8 If a new drive shaft is fitted the gear pin hole will need to be drilled ($1/8$ inch). This hole must be positioned to allow the correct

end float. It should also be arranged so that the angle between the centre line of any gear tooth and the centre line of the drive slot is 70º (Fig 4.10).

8 Ignition timing

1 Before setting the distributor static timing make quite sure that the correct static advance is known. On those engines which had 18º BTDC (some 1599 cc models) a second mark is made on the rear of the crankshaft pulley which is used against the 9º BTDC pointer to give the extra 9º advance.

2 The procedure for setting the timing is detailed from the point of installing the distributor. If the distributor is not removed and the timing is known to be in need only of fine adjustment then the procedures leading up to this stage can be ignored. Only the final setting of the opening of the points gap is necessary.

3 With the distributor removed turn the engine so that the crankshaft pulley mark is on the 9º (or 18º if appropriate) BTDC pointer (photo). At the same time the camshaft pulley timing mark should be at the No 1 piston TDC position (Fig 4.11). (If it is opposite this position then turn the crankshaft another revolution).

4 Prepare the mating faces of the distributor body flange and the oil pump flange by cleaning them thoroughly and applying a thin coat of 'Hylomar'.

5 Hold the distributor over the installation position with the vacuum advance unit facing towards the fuel pump and the rotor contact at about 11 o'clock as you look down on the distributor from the side of the engine (photo).

6 Line up the oil pump shaft tongue with the slot in the bottom of the distributor drive shaft (photo).

7 Put the distributor down into position. If you have everything correctly lined up the rotor tip should have moved clockwise to 12 o'clock and the mounting bolt holes should be in the centre of the flange slots.

8 If you make an error lift the distributor out and repeat the procedure. If the body does not go right down easily it will be because the oil pump drive shaft is not properly aligned.

9 Replace the three distributor securing bolts but do not tighten them. Set the contact breaker points gap if not already done.

10 Turn the body of the distributor anticlockwise until the points are closed.

11 Now turn the distributor body clockwise until the contact points are just about to open. This can be accurately gauged if a 12 volt 6 watt bulb is wired in parallel with the contact points. Switch on the ignition and when the points open the bulb should light.

12 Tighten the distributor clamp bolts (photo).

13 If a stroboscopic light is used for a final static ignition timing check, remove the lead from No 1 plug and then connect the strobe, one wire to the plug and the other to the plug lead. With the engine idling as slowly as possible shine the strobe light on to the timing case marker when the pulley pointer should appear stationary on the lower marker (9º advance).

9 If the engine speed is increased, then the effect of the vacuum and centrifugal advance controls can be seen and in fact, measured to some extent, in so far as the distance between the two crankcase timing markers represents 9º of crankshaft revolution.

9 Spark plugs and leads

1 The correct functioning of the spark plugs is vital for the correct running and efficiency of the engine. The plugs fitted as standard are listed in the specifications at the beginning of the Chapter.

2 At intervals of 3000 miles the plugs should be removed, examined and cleaned. If worn excessively, they should be replaced. This cleaning frequency may seem high to some people but experience has shown that it is worth the short time involved. The condition of the spark plug will also tell much about the overall condition of the engine.

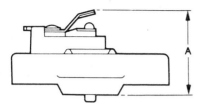

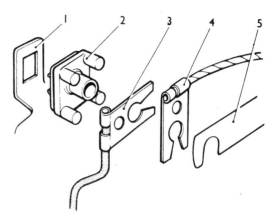

Fig 4.2 DISTRIBUTOR ROTOR — CONTACT SPRING HEIGHT
A = 1.38–1.44 inches

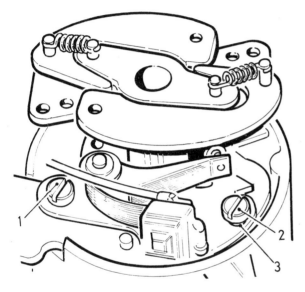

Fig 4.4 CONTACT POINTS AND CONDENSER LEAD FIXING
1 Base plate lug   4 LT wire from coil
2 Insulator/connector   5 Contact point spring
3 Condenser wire

Fig 4.3 CONTACT BREAKER POINTS — ROTOR REMOVED
1 Fixing screw   3 Adjusting slot
2 Fixing screw

Fig 4.6 DISTRIBUTOR
Circlip (arrowed) retaining the contact points mounting plate

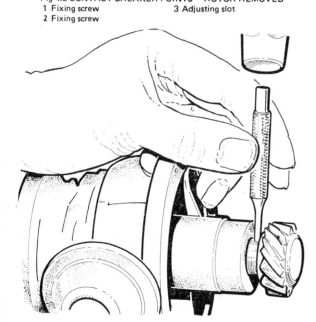

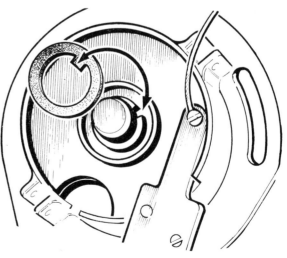

Fig 4.5 DISTRIBUTOR
Driving out the spring pin securing the drive gear to the mainshaft

Fig.4.7. DISTRIBUTOR
Positioning felt lubricator in slotted base.

3 If the insulator nose of the spark plug is clean and white, with no deposits, this is indicative of a weak mixture, or too hot a plug. (A hot plug transfers heat away from the electrode slowly - a cold plug transfers it away quickly).

4 If the tip and insulator nose is covered with sooty black deposits, then this is indicative that the mixture is too rich. Should the plug be black and oily, then it is likely that the engine is fairly worn, as well as the mixture being rich.

5 If the insulator nose is covered with light tan to greyish brown deposits, then the mixture is correct and it is likely that the engine is in good condition.

6 If there are any traces of long brown tapering stains on the outside of the white portion of the plug, then the plug will have to be renewed, as this shows that there is a faulty joint between the plug body and the insulator, and compression is being allowed to leak away.

7 Plugs should be cleaned by a sand blasting machine, which will free them from carbon more thoroughly than cleaning by hand. The machine will also test the condition of the plugs under compression. Any plug that fails to spark at the recommended pressure should be renewed.

8 The spark plug gap is of considerable importance, as, if it is too large or too small the size of the spark and its efficiency will be seriously impaired. The spark plug gap should be set to .030 inch for the best results.

9 To set it, measure the gap with a feeler gauge, and then bend open, or close, the outer plug electrode until the correct gap is achieved. The centre electrode should never be bent as this may crack the insulation and cause plug failure, if nothing worse.

10 When replacing the plugs it is important that the tapered contact seats of the plugs and cylinder head are clean and undamaged (photo).

11 Plugs must not be overtightened. As they are a different size (518 AF) from most other plugs it is worthwhile obtaining the proper socket and extension to fit a torque wrench.

10 Ignition system - faults and remedies

1 By far the majority of breakdown and running troubles are caused by faults in the ignition system either in the low tension or high tension circuits.

2 There are two main symptoms indicating ignition faults. Either the engine will not start or fire, or the engine is difficult to start and misfires. If it is a regular misfire, ie the engine is only running on two or three cylinders, the fault is almost sure to be in the secondary, or high tension, circuit. If the misfiring is intermittent, the fault could be in either the high or low tension circuits. If the car stops suddenly, or will not start at all, it is likely that the fault is in the low tension circuit. Loss of power and overheating, apart from faulty carburation settings, are normally due to faults in the distributor, or incorrect ignition timing.

3 If the engine fails to start and the car was running normally when it was last used, first check there is fuel in the petrol tank. If the engine turns over normally on the starter motor and the battery is evidently well charged, then the fault may be in either the high or low tension circuits. First check the HT circuit. NOTE: If the battery is known to be fully charged; the ignition light comes on, and the starter motor fails to turn the engine CHECK THE TIGHTNESS OF THE LEADS ON THE BATTERY TERMINALS and also the secureness of the earth lead to its CONNECTION TO THE BODY. It is quite common for the leads to have worked loose, even if they look and feel secure. If one of the battery terminal posts gets hot when trying to work the starter motor this is a sure indication of a faulty connection to that terminal.

4 One of the common reasons for bad starting is wet or damp plug leads and distributor. Remove the distributor cap. If condensation is visible internally, dry the cap with a rag and also wipe over the leads. Replace the cap.

5 If the engine still fails to start, check that current is reaching the plugs, by disconnecting each plug lead in turn at the spark plug end,

and hold the end of the cable about $^3/_{16}$ inch away from the cylinder block. Spin the engine on the starter motor.

6 Sparking between the end of the cable and the block should be fairly strong with a regular blue spark. (Hold the lead with rubber to avoid electric shocks). If current is reaching the plugs, then remove them and clean and regap them to .030 inch. The engine should now start.

7 If there is no spark at the plug leads take off the HT lead from the centre of the distributor cap and hold it to the block as before. Spin the engine on the starter once more. A rapid succession of blue sparks between the end of the lead and the block indicate that the coil is in order and that the distributor cap is cracked, the rotor arm faulty, or the carbon brush in the top of the distributor cap is not making good contact with the spring on the rotor arm. Possibly the points are in bad condition. Clean and reset them as described earlier in this Chapter.

8 If there are no sparks from the end of the lead from the coil, check the connections at the coil end of the lead. If it is in order start checking the low tension circuit.

9 Use a 12v voltmeter or a 12v bulb and two lengths of wire. With the ignition switch on and the points open, test between the low tension wire to the coil (it is marked SW or +) and earth. No reading indicates a break in the supply from the ignition switch. Check the connections at the switch to see if any are loose. Refit them. A reading shows a faulty coil or condenser, or broken lead between the coil and the distributor.

10 Take the condenser wire off the points assembly and with the points open, test between the moving point and earth. If there now is a reading, then the fault is in the condenser. Fit a new one.

11 With no reading from the moving point to earth, take a reading between earth and the CB or − terminal of the coil. A reading here shows a broken wire which will need to be replaced between the coil and distributor. No reading confirms that the coil has failed and must be replaced. Remember to refit the condenser wire to the points assembly. For these tests it is sufficient to separate the points with a piece of dry paper while testing with the points open.

12 The Victor is fitted with a device which boosts the output from the coil when the starter is operated. (When the starter is used battery voltage tends to drop due to the load placed upon it). Quite simply, the coil is rated for a continuous 6 volt supply. As the vehicle system is 12 volt a resistor is fitted into the LT supply to the coil so that under normal running conditions the coil only receives a 6 volt supply. However, when the starter is operated the system voltage drops. This is usual. In addition to the normal LT feed to the coil therefore, an additional feed is taken from the starter solenoid switch direct to the coil. This feed only operates when the solenoid starter terminals are closed, ie when the starter is turning. Consequently, for the brief time when the voltage drops from 12 to about 8 volts is fed direct to the 6 volt coil providing a temporary starting boost.

Certain checks are necessary to ensure that:

a) The starter feed is functioning properly - otherwise only about 2 volts would reach the coil on starting.

b) The resistor is in good order - otherwise 12 volts or no volts may reach the 6 volt coil.

The tests detailed are clarified by reference to the wiring connections given in Fig 4.14.

A (i) To check the current supply to the coil through the resistor wire, disconnect the resistor wire and connect it to earth via a voltmeter. With contact points closed and ignition switched on the reading should be 6 volts (approx). If not then there is a fault in the wire, the ignition switch, or the feed to the ignition switch.

(ii) With the connections still made, operate the starter motor. The voltage should jump to 9v (approx) whilst the starter is turning,

If the wire is not faulty and the voltage does not rise, then the starter solenoid switch must be faulty and will need renewal.

B (i) To check the primary (LT) coil winding points and condenser, connect the voltmeter to the −(CB) terminal of the coil leaving both

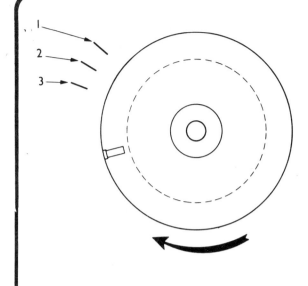

Fig 4.8 IGNITION TIMING MARKS — DRIVE BELT COVER
(LATER MODELS)
1 TDC   3 18° BTDC
2 9° BTDC

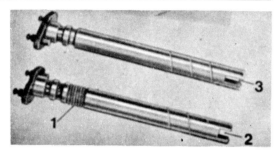

Fig.4.9. Distributor mainshaft differences in later
versions

1 Oil scroll return   3 Narrow slot in early
2 Wider slot   version

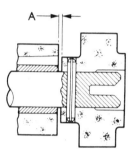 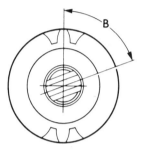

Fig 4.10 DISTRIBUTOR
Mainshaft drive gear pinned position
A = End float .085—.175 inch   B = Pin position to slot 70°

8.3 Ignition timing. Crankshaft pulley mark
on 9° BTDC pointer

8.5 Ignition timing. Position of distributor
rotor prior to replacement

8.6 Ignition timing. Oil pump spindle tongue
(arrowed) prior to distributor replacement
should be lined up with slot in distributor shaft

8.12 Ignition timing. Tightening body securing bolts

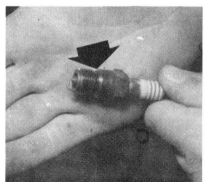

9.10 Spark plug. Note bevelled seat (arrowed)

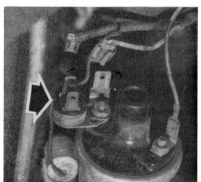

10.13 Coil - resistor (arrowed) fitted to early
versions

coil wires connected also. Switch on the ignition with the contact points OPEN. The voltage should be 12v (approx). If the reading is low or zero, then there is a fault in the coil primary winding or a short circuit at the contact points or condenser.

(ii) With the same connections, close the contact breaker points. With the ignition still on the reading should be 0—.2 volts. If the voltage is greater then the contact points are dirty, the wire from the — (CB) coil terminal is broken, or the distributor body to earth resistance is very high. Should indications be that the resistance in the wiring harness is removed and the wires separated a competent electrician might succeed in fitting a new resistance wire according to the resistance requirement as given in the specifications.

13 Early models are slightly different in that the resistor is fitted on to the coil terminal rather than being incorporated in the feed wire itself (photo). Connections for check A (i) and (ii) would be as shown in Fig 4.12.

14 In addition another check under the A (i) heading would be to check that the 12 volt supply was, in fact, reaching the resistor. For this the voltmeter would be connected as shown in Fig 4.13.

15 Should indications be that the resistance in the wiring harness is faulty the whole harness may need replacement as this particular resistance wire is not supplied or serviced separately. However, if the wiring harness is removed and the wires separated a competent electrician might succeed in fitting a new resistance wire. On early models it is simple enough to fit a new resistor onto the coil terminal. Another alternative with the later resistance wire is to bypass it altogether and rig an early type resistor into the circuit.

11 Misfiring - diagnosis and remedies

1 If the engine misfires regularly run it at a fast idling speed. Pull off each of the plug caps in turn and listen to the note of the engine. Hold the plug cap in a dry cloth or with a rubber glove as additional protection against a shock from the HT supply.

2 No difference in engine running will be noticed when the lead from the defective circuit is removed. Removing the lead from one of the good cylinders will accentuate the misfire.

3 Remove the plug lead from the end of the defective plug and hold it about 3/16 inch away from the block. Restart the engine. If the sparking is fairly strong and regular the fault must lie in the spark plug.

4 The plug may be loose, the insulation may be cracked, or the points may have burnt away giving too wide a gap for the spark to jump. Worse still, one of the points may have broken off. Either renew the plug, or clean it, reset the gap, and then test it.

5 If there is no spark at the end of the plug lead, or if it is weak and intermittent, check the ignition lead from the distributor to the plug. If the insulation is cracked or perished, renew the lead. Check the connections at the distributor cap.

6 If there is still no spark, examine the distributor cap carefully for tracking. This can be recognised by a very thin black line running between two or more electrodes, or between an electrode and some other part of the distributor. These lines are paths which now conduct electricity across the cap thus letting it run to earth. The only answer is a new distributor cap.

7 Apart from the ignition timing being incorrect, other causes of misfiring have already been dealt with under the section dealing with the failure of the engine to start. To recap - these are that:
a) The coil may be faulty giving an intermittent misfire.
b) There may be a damaged wire or loose connection in the low tension circuit.
c) The condenser may be short circuiting.
d) There may be a mechanical fault in the distributor - a broken driving spindle or contact breaker spring.

8 If the ignition timing is too far retarded, it should be noted that the engine will tend to overheat, and there will be a quite noticeable drop in power. If the engine is overheating and the power is down, and the ignition timing is correct, then the carburettor should be check, followed by valves.

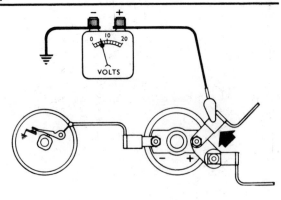

Fig 4.12 LT circuit test connection (early models) - see Section 10, paragraph 13

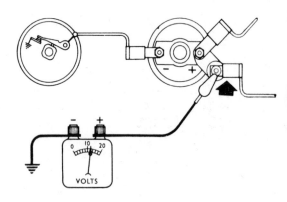

Fig 4.13 LT circuit test connection (early models) - see Section 10, paragraph 14

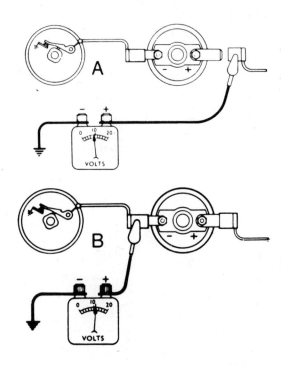

Fig 4.14 LT CIRCUIT TEST CONNECTIONS — SEE SECTION 10, PARAGRAPH 12
■ A = Test A (i) and A (ii)   B = Test B (i) and B (ii)

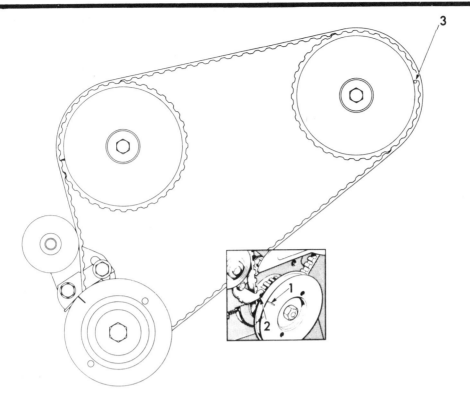

Fig 4.11 IGNITION TIMING — NO 1 PISTON 9° BTDC ON COMPRESSION STROKE

1 Crankshaft pulley mark   2 9° BTDC pointer   3 Camshaft pulley timing mark

White deposits and damaged porcelain insulation indicating overheating

Broken porcelain insulation due to bent central electrode

Electrodes burnt away due to wrong heat value or chronic pre-ignition (pinking)

Excessive black deposits caused by over-rich mixture or wrong heat value

Mild white deposits and electrode burnt indicating too weak a fuel mixture

Plug in sound condition with light greyish brown deposits

Chapter 5 Clutch and actuating mechanism

Contents

Specifications

Make	Borg and Beck or Laycock
	VX 4/90 Laycock only
Type	Diaphragm sprung

	Diameter	Springs	Colour code
Size 1599 cc	7½''	4	Yellow/green
	8''	6	Grey/violet
1925 cc	7½''	4	woven wire facings
	8''	6	Grey/violet
	8½''	6	Grey/violet

Actuating arm free travel ... ... $1/5$ inch (5 mm)

Torque wrench setting

Clutch cover to flywheel bolts ... ... 14 lb/ft - dry threads

1 General description

The clutch consists of an integral pressure plate and diaphragm spring assembly with a single dry plate friction disc between the pressure plate assembly and the flywheel.

The bellhousing on the gearbox encloses the whole unit but only the top half of the bellhousing bolts to the engine. Consequently, there is a semi-circular steel plate bolted to the lower half of the bellhousing to act as a cover.

The clutch is operated mechanically by a Bowden cable direct from the clutch pedal. This actuates a clutch release lever and thrust bearing, the lever pivoting on a ball pin inside the bellhousing and projecting through an aperture in the bellhousing opposite to the pin. Adjustment of free play is effected at the end of the cable where it is attached to the clutch operating lever.

2 Clutch cable - removal and replacement

1 Remove the actuating arm return spring from the bracket on the gearbox (photo).
2 Remove the adjuster nut from the end of the cable (photo).
3 Draw the cable out through the hole in the bellhousing (photo).
4 Uncover the pedal mounting bracket inside the car and take off the clips securing the clevis pin to the top of the pedal and take out the pin.
5 Detach the clevis from the end of the cable.

6 Undo the anchor nut securing the cable outer to the bracket (Fig 5.1).
7 Pull the cable out from inside the engine compartment and unclip it from the sump before taking it away from the car (photo).
8 Replacement of the cable is a reversal of this procedure with attention to the following.
9 When fitting the cable outer into the bellhousing aperture use an insulator collar even if one was not used before. Make one of your own if necessary. A lot of engine noise will be kept out of the car (Fig 5.3).
10 Fit the pedal end of the cable and the locknut before the clutch end.
11 Assemble the insulator, pressure pad washer and nuts in that order after the end of the cable has been passed through the hole in the operating arm.
12 Adjust the release arm clearance and refit the return spring.

3 Clutch - adjustment

1 The free play in the clutch pedal cannot be determined accurately from the pedal. It is necessary to check the gap between the pressure pad/insulator and actuating arm.
2 To measure the gap the return spring is first unhooked from the arm. Then prop or get someone to hold the pedal in the fully up position.
3 Move the actuating arm until it can be felt to be up against the clutch and pull the cable to eliminate any end play there may be. The

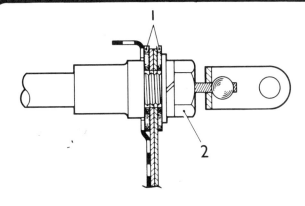

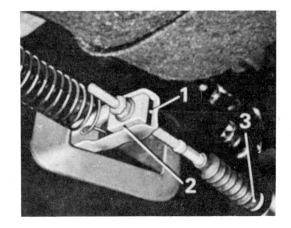

Fig 5.1 CLUTCH CABLE — ANCHORAGE TO PEDAL SUP-
PORT BRACKET — CROSS SECTION
1 Insulating washers   2 Securing nut

Fig 5.2 CLUTCH CABLE — ANCHORAGE TO CLUTCH ACTU-
ATING ARM
1 Insulator block   3 Boot fitted in outer cable
2 Pressure pad   groove

Fig 5.3 Clutch cable. Rubber insulator 'A' fitted between cable
outer and bell housing on later models

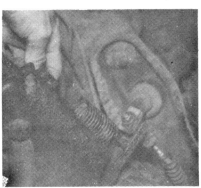

2.1 Detaching the clutch cable return spring

2.2 Removing the clutch cable adjuster nut

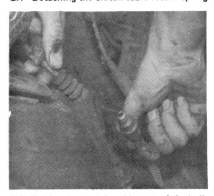

2.3 Pulling the clutch cable out of the bellhousing

2.7 Removing the cable from the sump clip

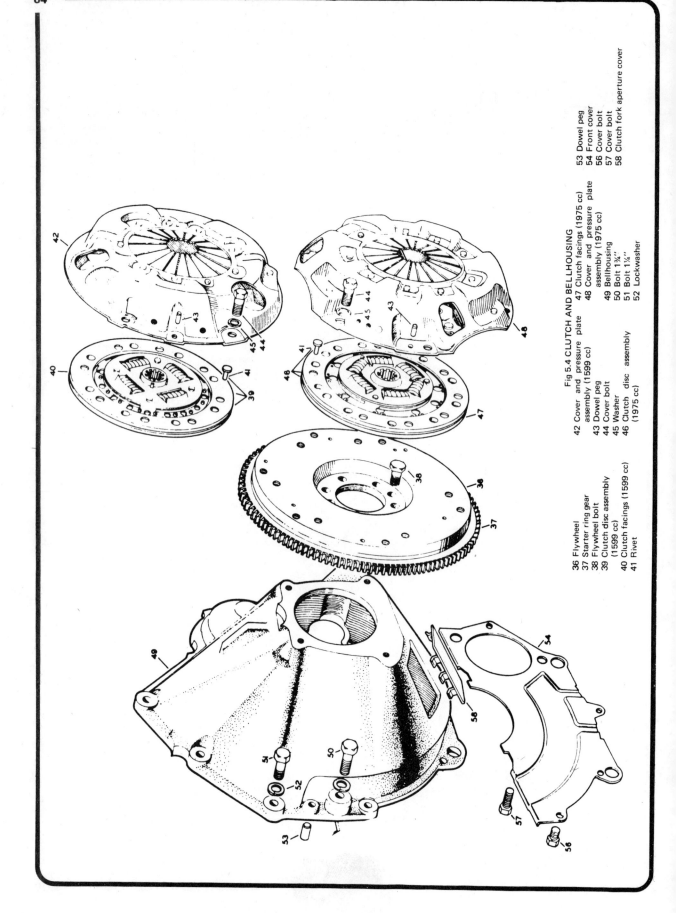

Fig 5.4 CLUTCH AND BELLHOUSING

36 Flywheel
37 Starter ring gear
38 Flywheel bolt
39 Clutch disc assembly (1599 cc)
40 Clutch facings (1599 cc)
41 Rivet

42 Cover and pressure plate assembly (1599 cc)
43 Dowel peg
44 Cover bolt
45 Washer
46 Clutch disc assembly (1975 cc)

47 Clutch facings (1975 cc)
48 Cover and pressure plate assembly (1975 cc)
49 Bellhousing
50 Bolt 1¾"
51 Bolt 1½"
52 Lockwasher

53 Dowel peg
54 Front cover
56 Cover bolt
57 Cover bolt
58 Clutch fork aperture cover

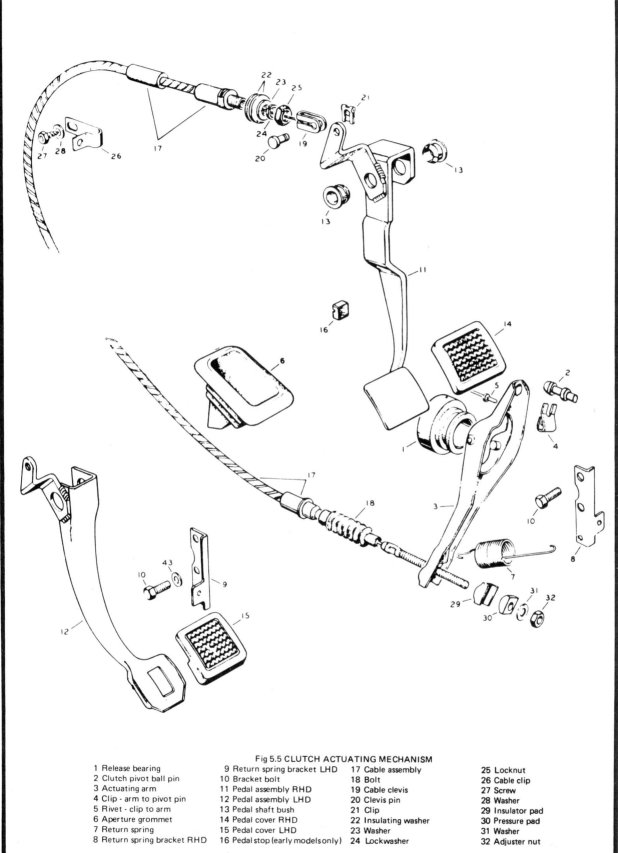

Fig 5.5 CLUTCH ACTUATING MECHANISM

1 Release bearing	9 Return spring bracket LHD	17 Cable assembly	25 Locknut
2 Clutch pivot ball pin	10 Bracket bolt	18 Bolt	26 Cable clip
3 Actuating arm	11 Pedal assembly RHD	19 Cable clevis	27 Screw
4 Clip - arm to pivot pin	12 Pedal assembly LHD	20 Clevis pin	28 Washer
5 Rivet - clip to arm	13 Pedal shaft bush	21 Clip	29 Insulator pad
6 Aperture grommet	14 Pedal cover RHD	22 Insulating washer	30 Pressure pad
7 Return spring	15 Pedal cover LHD	23 Washer	31 Washer
8 Return spring bracket RHD	16 Pedal stop (early models only)	24 Lockwasher	32 Adjuster nut

gap (of $^1/_5$ inch) between arm and pad should now be present. Adjust the nuts as necessary to obtain this gap.

4 Too little or no gap will wear out the thrust race prematurely. If very badly adjusted this way clutch slip could occur. Too much gap will result in excessive pedal movement before the clutch disengages.

5 Do not forget to refit the return spring. If the spring is broken or disconnected it will immediately be apparent by looseness in the pedal at the top end of its travel. The clutch will work but the actuating arm will rattle and cause wear on the thrust bearing also.

---

4 Clutch pedal and shaft - renewal of bushes

---

1 Should excessive play develop in the movement of the pedal on the pivot shaft the bushes may be renewed.

2 Uncover the mounting bracket and disconnect the clevis pins of both the clutch cable and the brake master cylinder attachment.

3 Pull out the spring pins at each end of the pedal shaft and pull out the shaft.

4 Remove the parking brake lever (RHD) as described in Chapter 9.

5 Take out the brake pedal.

6 The clutch pedal can be manoeuvred out of the bracket.

7 Renew the nylon bushes between the pedals and the shaft and the shaft and bracket. They can be pressed out and in without difficulty.

---

5 Clutch assembly - removal and inspection

---

1 Remove the gearbox (see Chapter 6).

2 To remove the clutch bellhousing the engine has to be lowered and moved to one side or taken out completely. This is to get access to the two top bolts on the left hand side (Fig 5.7).

3 If the engine is not being removed then disconnect the exhaust pipe from the manifold and the clutch operating cable. Pull out the actuating arm (Fig 5.6).

4 The right hand engine mounting bracket has to be unbolted from the engine so the engine must be supported - preferably by a sling from above. If supported from underneath remember that it has to be lowered and swung to one side.

5 Undo the bellhousing bolts and take off the bellhousing.

6 Mark the position of the clutch cover relative to the flywheel.

7 Slacken off the bolts holding the clutch cover to the flywheel in a diagonal sequence, undoing each bolt a little at a time. This keeps the pressure even all round the diaphragm spring and prevents distortion. When all the pressure on the bolts is released remove them, lift the cover off the dowel pegs and take it off together with the friction disc which is between it and the flywheel.

8 Examine the diaphragm spring for signs of distortion or fracture.

9 Examine the pressure plate for signs of scoring or abnormal wear.

10 If either the spring or the plate is defective it will be necessary to replace the complete assembly with an exchange unit. The assembly can only be taken to pieces with special equipment and in any case individual parts of the assembly are not obtainable as regular spares. NOTE: Some models are fitted with the Laycock clutch assembly. On these versions the diaphragm spring, driving plate and pressure plate can be separated as they are simply held together by a large retaining ring and no rivets are used. The relative position of the three items should be marked. The retaining ring and anti-rattle springs can then be detached and the assembly comes apart. On assembly the pressure points should be greased sparingly with a heavy lubricant (Castrol MS3). Make sure the retaining ring is replaced with the flat sections under the pressure plate lugs and the curved sections against the edge of the diaphragm spring.

11 Examine the friction disc for indications of uneven wear and scoring of the friction surfaces. Contamination by oil will also show as hard and blackened areas which can cause defective operation. If the clearance between the heads of the securing rivets and the face of the friction lining material is less than .025 inch it would be worthwhile to fit a new disc also. Around the hub of the friction disc are

four springs acting as shock absorbers between the hub and the friction area. These should be intact and tightly in position.

8 The face of the flywheel should be examined for signs of scoring or uneven wear and if necessary it will have to be renewed and replaced or reconditioned. See Chapter 1, for details of flywheel removal.

---

6 Clutch assembly - replacement

---

1 Replacement of the clutch cover and friction plate is the reverse of the removal procedure but not quite so straightforward, as the following paragraphs will indicate.

2 If the clutch assembly has been removed from the engine with the engine out of the car, it is a relatively easy matter to line up the hub of the friction disc with the centre of the cover and flywheel. The cover and friction plate are replaced onto the flywheel with the holes in the cover fitting over the three dowels on the flywheel. The friction plate is supported with a finger while this is being done (photo).

3 Note that the friction plate is mounted with the longer hub of the boss towards the flywheel. Usually the replacement disc is marked 'flywheel side' to prevent a mistake being made (photo).

4 Replace the cover mounting bolts finger tight sufficiently to just grip the friction plate. Then set the friction plate in position so that the hub is exactly concentric with the centre of the flywheel and the cover assembly. An easy way of doing this is to make a temporary mandrel using a bar from a socket set which should fit fairly closely in the flywheel bush. Wrap a few turns of adhesive tap round the bar near the end which will make a snug fit inside the splined boss of the friction plate. Use this as a centring device. It is most important to get this right when replacing the clutch to an engine which is still in the car. Otherwise, difficulty and possibly damage could occur when refitting the gearbox (photo).

5 Tighten up the cover bolts one turn at a time in a diagonal sequence to maintain an even pressure. Final torque setting should be 14 lb/ft with clean dry bolt threads.

6 Replace the bellhousing (photo). Position the engine back onto the right hand mounting bracket. Then replace the gearbox and propeller shaft.

---

7 Clutch actuating lever and thrust release bearing - removal, inspection and replacement

---

1 Remove the gearbox as described in Chapter 6.

2 Move the lever sideways so that the end over the ball pivot pin is freed by springing back the retaining clip.

3 The lever can then be disengaged and drawn out of the bellhousing (photo).

4 The clutch release bearing may then be taken off.

5 If the bellhousing is removed inspect the pivot pin ball for signs of wear and flats. If necessary, it can be removed by driving it out of the bellhousing with a drift. A new one can be driven in with a soft headed hammer.

6 If the release bearing is obviously worn and is noisy it should be replaced. Do not clean the release bearing in any oil solvent liquid as the ball races have been pre-packed with grease and such cleaning would wash it out.

7 Replace the operating lever and release bearing in the reverse order of dismantling. Note that the radiused face of the thrust bearing goes towards the clutch.

8 Ensure also that the spring retaining clip on the clutch end of the lever fastens securely over the mushroom head of the ball pivot pin.

9 Replace the gearbox as described in Chapter 6.

---

8 Clutch pilot bush - renewal

---

1 In the centre of the flywheel is a bushed hole in which runs the input shaft of the gearbox. If the bush is badly worn the clutch oper-

6.2 Positioning driven plate and clutch cover together onto the flywheel

6.3 New clutch driven plate in relation to flywheel

6.4 Centring the clutch driven plate by using the gearbox input shaft

6.6 Offering up the bellhousing to the engine block. Note lower cover plate resting behind the flywheel

7.3 View through rear of bellhousing - of clutch actuating lever being pulled out

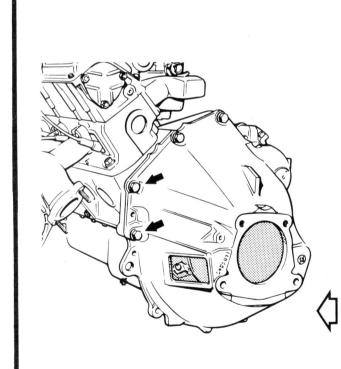

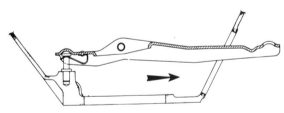

Fig 5.6 Clutch actuating arm. Cross section to show pivot pin and clip. Pull in direction of arrow to remove the arm

Fig 5.7 CLUTCH BELLHOUSING
To remove bolts (arrowed) engine must be moved to one side and down

ation will be unsatisfactory and out of balance.

2 It is impossible to judge the condition of the bush unless you can obtain a bar of exactly the same diameter as the gearbox shaft to test it. With the engine removed from the car it is possible to measure it but once again unless the gearbox is also removed it is impossible to check the fit of the two parts concerned.

3 The old bush can be removed by finding a bolt which can be forced into the soft metal of the bush. Fit a nut and spacer tube on the bolt, force the bolt into the bush and then draw out the bush by turning the nut.

4 Replacement of the bush is best done using a proper mandrel which will ensure that it is not distorted or damaged when being driven in. It is most important that the shaft is an easy fit in the bush on reassembly.

Fault Finding Chart

Symptom	Reason/s	Remedy
Judder when taking up drive	Loose engine or gearbox mountings or over flexible mountings	Check and tighten all mounting bolts and replace any 'soft' or broken mountings
	Badly worn friction surfaces or friction plate contaminated with oil carbon deposit	Remove clutch assembly and replace parts as required. Rectify any oil leakage points which may have caused contamination
	Worn splines in the friction plate hub or on the gearbox input shaft	Renew friction plate and/or input shaft
	Propeller shaft or rear axle mounting faults	Examine propeller shaft universal joints and rear axle to suspension attachment points
Clutch spin (or failure to disengage) so that gears cannot be meshed	Clutch actuating cable clearance from fork too great	Adjust clearance
	Clutch friction disc sticking (usually apparent after standing idle for some length of time)	As temporary remedy engage top gear, apply handbrakes, depress clutch and start engine. (If very badly stuck engine will not turn). When running rev up engine and slip clutch until disengagement is normally possible. Renew friction plate at earliest opportunity
	Damaged or misaligned pressure plate assembly	Replace pressure plate assembly
Clutch slip - (increase in engine speed does not result in increase in car speed - especially on hills)	Clutch actuating cable clearance from fork too small resulting in partially disengaged clutch at all times	Adjust clearance
	Clutch friction surfaces worn out (beyond further adjustment of operating cable) or clutch surfaces oil soaked	Replace friction plate and remedy source of oil leakage

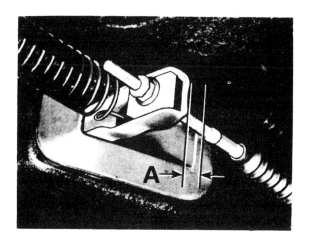

Fig 5.8 CLUTCH RELEASE BEARING ACTUATING ARM
Free travel 'A' = $\frac{1}{5}$ inch (5 mm)

Fig 5.9 Clutch pedal. Rubber pedal stop (arrowed) removed on later models to increase release bearing travel

Chapter 6 Gearbox

Contents

Specifications

General

	3 speed		4 speed	
No of gears	3 forward, 1 reverse		4 forward, 1 reverse	
Type	Helical cut constant mesh with straight cut reverse gears. Synchro-mesh on all forward speeds			
Change mechanism	Steering column		Floor mounted remote lever	
Oil capacity	2.1 pints (Imp)		2.5 pints (Imp)	
- with overdrive	3 pints		3 pints	
Ratios:	1599 cc	1975 cc	1599 cc	1975 cc
First	3.2:1	2.897:1	3.3:1	2.786:1
Second		1.671:1	2.145:1	1.981:1
Third	1:1			1.413:1
Fourth	—			1:1
Reverse		3.064:1		3.064:1
Overdrive	—		3rd	1.1:1
			4th	1:.778

Mainshaft

Diameter	1.4738—1.4744
Gear to shaft clearance	.0016—.0032
1st gear sleeve diameter (4 speed only)	1.3484—1.3490 in
1st gear clearance on sleeve (4 speed only)	.0020—.0041 in

Laygear

Length (3 speed)	6.141—6.144 in
(4 speed)	7.141—7.144 in
Thrust washer thickness	.0615—.0635 in
End float in casing	.0048—.0177 in

Reverse pinion

Overall length (3 speed)	1.492—1.496 in
End float in casing (3 speed)	.004—.014 in
Shaft diameter	.779—.7795 in
Pinion clearance on shaft	.0025—.0040 in

Speedometer gears

Driving gear on mainshaft	5 starts (worm)		
	Axle ratio	Tyre size	No of teeth
Driven gears	8:33	5.60—13	18
		6.2—13	19

	6.9—13	18
	165—13	18
10:39	5.60—13	17
	6.2—13	18
	6.9—13	17
	165—13	17
	6.95—13	17
	175/70HR—13	18
10:41	5.60—13	18
	6.25—13	19
	6.95—13	18
	1655R—13	18
11:38	6.9—13	15
	165—13	15
11:34	6.95—13	14
	165 SR—13	14
11:41	5.60—13	16
	6.25—13	17
	6.95—13	16
	165 SR—13	16

Circlips and shims - available thicknesses

Circlips	.059—.061 in
	.062—.064 in
	.065—.067 in
	.068—.070 in
	.071—.073 in
	.074—.076 in
	.077—.079 in
Shims	.003 in
	.005 in
	.010 in

Overdrive

Make	Laycock Type J
Oil capacity (with gearbox)...	3 pints
Hydraulic pressure - residual	20 lb sq in
- operating	300—340 lb sq in
Relief valve plug)	
Pump plug)	Tightening torque 16 lb ft
Pressure filter plug)	

Automatic transmission

Gear ratios (GM) **1st**	2.4:1
2nd	1.48:1
3rd...	1:1
Reverse	1.92:1
Oil capacity	BW - 11 pints
	GM - 9 pints
Stall speed	BW - 1550 rpm
	GM - 2100—2150 rpm

Approximate change speeds in 'D' range

	BW		GM	
	Change	Speed	Change	Speed
Minimum throttle...	1—2	6—8 mph	1—2	10 mph
	2—3	13—20 mph	2—3	12 mph
Closed throttle	3—1	4—6 mph	3—2	10 mph
	—	—	2—1	8 mph
90% throttle	—	—	1—2	32 mph
	—	—	2—3	43 mph
Full throttle	1—2	28—35 mph	1—2	35 mph
	2—3	46—53 mph	2—3	58 mph
	3—2	43 mph	3—2	52 mph
	3—1	23 mph	3—1	32 mph

Torque wrench settings

	BW	GM
Flexplate to crankshaft bolts	26 lb ft	25 lb ft
Torque converter to flexplate bolts	30 lb ft	42 lb ft
Converter housing to transmission bolts	10 lb ft	25 lb ft
Extension housing to transmission bolts	10 lb ft	20 lb ft
Transmission sump to case bolts	10 lb ft	7 lb ft

1 General description

The standard gearbox fitted is an all synchromesh 3 forward speed and 1 reverse with steering column change. However, the optional 4 speed all synchromesh option with floor mounted change lever is usually taken and is the one detailed in this manual. The 3 speed version is basically very similar and differences are shown.

All forward gears are constant mesh and helically cut and gear engagement is by hubs with sliding sleeves engaging teeth on the gears through intermediate synchronising rings.

The gearbox 'cover' is at the bottom of the box and the forward gear selector forks are mounted on rails one at each side of the casing. The selector fork operating levers are mounted on a cross shaft across the casing. The reverse gear selector fork is mounted in the cover plate on four speed models.

The laygear runs on needle roller bearings on the layshaft and end float is governed by a thrust washer at each end.

An oil drain plug is located in the cover plate centre on 3 speed models and on the edge of the cover on 4 speed versions. The filler/level plug is located half way up the left side.

2 Gearbox - removal

1 If overdrive is fitted read the overdrive section before doing anything. Jack up the car in the centre of the right hand body side frame member, and then support the car at the front and rear of this side member on proper stands (photo). If a pit is used this is not necessary, of course. If wheel ramps are used put them at the front and rear wheels on the same side of the car. In this way access to the gearbox and rear of the propeller shaft is equally satisfactory. Block the wheels resting on the ground. Drain the gearbox oil.
2 Disconnect the propeller shaft flange bolts at the rear (as described in Chapter 7). Lower the rear to the ground but before pulling the front end out of the gearbox obtain a plastic bag and rubber band to put over the end of the extension casing to catch any remaining oil (photo).
3 Draw the front end of the propeller shaft out of the gearbox and secure the plastic bag over the extension of the gearbox.
4 On three speed gearboxes with steering column change levers there is a cross shaft from the side of the gearbox to a bushed bracket bolted to the side frame. The clip and retaining pin securing the gearbox end of this shaft to the yoke of the gearbox shaft should be removed.
5 With floor mounted change levers on 4 speed boxes remove the upper and lower retaining plates securing the rubber shroud round the lever to gain access to the bottom end of the lever (photo).
6 The lever pivots in an inverted U shaped carrier. On earlier models this pivot pin is held in position by a retaining nut and after undoing this the pin may be withdrawn and the lever lifted out. On later models the pivot pin is held by an 'E' clip (photo).
7 Disconnect the speedometer cable by undoing the knurled retainer round the end of the outer cable on the right hand side of the rear extension (photo).
8 Unhook the clutch operating lever return spring from the bracket bolted on the side of the casing. If the clutch is going to be dismantled and/or engine removed disconnect the clutch cable also.
9 Remove the two lower bolts which secure the gearbox to the clutch housing. These bolts fit from inside the housing into the gearbox and access to them is through the lower apertures in the housing. Use a cranked ring spanner to loosen and remove them (photo).
10 Support the edge of the clutch housing with a jack in preparation for removing the gearbox support crossmember.
11 Mark the crossmember so as to prevent confusion as to which way round it goes on replacement.
12 Undo the two bolts holding the crossmember at each end to the side rails and remove the nut securing it to the mounting stud in the centre. Take the crossmember off (photo).
13 Carefully lower the jack under the bellhousing just enough to

permit access to the two bolts which secure the top of the gearbox casing to the bellhousing. These bolt through the lugs on the gearbox into the bellhousing and are readily undone with a socket extension. Even though all four bolts are removed the gearbox will not fall.
14 Pull the gearbox to the rear, supporting it well so it does not drop and then take it out from under the car.

3 Gearbox - dismantling

1 Place the complete unit on a firm bench or table and ensure that you have the following tools (in addition to the normal range of spanners etc) available:

a) Good quality circlip pliers, 2 pairs - 1 expanding and 1 contracting.
b) Copper headed mallet, at least 2 lb.
c) Drifts, steel $3/8$ inch and brass $3/8$ inch.
d) Small containers for needle rollers.
e) Engineer's vice mounted on firm bench.
f) Method of heating, such as blow lamp or butagas stove.

Any attempt to dismantle the gearbox without the foregoing is not necessarily impossible, but will certainly be very difficult and inconvenient, resulting in possible injury or damage.

Read the whole of this section before starting work.

Take care not to let the synchro hub assemblies come apart before you want them to. It accelerates wear if the splines of hub and sleeve are changed in relation to each other. As a precaution it is advisable to make a line up mark with a dab of paint.

Before finally going ahead with dismantling first ascertain the availability of spare parts - particularly shims and selective circlips which could be difficult.
2 On four speed boxes remove the gearchange mechanism by undoing the securing clips which locate the pins in both the selector shaft and control rod.
3 Undo the two bolts holding the gear lever carrier to the top of the rear cover.
4 Remove the flexible mounting from the rear cover.
5 Remove the overdrive unit from the adaptor and draw it off.
6 With the gearbox inverted remove the cover plate.
7 Undo bolts securing the rear extension (or overdrive adaptor) to the gear casing. Turn it so that the rear end of the layshaft is exposed.
8 From the rear, drive the shaft out through the front of the casing. Note that there is a locking bolt in a recess in the front end of the shaft which must not be lost.
9 When the layshaft has been removed carefully lift up the laygear, keeping it horizontal. Remove the needle rollers and spacers from each end.
10 Remove the thrust washers from each end of the casing round the layshaft openings.
11 The selector striking levers are held to the cross shaft by tubular spring pins. These are driven downwards with a flat nosed punch just far enough to release the levers on the shaft. Manoeuvre the shaft to the most advantageous position for driving out. If driven too far they might jam against the side of the casing.
12 On early model 4 speed boxes the cross shaft is used for the reverse lever stop against a spring loaded ball in the end housing. Remove the spring housing and ball. The end cover may also be removed now. On later 4 speed boxes this is not necessary. On three speed boxes the striking levers and shaft should be marked with a dab of paint to make quite sure that they go back in precisely the same way. The assemblies are matched. Draw out the cross shaft and lift out the striking levers.
13 The selector forks are also held by spring pins to their respective rails. These should be driven out similarly, just far enough to clear the forks from the rails without jamming against the side of the casing. On 3 speed gearboxes the 1st/reverse fork is not sufficiently supported unless reverse gear is engaged when driving out the pin.
14 The detent balls and springs for the selector rails are contained in recesses in the casing sides. Remove the screwed plug to release the

2.1 Stand supporting body side rail. Note propeller shaft already removed

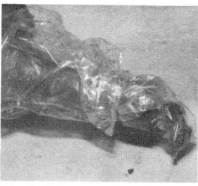

2.2 Plastic bag wrapped round gearbox to contain any oil

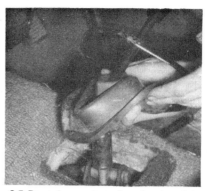

2.5 Removing gear lever shroud and retaining plates

2.6 Removing floor change lever pivot pin

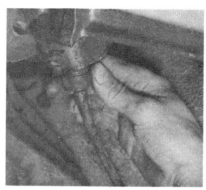

2.7 Undoing the speedo cable union

2.9 Removing the lower gearbox mounting bolts through the apertures in the bellhousing

2.12 Removing the gearbox support cross-member securing bolts

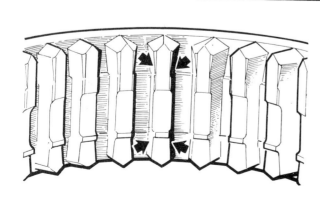

Fig 6.1 SYNCHRO HUBS — OUTER SLEEVE (SECTION 6)
Illustration of 'keystone' shape of engagement dogs on all hubs in 4 speed box and 2nd/3rd in 3 speed

springs and balls.

15 Once again, rotate the rear cover so as to expose the ends of the selector fork rails which are then drifted out from the rear to the front of the casing. Take care to watch that the forks do not jam while the rails are being drifted out through them.

16 On three speed gearboxes drift out the reverse pinion shaft next otherwise the mainshaft cannot be taken out. On four speed gearboxes note that there is a spacer collar between the rear face of the pinion and the casing.

17 Withdraw the mainshaft and rear cover assembly from the casing. Collect up the needle rollers from the nose of the mainshaft or the counterbore of the input shaft - also the spacer ring.

18 Undo the five set screws holding the input shaft bearing cover to the front of the casing and withdraw the input shaft assembly.

19 On four speed boxes the reverse gear selector fork and striking fork are pinned to a common shaft in the cover. If necessary, they may be removed by driving out the spring pins through the drain plug hole. Before driving out the shaft remove the detent spring and ball by undoing the screwed plug in the housing.

20 The gearbox casing is now stripped out. Thoroughly flush out the interior of the casing with paraffin and water.

4 Mainshaft - dismantling

1 The mainshaft is held into the extension cover by a circlip behind the main bearing. The bearing is also a tight fit and to avoid damage the cover should be warmed over a suitable heat source first. Remove the rubber mounting block before holding the cover over a naked flame. Contract the circlip to release it from the bore of the casing, support the casing against the vice jaws and drive the shaft out from the rear with a soft faced mallet.

2 Remove the speedometer driven gear and spindle by undoing the two set screws, marking the position of the flat on the housing relative to the cover, and lifting it out.

3 With long nosed pliers remove the circlip inside the extension cover which retains the bearing.

4 Warm the extension cover over a heat source such as a butane gas camping stove and then clamp the flange in a vice.

5 Tap the tail end of the protruding mainshaft with a hammer and block of wood to drive the shaft and bearing out of the cover.

6 Without the services of a press it is essential to have an assistant when dismantling the shaft. The synchro hubs, gear sleeve and bearing are very tightly fitted and considerable force must be carefully applied to get them off.

7 Starting with the rear end of the shaft remove the circlips retaining the speedometer drive worm gear and drive off the gear with a suitable drift. It is keyed to the shaft with a small barrel key which should not be lost.

8 Remove the circlip on the shaft which retains the bearing by its inner race.

9 Support the front face of 1st gear over the jaws of the vice adjusting the jaw width to give maximum support to the gear without touching the gears below. On 4 speed shafts the gear is next to the bearing but on three speed versions the 1st/reverse hub assembly comes in between it and the bearing.

10 With one person holding the assembly firmly the rear end of the shaft needs firm striking with a heavy soft headed mallet. The shaft will be driven through the gears.

11 On four speed shafts repeat this operation with the front face of 2nd gear supported over the vice jaws in order to drive the shaft out through 2nd gear, 1st/2nd synchro hub and the centre sleeve on which 1st gear revolves.

12 Take note of the thrust washer (four speed shaft) and any shims (both) fitted between the bearing and adjacent gear/hub.

13 The rear end of the shaft now being clear up to the shoulder remove the circlip from the opposite end which retains the 3rd/4th speed synchro hub in position.

14 Support the rear face of 3rd gear over the vice jaws and drive the nose of the shaft down through the gear and 3rd/4th synchro hub

assembly. With the exception of the hub assemblies (dealt with in a later section), the mainshaft is now dismantled.

5 Input shaft - dismantling

1 The shaft and bearing are retained in the front cover by a circlip which also locks into a groove in the bearing outer race.

2 Grip the cover sleeve with the gear upwards and expand the circlip sufficiently to clear the groove in the bearing. At the same time tap the end of the shaft on the bench or a solid wood block to move it out of the casing.

3 To get the bearing off the shaft grip the shaft across the cover of the vice at a place clear of the splines and drift the bearing down off it.

6 Synchro hubs - dismantling and inspection

1 Synchro hubs are only too easy to dismantle - you just push the centre out and the whole thing flies apart. The point is to prevent this happening before you are ready. Do not dismantle the hubs without reason and do not mix up the parts of the two hubs.

2 The most important check to make is for any backlash in the splines between the outer sleeve and inner hub. If any is noticeable the whole assembly must be renewed.

3 Mark the hub and sleeve so that you may reassemble them on the same splines. With the hub and sleeve separated the teeth at the ends of the splines which engage with corresponding teeth of the gear wheels must be checked for damage or wear.

4 Do not confuse the keystone shape at the ends of the teeth with wear. This shape matches the gear teeth shape and is a design characteristic to minimise jump out tendencies.

5 If the synchronising cones are being renewed it is sensible also to renew the sliding keys and springs which hold them in position.

7 Synchro hubs - reassembly

1 Hub assemblies are different from each other in the same box and different between 3 and 4 speed gearboxes.

3 On 3 speed boxes the reverse/1st assembly has a hub with a groove running round it and a sliding key retainer plate is fitted at the end with the projecting centre. Make sure the retainer is securely fixed.

3 A spring clip with both ends turned out is fitted into the groove and the keys placed over it. One key has a slot in it and this should go over one end of the spring.

4 The other spring has one turned out end and this is to be fitted in the end of the hub so that the turned out and hooks into the key with the slot and the ring fits anticlockwise from the slotted key.

5 The outer sleeve fits over the hub so that the selector fork groove of the sleeve is at the same end as that of the hub with the key retainer plate fitted.

6 The 2nd/3rd speed hub on the 3 speed box has offset pips on the sliding keys and this offset should be towards the protruding hub centre.

7 The springs are fitted anticlockwise with the leading turned out end fixed into the slotted key.

8 The outer sleeve of the 2nd/3rd speed hub is fitted so that the selector fork groove faces the same way as the protruding hub centre.

9 On 4 speed gearboxes the synchro hubs are both assembled in the same manner as for the 2nd/3rd hub of the 3 speed box. Note that the sliding keys of the 3rd/4th gear hub assembly are shorter than those for the 1st/2nd gear hub.

8 Gearbox components - inspection

1 It is assumed that the gearbox has been dismantled for reasons of excessive noise, lack of synchromesh on certain gears or for failure to

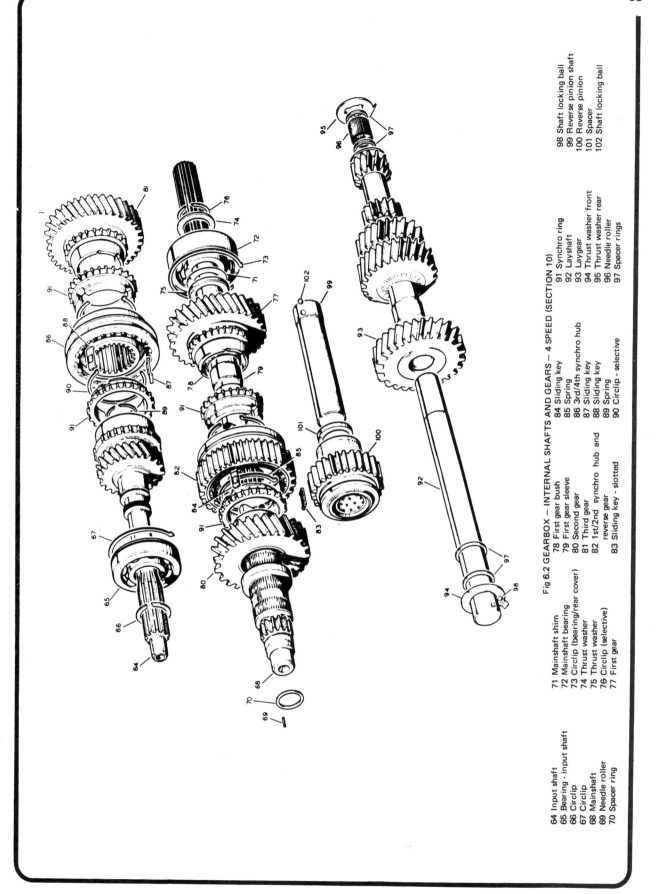

Fig 6.2 GEARBOX – INTERNAL SHAFTS AND GEARS – 4 SPEED (SECTION 10)

64 Input shaft
65 Bearing - input shaft
66 Circlip
67 Circlip
68 Mainshaft
69 Needle roller
70 Spacer ring

71 Mainshaft shim
72 Mainshaft bearing
73 Circlip (bearing/rear cover)
74 Thrust washer
75 Thrust washer
76 Circlip (selective)
77 First gear

78 First gear bush
79 First gear sleeve
80 Second gear
81 Third gear
82 1st/2nd synchro hub and reverse gear
83 Sliding key - slotted

84 Sliding key
85 Spring
86 3rd/4th synchro hub
87 Sliding key
88 Sliding key
89 Spring
90 Circlip - selective

91 Synchro ring
92 Layshaft
93 Laygear
94 Thrust washer front
95 Thrust washer rear
96 Needle roller
97 Spacer rings

98 Shaft locking ball
99 Reverse pinion shaft
100 Reverse pinion
101 Spacer
102 Shaft locking ball

stay in gear. If anything more drastic than this (total failure, seizure or gear case cracked) it would be better to leave well alone and look for a replacement, either secondhand or exchange unit).

2 Examine all gears for excessively worn, chipped or damaged teeth. Any such gears should be replaced.

3 Check all synchromesh rings for wear on the bearing surfaces, which normally have clearly machined oil reservoir lines in them. If these are smooth or obviously uneven, replacement is essential. Also, when the rings are fitted to their gears - as they would be when in operation - there should be no rock. This would signify ovality, or lack of concentricity. One of the most satisfactory ways of checking is by comparing the fit of a new ring with an old one on the gearwheel cone.

The teeth and cut-outs in the synchro rings also wear and for this reason also it is unwise not to fit new ones when the opportunity avails.

4 All ball race bearings should be checked for chatter and roughness after they have been flushed out. It is advisable to replace these anyway even though they may not appear too badly worn.

5 Circlips which are all important in locating bearings, gears and hubs should also be checked to ensure that they are undistorted and undamaged. In any case a selection of new circlips of varying thicknesses should be obtained to compensate for variations in new components fitted, or wear in old ones. The specifications indicate what is available.

6 The thrust washers at the ends of the laygear should also be replaced, as they will almost certainly have worn if the gearbox is of any age.

7 Needle roller bearings between the input shaft and mainshaft and in the laygear are usually found in good order, but if in any doubt replace the needles as necessary.

8 For details of inspecting the synchro hub assemblies refer to Section 6.

9 Input shaft - reassembly

1 The bearing can be driven onto the shaft with a piece of tube with an inside diameter of 1 $1/8$ inch which will go over the shaft and butt against the inner race of the bearing. Do not drive the bearing on by the outer race. The circlip groove is off centre of the bearing and it should be nearest the gear on the shaft.

2 Make sure the bearing is driven fully up to the gear.

3 Put the circlip into the housing, expanding it with circlip pliers and then put the shaft and bearing in. Tap the shaft down so that the bearing first goes through the circlip and then make sure it is driven in far enough for the circlip to engage the groove.

10 Mainshaft - 4 speed gearbox - reassembly

1 Start with the tail end of the mainshaft and first place 2nd gear (the middle sized one of the three loose gears you have) onto the shaft with the gear teeth next to the shoulder of the shaft.

2 Place a synchro ring over the gearwheel cone.

3 Put the 1st/2nd gear synchro hub assembly (the one with the straight cut teeth on the outer sleeve) onto the shaft so that the teeth of the sleeve are nearest to the gear already fitted (photo)'

4 The hub centre will need driving onto the splines. A piece of 1 $1/8$ inch ID tube is ideal for this as it will be necessary to drive only the hub centre. It is also necessary to make sure that the cut-outs in the synchro ring engage with the sliding keys in the hub when it is driven fully home. If you do not have a long enough piece of tube then use a drift (photo) or support the hub centre across the vice jaws and drive the shaft into it with a soft mallet.

5 The hub sleeve for first gear is also a drive fit and goes on next. It helps to heat it up. It is important to make sure that the edges of this sleeve are not nicked, burred or spread in the process of fitting. If two people are available it can be done with the vice jaw method. Make sure it butts tight up to the hub of the synchro assembly (photos).

6 Fit a synchro ring into the hub assembly, lining up the cut-outs with the sliding keys.

7 Place 1st gear (the largest) onto the shaft with the cone section fitting into the synchro ring (photo).

8 Fit the large thrust washer.

9 At this stage it is theoretically necessary to check the measurement from the front face of the shoulder on which 3rd gear runs to the rear face of the thrust washer just fitted. This is because the longitudinal position of the mainshaft in the casing is controlled by the position of the rear bearing which goes on next. The measurement referred to should be between 5.781 inch—5.783 inch. The design is such that shims need adding between the thrust washer and bearing to make up the correct distance.

10 Provided that only the bearing and synchro rings have been renewed one may replace the shims originally fitted without trepidation. If the synchro hub assembly and gears have been renewed then the shim thickness may need altering. For this, a large caliper gauge will need to be acquired to carry out the necessary measurement. Shim thickness can then be calculated. Available shims are listed in the specifications (photo).

11 With the thrust washer and shims in position the rear bearing is driven onto the shaft in the same way as the hubs. Replace the large circlip behind the bearing first - otherwise it will have to be spread excessively in order to get it in position afterwards. Be careful not to trap the shim in the circlip groove while the bearing is driven on (photo).

12 Having ensured that the bearing is driven fully up to the shims and thrust washer fit the thrust collar and circlip in the shaft groove behind the bearing inner race. This is where a circlip of a different thickness may need selecting. Too thick a circlip will not go in, and too thin a circlip will allow the bearing to creep fractionally along the shaft until it butts up against the circlip. Select one which is a snug fit (photos).

13 The speedometer drive gear is next fitted to the tail shaft. Line up the keyway first. Here again the correct thickness of the circlip on each side of the gear will prevent movement of the gear on the shaft (photos).

14 Turning to the front of the shaft fit third gear (the only loose gear left!) onto the nose with the flat side up against the shoulder (photo).

15 Place a synchro ring over the gear cone and put the 3rd/4th hub assembly onto the shaft with the selector fork groove in the sleeve towards the front of the shaft. This hub will need driving on in the same way as the other and once again the sliding keys must line up and fit into the synchro ring cut-outs. Make sure that the hub assembly is driven on fully up to the third gear (photos).

16 Select a circlip which is a tight fit in the groove to retain the hub assembly on the shaft (photo).

17 Before fitting the mainshaft back into the rear extension cover fit a new rear oil seal. The old one can be taken out by clamping it in the vice and pulling the casing out (photo).

18 Carefully tap the new seal into position keeping it square and undistorted (photo). Soak the felt ring with oil (NB This job can be done with the gearbox installed and propeller shaft removed).

19 Warm the extension housing so that the main bearing on the shaft will enter easily (photo).

20 When the bearing is in position make sure that the retaining circlip fits the housing groove properly (photo).

21 Fit the gearbox mounting to the extension cover ensuring it is the correct way round (see Section 16).

11 Mainshaft - 3 speed gearbox - reassembly

1 Start with the tail end of the mainshaft and first place 1st gear (the largest loose one) onto the shaft with the gear teeth next to the shoulder of the shaft (photo).

2 Place a synchro ring over the gearwheel cone (photo).

3 Put the 1st/reverse hub assembly (the one with the straight cut teeth on the outer sleeve on to the shaft so that the teeth of the

10.3 2nd gear, synchro ring and 1st/2nd gear synchro hub being put onto the rear end of the mainshaft

10.4 Driving 1st/2nd gear synchro hub onto the shaft splines

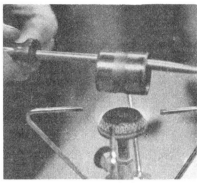

10.5a Heating 1st gear hub sleeve

10.5b Showing the hub sleeve position on the shaft butted up to the synchro hub assembly

10.7 Fitting first gear. Note that the synchro ring is in position in the synchro hub

10.10 Placing the thrust washer and shim in position

10.11 Driving the bearing onto the shaft. Note the large circlip between the bearing and gear (arrowed)

10.12a Rear thrust collar being fitted

10.12b Circlip being fitted

10.13a Tapping the speedo drive gear up to one circlip

10.13b Fitting the second circlip

10.14 Fitting 3rd gear to the front of the shaft

10.15a Placing the synchro ring and 3rd/4th hub onto the front of the mainshaft

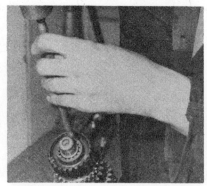

10.15b Driving it on to the splines. The outer sleeve has not yet been assembled to the hub

10.16 Fitting the circlip to retain 3rd/4th synchro hub

10.17 Pulling off the rear extension cover oil seal

10.18 Fitting a new rear extension oil seal

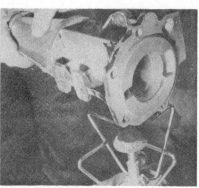

10.19 Warming the rear extension cover prior to fitting the mainshaft assembly into it

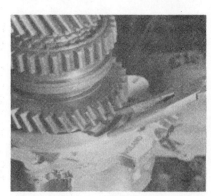

10.20 Fitting the mainshaft bearing circlip into the rear cover

11.1 Fitting first gear to 3 speed mainshaft

11.2 Positioning synchro ring for 1st gear

11.4 Fitting 1st/reverse clutch hub

11.5 Replacing main bearing. Note shims between bearing and hub

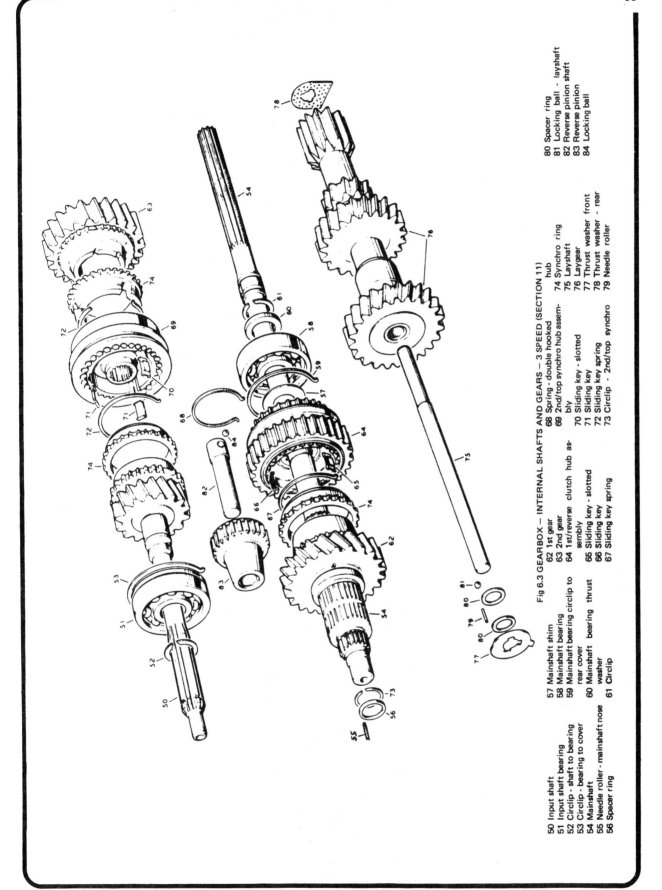

Fig 6.3 GEARBOX — INTERNAL SHAFTS AND GEARS — 3 SPEED (SECTION 11)

50 Input shaft
51 Input shaft bearing
52 Circlip - shaft to bearing
53 Circlip - bearing to cover
54 Mainshaft
55 Needle roller - mainshaft nose
56 Spacer ring
57 Mainshaft shim
58 Mainshaft bearing
59 Mainshaft bearing circlip to rear cover
60 Mainshaft bearing thrust washer
61 Circlip
62 1st gear
63 2nd gear
64 1st/reverse clutch hub assembly
65 Sliding key - slotted
66 Sliding key
67 Sliding key spring
68 Spring - double hooked
69 2nd/top synchro hub assembly
70 Sliding key - slotted
71 Sliding key
72 Sliding key spring
73 Circlip - 2nd/top synchro hub
74 Synchro ring
75 Layshaft
76 Laygear
77 Thrust washer front
78 Thrust washer - rear
79 Needle roller
80 Spacer ring
81 Locking ball - layshaft
82 Reverse pinion shaft
83 Reverse pinion
84 Locking ball

sleeve are nearest the gear already fitted.

4 Drive on the hub assembly as described in paragraph 4 of the preceding section (photo).

5 At this stage it is theoretically necessary to check the measurement from the front face of the shoulder on which 2nd gear runs to the rear abutment face of the hub just fitted. This is because the longitudinal position of the mainshaft in the casing is controlled by the position of the rear bearing which goes on next. The measurement referred to should be between 4.781–4.783 inches. The design is such that the shims need adding between the hub face and bearing to make up the correct distance (photo).

6 Provided that only the bearing and synchro ring has been renewed one may replace the shims originally fitted without trepidation. If the hub assembly and gear have been renewed then the shim thickness may need altering. For this a large caliper gauge will need to be acquired to carry out the necessary measurement. Shim thickness can then be calculated. Available shims are listed in the specifications.

7 Continue assembly of the mainshaft as described for the 4 speed shaft in the preceding section from paragraph 11 onwards. Note that there is no thrust washer behind the shims and references to 3rd and 4th gears are, in fact, 2nd and 3rd gears in this case.

12 Gearbox - 4 speed - reassembly

1 Make sure the mating faces of the casing and rear extension cover are clean, fit a new gasket in position and place the mainshaft assembly into the casing. Do not replace any bolts yet (photo).

2 Rotate the cover (or overdrive adaptor) until the reverse pinion shaft hole is clear. Put the locking ball into the recess in the reverse pinion shaft and then guide the plain end into the casing.

3 Put the spacer ring over the shaft followed by the pinion. The pinion teeth chamfered ends should face the front of the casing (photo).

4 Rotate the shaft so that the locking ball lines up with the notch in the casing and then drive it fully home until the end is flush with the casing (photo).

5 Fit the rear cover bolts but do not tighten them up fully at this stage. On units with overdrive do not forget to fit the inhibitor switch mounting bracket.

6 The needle rollers should next be prepared for fitting the input shaft onto the nose of the mainshaft. This can be done by either fitting them in the counterbore of the input shaft or around the nose of the mainshaft. (The latter method is less likely to cause dislodging of the needles on assembly). Use a little grease - not too much to hold the needles in position (photo).

7 The spacer must be installed correctly. It is positioned at the mainshaft end of the needle rollers.

8 Check the input shaft mating surfaces on the cover and casing, and position a new gasket on the flange.

9 Fit a synchro ring (the remaining one) into the 3rd/4th synchro hub so that the cut-outs engage the sliding keys.

10 Fit the input shaft into the casing so that the counterbore engages over the nose of the mainshaft without dislodging the needle rollers. (photo).

11 Replace the front cover bolts but do not tighten them fully at this stage.

12 The selector forks and rails are fitted next. It is best to have new cylindrical pins to secure the forks to the shaft. In subsequent paragraphs remember that you are working with the gearbox inverted so references to the left and right side are based on the bore being the proper way up and looking from rear to front.

13 First/second selector fork has legs of unequal length and the rail is fitted from the front of the casing. The striking lug is fitted to the rail with the jaw for the lever towards the casing front.

14 Place the rail into the casing from the front on the left side. The three detent grooves are at the front end of the shaft and face the top of the casing when finally positioned.

15 Pass the shaft through the striking lug.

16 Fit the selector fork into the 1st/2nd selector hub groove with the

recessed face of the fork facing the front of the casing.

17 Pass the rail through the fork boss and tap it home as far as it will go. The front end will come clear of the front of the casing (photo).

18 Pin the striking lug and selector fork to the rail using a flat nosed punch to fit the pins (photo).

19 The 3rd/4th selector fork rail is fitted on the other side of the casing. The selector fork should be fitted into the groove in the outer sleeve of the 3rd/4th gear hub with the recessed face facing the front of the casing like the other.

20 No separate striking lug is fitted on this rail. There is a cut-out in the rail itself.

21 Pin the fork to the rail so that the cut-out faces the interior of the casing (photo).

22 The cross shaft and striking levers are next assembled.

23 A conventional lip type seal is fitted into the casing for the right hand end of the shaft. This should be prised out and renewed while the opportunity presents itself. Lubricate the new seal lip with molybdenum paste or grease and drive it in open side first until it butts up against the shouldered recess in the casing (photos).

24 Insert the cross shaft, spigot end first into the casing from the right hand side.

25 Take up the striking lever which has two legs - one long - and put the shaft through it so that the long leg points to the bottom of the bore and the boss faces the side of the casing (photo).

26 Pass the shaft next through the other striking lever, the leg pointing to the top of the box and the boss facing the side of the casing (photo).

27 Manoeuvre both levers to line up with the holes in the shaft making sure that the set screw recess on the right hand end of the shaft faces the front of the casing. If this is not done correctly the operating lever on the end of the shaft cannot be clamped on in the correct position.

28 Refit the spring pins to lock the striking levers to the shaft (photos).

29 The laygear is fitted next. The front end has 26 needle rollers and the rear 25. Each set has a spacer ring at each end.

 Put the needles and spacers in position using grease to prevent them dropping out.

30 Fit the thrust washers into the casing with the dimpled faces facing inwards. The washer with the flat edge goes at the rear with the edge in line with the casing edge.

31 The circular front washer is positioned so that the tab engages in the groove (photo).

32 Carefully lower the laygear into the casing (large gear to the front) taking care not to disturb the thrust washers or needle rollers (photo). Line up the holes of the casing and the gear.

33 Put the locking ball in the recess of the layshaft and introduce the plain end of the layshaft from the front of the casing end into the gear without upsetting the needle rollers (photo).

34 Tap it gently through the gear. The hole at the other end of the casing will be covered by the rear cover flange so to ensure that the needle rollers are not disturbed the bolts can be removed and the cover rotated to expose the hole. If the hole is left covered make sure that the cover bolts are not fully tightened. If they are air may be trapped which could prevent the shaft being driven fully home.

35 Turn the shaft to line up the locking ball with the recess at the front of the casing and drive the shaft fully home.

36 At this stage rotate the mainshaft to ensure that everything revolves freely and smoothly.

37 Fully tighten the input shaft flange bolts and rear cover bolts and check once again that the shafts revolve freely.

38 Drive in the two cups that seal the selector fork rail holes in the front of the casing. They should be driven in open end first, just flush with the casing (photo).

39 Refit the detent balls, springs and screwed plugs into each side of the casing (photo).

40 The cover incorporates the reverse selector fork and rail. Having made sure that the mating surfaces are clean, fit a new gasket and replace the cover so that the fork engages the groove in the reverse gear pinion (photo).

41 Replace the cover bolts and tighten them.

42 Refit the detent ball and spring followed by the screwed plug into

12.1 Replacing the mainshaft into the gearbox casing

12.3 Assembling the reverse pinion and shaft

12.4 Reverse pinion shaft showing locking ball just before being driven fully home

12.6 Fitting needle rollers in input shaft counterbore

12.10 Replacing the input shaft into the casing. In this instance the synchro ring is fitted on the gear cover rather than in the synchro hub on the mainshaft.

12.17 First/second gear selector rail with the fork and lug not yet pinned in position. The front of the casing is to the left of the photo

12.18 Pinning the 1st/2nd selector fork to the rail

12.21 Pinning the fork to the rail

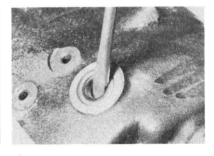

12.23a Prising out the old seal

12.23b Fitting a new seal for the cross shaft in the right hand side of the casing

12.25 Striking lever in correct position relative to 3rd/4th selector fork rail (before cross shaft has been put through it)

12.26 Striking lever in correct position relative to 1st/2nd selector fork rail (before cross shaft has been put through it)

12.28a Placing the pin in position on the striking lever

12.28b Pinning the striking levers to the cross shaft

12.31 Laygear front thrust washer in position

12.32 Lowering the laygear into the casing

12.33 Fitting the lay shaft

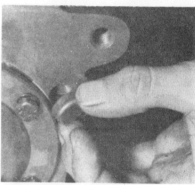

12.38 Fitting the selector fork rail blanking plugs to the front of the casing

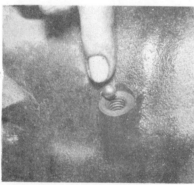

12.39 Replacing the detent ball (prior to spring and plug) in the casing

12.40 Refitting the cover plate and reverse selector rail. Note fork which will engage the pinion groove

12.41 Tightening gear casing cover bolts

12.43 Fitting speedometer driven gear and spindle with the housing

12.45 Fitting a new 'O' sealing ring at the end of the cross shaft

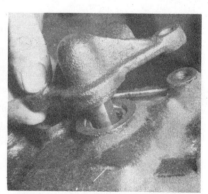

12.46a Replacing the end housing

12.46b Replacing the ball

12.46c Replacing the spring and plug

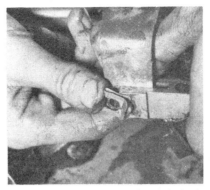

14.3a Removing the control rod clevis pin clips

14.3b Lifting away the selector bar

14.4 Gear lever 'U' carrier mounting bolts

14.5 Cross shaft selector coupling

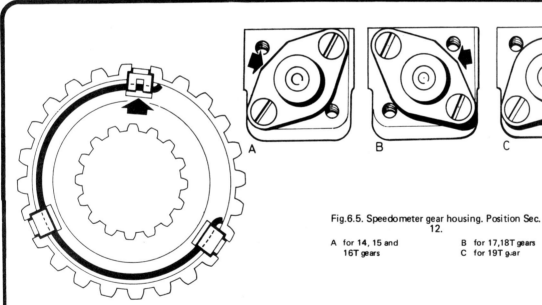

Fig.6.5. Speedometer gear housing. Position Sec. 12.

A for 14, 15 and 16T gears

B for 17,18T gears
C for 19T gear

Fig 6.4 SYNCHRO HUB (3 SPEED) REVERSE/1st GEAR (SECTION 11)
Location of central spring for sliding keys. One end engages over slotted key (arrowed)

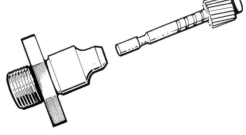

the cover if they have been taken out.

43 Fit the speedometer driven gear not forgetting the thrust pad, a new seal (with circular spring on the small inner lip) and the housing (photo). The housing should have been marked on removal. If not then the position of the flat on the housing depends on the number of teeth on the gear. Fig 6.5. shows the flat position for the various numbers of teeth.

44 Early versions incorporated the reverse override spring in the form of a detent on the end of the cross shaft. The detent ball and spring are fitted onto the casing at the left end of the cross shaft.

45 Fit a new 'O' ring in the casing recess (photo).

46 Replace the end housing and put the ball spring and spring housing plug into position (photos).

47 Later models, which incorporate the reverse stop mechanism in the change lever, have a plain blanking plug fitted instead of the housing.

13 Gearbox - 3 speed - reassembly

1 Reassembly of the 3 speed box follows exactly the same order and procedure as the 4 speed. The only difference is that some things are omitted making it somewhat simpler. This description, therefore, refers directly to the preceding Section and states any differences in the paragraphs where they occur.

paragraph 2	overdrive is not fitted to 3 speed gearboxes
paragraph 3	no spacer ring is fitted
paragraph 9	for 3rd/4th speed hubs read 2nd/3rd
paragraph 13	for 1st/2nd selector fork read reverse/1st. There is no striking lug fitted to the shaft
paragraph 15	not applicable
paragraph 16	for 1st/2nd read reverse/1st
paragraph 18	no striking lug. While fitting the pin engage reverse gear to provide support for the rear end of the rail
paragraph 19	for 3rd/4th read 2nd/3rd
paragraph 24	on LH drive models the shaft is inserted from the other side.
paragraphs 25/26	both striking levers are the same. They are fitted to the shaft differently according to RHD or LHD as shown in Fig 6.10
paragraph 27	There is a yoke fitted as opposed to a set screw recess and this should face down and incline to the front of the casing as shown in Fig 6.11
paragraphs 40-42	The cover is simply a cover
paragraph 47	This applies to all 3 speed versions

14 Gearchange mechanism - 4 speed gearbox

1 The floor change mechanism is normally fitted only to 4 speed gearboxes. It is possible to remove the mechanism and linkage from the gearbox without removing the gearbox from the car.

2 Disconnect the gearchange lever inside the car as described in Section 2, paragraphs 5 and 6.

3 The selector bar and control rod on early models are disconnected underneath by removing the clips securing the pivot pins (photos).

4 The U shaped carrier and pivot shaft is held to the top of the casing by two bolts (photo).

5 The gearbox cross shaft coupling is held by a set screw which engages a recess in the cross shaft (photo).

6 A rubber boot is fitted between the casing and the coupling.

7 On later models the same principles exactly are employed but the reverse stop device is incorporated in the gear lever and the control rod runs more directly to a quadrant arm on the end of the cross shaft. Furthermore the change lever end of the selector bar runs in a grooved adjuster in the pivot shaft. It pivots on the casing by a shouldered bolt rather than a clevis pin as before.

8 On early models it is important to check that the relative dimensions between the clevis pin centres on the control rod are as indicated in Fig 6.14.

9 On later versions when the mechanism is assembled the grooved adjuster should be set so that all gears including reverse are obtained without difficulty.

10 On later models a lift collar on the change lever operates a cable which lifts a ratchet to allow the lever to be moved further over to engage reverse (Fig 6.15).

11 The cable is held to the lifting collar by a grub screw and access to this is possible after the knob has been pulled off the splined shaft.

12 The lower end of the cable is accessible after removing the lever assembly from the gearbox. The stepped abutment and the shift finger are both primed to the lever and the pins must be driven out to release the cable and spring.

13 On overdrive models the lever knob incorporates the overdrive switch and is screwed to the lever shroud. If the top of the grip is prised off the wires can be disconnected and the grip unscrewed.

15 Gearchange mechanism - 3 speed gearbox

1 The steering column change is only fitted normally to the 3 speed gearbox. The complete linkage is accessible without removing the gearbox from the car.

2 Most of the gearchange difficulty encountered with older high mileage column change mechanisms is due to wear in the link rod clevises and pins and at the pivot pin for the change lever. Adjustment of the link rods does not affect operation - it merely repositions the change lever. In other words backlash in the linkage cannot be compensated by adjustment.

3 The correct position of the change lever should be radially 5º above horizontal and 3.3 inches from the top edge of the steering wheen when held in the 2nd/3rd speed plane (Figs 6.19 and 6.21).

4 Radial position is adjusted by the control rod which has a threaded adjuster at the gearbox end and height is adjusted by the selector rod which has a threaded adjuster at the steering column end.

5 The change lever is retained in its housing by the pivot pin which if driven out, will release the lever. Washers are fitted on the pin between lever and housing to reduce vibration.

6 The selector lever at the bottom of the column can be removed after removing its pivot bolt and disconnecting the selector rod.

7 The cross shaft between gearbox and side frame member at the lower end is bushed at the bracket end.

8 To renew the bush or the rubber boot surrounding it the bracket must be unbolted from the side frame member. Push the bush out of the boot and the boot can be pushed out of the bracket.

9 The bellcrank operated by the selector rod operates a pin in a grooved collar fitted to the cross shaft. The pin can be screwed in or out of the bellcrank so that it runs properly in the groove but without jamming in the bottom. It normally projects ½ inch from the bellcrank arm.

16 Gearbox - replacement

1 Replacement of the gearbox is a reversal of the removal procedure but certain matters have to be remembered.

2 With 4 speed gearboxes the change mechanism should be assembled and fitted, and all gears engaged before re-installation.

3 With three speed boxes the change mechanism has to be fitted afterwards. If you have overhauled the gearbox do not neglect the change mechanism as it is subject to wear and this results in a sloppy change action.

4 The clutch actuating lever is fitted by a spring clip to a ball ended stud in the bellhousing. Make sure this is fitted correctly as the gearbox input shaft has to be passed through the thrust bearing when the gearbox is replaced.

5 Do not forget to fit a new gasket between the gearbox facc and the bellhousing. Hold it in position with some grease during assembly. Do not use sealing compound.

6 Make sure that the rear mounting and crossmember are fitted the correct way round.

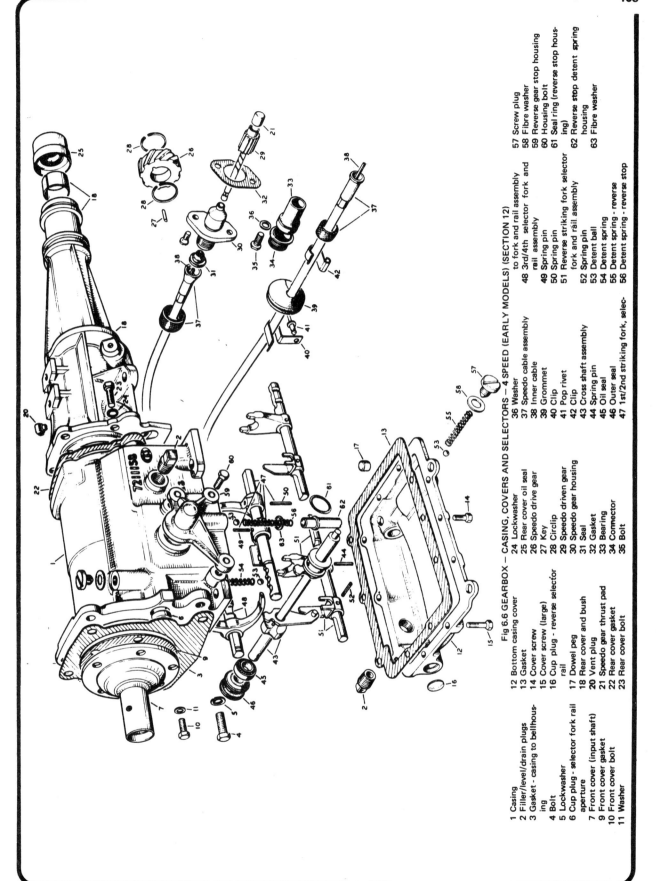

Fig 6.6 GEARBOX — CASING, COVERS AND SELECTORS — 4 SPEED (EARLY MODELS) (SECTION 12)

1 Casing
2 Filler/level/drain plugs
3 Gasket - casing to bellhousing
4 Bolt
5 Lockwasher
6 Cup plug - selector fork rail aperture
7 Front cover (input shaft)
9 Speedo gear thrust pad
10 Front cover bolt
11 Washer

12 Bottom casing cover
13 Gasket
14 Cover screw
15 Cover screw (large)
16 Cup plug - reverse selector rail
17 Dowel peg
18 Rear cover and bush
20 Vent plug
21 Speedo gear gasket
22 Rear cover gasket
23 Rear cover bolt

24 Lockwasher
25 Rear cover oil seal
26 Speedo drive gear
27 Key
28 Circlip
29 Speedo driven gear
30 Speedo gear housing
31 Seal
32 Gasket
33 Bearing
34 Connector
35 Bolt

36 Washer
37 Speedo cable assembly
38 Inner cable
39 Grommet
40 Clip
41 Pop rivet
42 Clip
43 Cross shaft assembly
44 Spring pin
45 Oil seal
46 Outer seal
47 1st/2nd striking fork, selec-

to fork and rail assembly
48 3rd/4th selector fork and rail assembly
49 Spring pin
50 Spring pin
51 Reverse striking fork selector fork and rail assembly
52 Spring pin
53 Detent ball
54 Detent spring
55 Detent spring - reverse
56 Detent spring - reverse stop

57 Screw plug
58 Fibre washer
59 Reverse gear stop housing
60 Housing bolt
61 Seal ring (reverse stop housing)
62 Reverse stop detent spring housing
63 Fibre washer

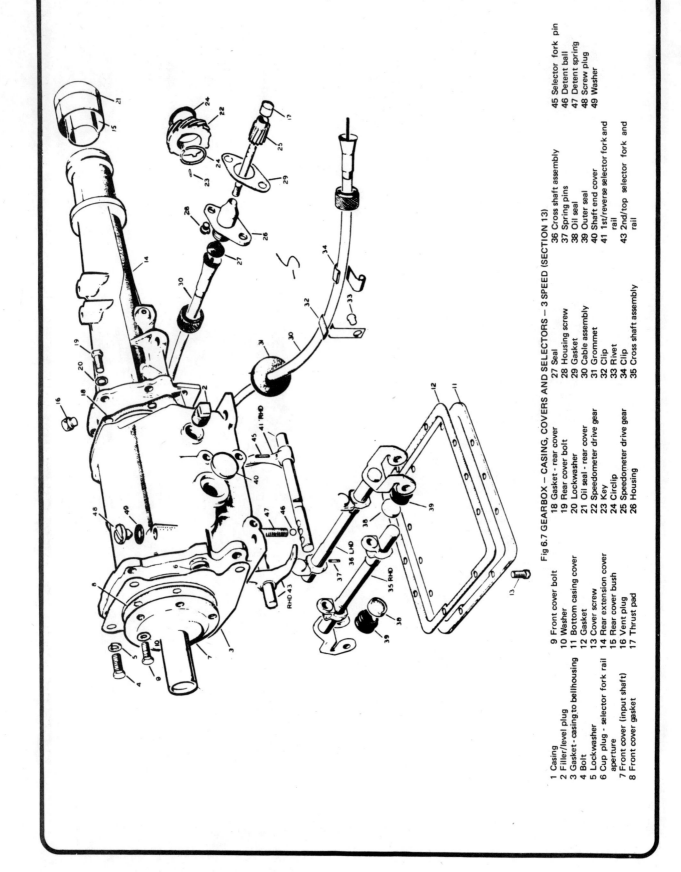

Fig 6.7 GEARBOX – CASING, COVERS AND SELECTORS – 3 SPEED (SECTION 13)

1 Casing	18 Gasket - rear cover	36 Cross shaft assembly
2 Filler/level plug	19 Washer	37 Spring pins
3 Gasket - casing to bellhousing	20 Lockwasher	38 Oil seal
4 Bolt	21 Oil seal - rear cover	39 Gasket
5 Lockwasher	22 Speedometer drive gear	30 Cable assembly
6 Cup plug - selector fork rail aperture	23 Key	31 Grommet
7 Front cover (input shaft)	24 Circlip	32 Clip
8 Front cover gasket	25 Speedometer drive gear	33 Rivet
9 Front cover bolt	26 Housing	34 Clip
10 Washer	27 Seal	35 Cross shaft assembly
11 Bottom casing cover	28 Housing screw	36 Cross shaft assembly
12 Gasket	29 Gasket	37 Spring pins
13 Cover screw	30 Cable assembly	38 Oil seal
14 Rear extension cover	31 Grommet	39 Outer seal
15 Rear cover bush	32 Clip	40 Shaft end cover
16 Vent plug	33 Rivet	41 1st/reverse selector fork and rail
17 Thrust pad	34 Clip	43 2nd/top selector fork and rail
	35 Cross shaft assembly	45 Selector fork pin
		46 Detent ball
		47 Detent spring
		48 Screw plug
		49 Washer

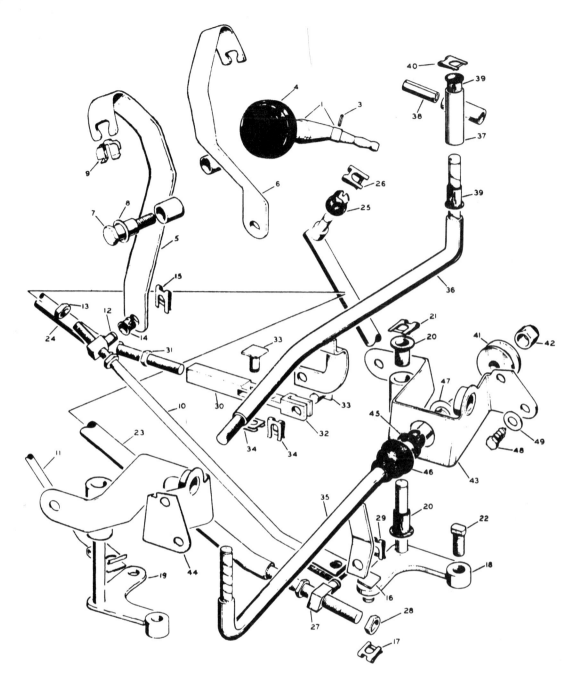

Fig 6.8 GEARCHANGE MECHANISM – 3 SPEED (SECTION 15)

1 Change lever assembly	15 Clip	28 Locknut	41 Cross shaft collar
3 Spring pin	16 Clevis pin	29 Clip	42 Self-locking nut
4 Lever grip	17 Clip	30 Yoke (LHD)	43 Cross shaft mounting bracket RHD
5 Selector lever assembly RHD	18 Bell crank lever RHD	31 Locknut (LHD)	
6 Selector lever assembly LHD	19 Bell crank lever LHD	32 Clevis (LHD)	44 Cross shaft mounting bracket LHD
7 Pivot bolt	20 Bush	33 Clevis pin (LHD)	
8 Washer	21 Clip	34 Clip (LHD)	45 Cross shaft bearing
9 Lever slipper	22 Cross shaft operating pin	35 Cross shaft assembly RHD	46 Boot
10 Selector rod RHD	23 Control rod RHD	36 Cross shaft assembly LHD	47 Washer
11 Selector rod LHD	24 Control rod LHD	37 Coupling	48 Bracket screw
12 Adjuster	25 Control rod bush	38 Spring pin	49 Washer
13 Locknut	26 Clip	39 Coupling bush	
14 Bush	27 Adjuster	40 Clip	

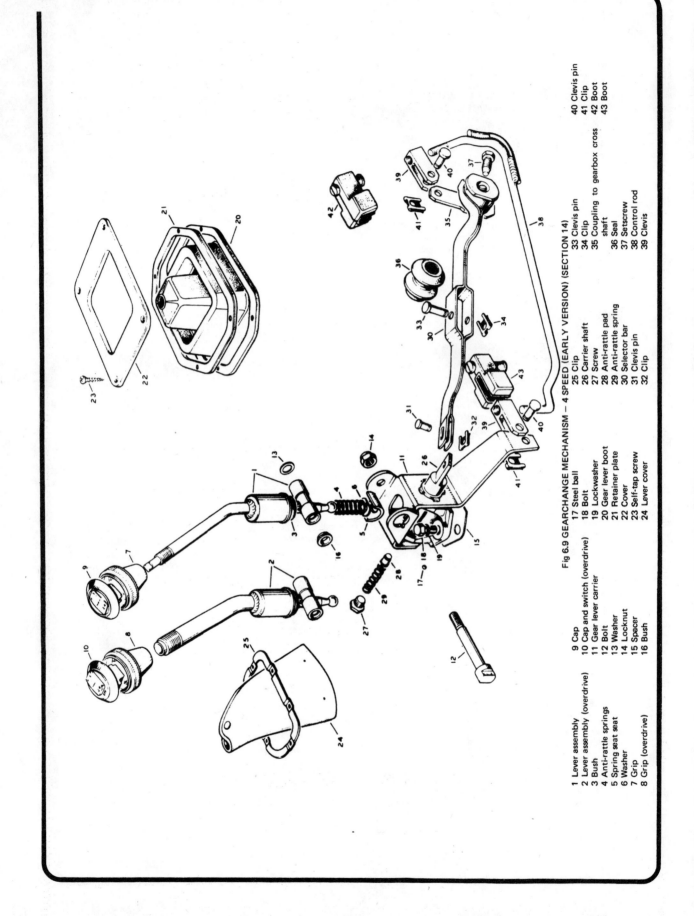

Fig 6.9 GEARCHANGE MECHANISM – 4 SPEED (EARLY VERSION) (SECTION 14)

1 Lever assembly	9 Cap	17 Steel ball	25 Clip	33 Clevis pin	40 Clevis pin
2 Lever assembly (overdrive)	10 Cap and switch (overdrive)	18 Bolt	26 Carrier shaft	34 Clip	41 Clip
3 Bush	11 Gear lever carrier	19 Lockwasher	27 Screw	35 Coupling to gearbox cross	42 Boot
4 Anti-rattle springs	12 Bolt	20 Gear lever boot	28 Anti-rattle pad	shaft	43 Boot
5 Spring seat seat	13 Washer	21 Retainer plate	29 Anti-rattle spring	36 Seal	
6 Washer	14 Locknut	22 Cover	30 Selector bar	37 Setscrew	
7 Grip	15 Spacer	23 Self-tap screw	31 Clevis pin	38 Control rod	
8 Grip (overdrive)	16 Bush	24 Lever cover	32 Clip	39 Clevis	

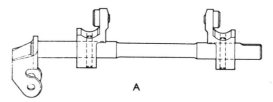

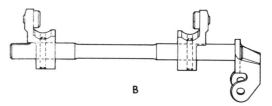

Fig 6.10 GEARBOX CROSS SHAFT — 3 SPEED
Assembly of striking levers on shaft

A - LHD   B - RHD

A

B

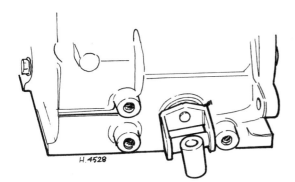

H.4528

Fig 6.11 GEARBOX CROSS SHAFT — 3 SPEED (SECTION 13)
Illustration of yoke position facing down and forwards

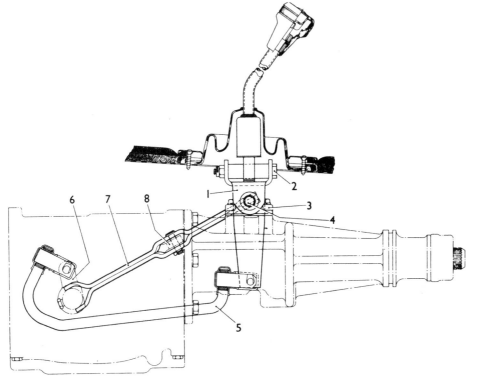

Fig 6.12 GEARCHANGE MECHANISM — 4 SPEED (EARLY VERSION) (SECTION 14)
Assembled longitudinal cross section showing main features

1 'U' shaped carrier	3 Carrier bracket	5 Control rod	7 Selector bar
2 Lever pivot	4 Carrier pivot	6 Gearbox cross shaft coupling	8 Pivot bracket

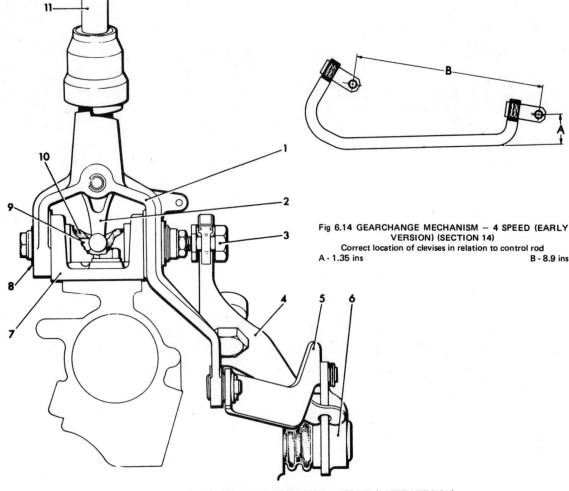

Fig 6.14 GEARCHANGE MECHANISM — 4 SPEED (EARLY VERSION) (SECTION 14)
Correct location of clevises in relation to control rod
A - 1.35 ins   B - 8.9 ins

Fig 6.13 GEARCHANGE MECHANISM — 4 SPEED (LATER VERSION)
Assembled lateral cross section showing main features (Section 14)

1 Carrier	6 Gearbox cross shaft coupling	9 Pad and spring
2 Lever finger	pivot	7 Carrier bracket	10 Pivot shaft
3 Grooved adjuster on carrier	4 Selector bar	8 Pivot bush	11 Gear lever
	5 Control rod		

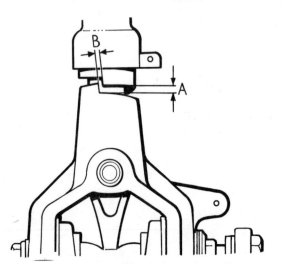

Fig 6.16 GEARCHANGE MECHANISM — 4 SPEED (LATER VERSION) (SECTION 14)
A - .020–.040 inch
B - .012–.020 inch with 1st or 2nd gear engaged

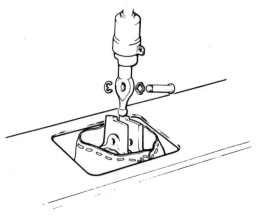

Fig 6.17 GEARCHANGE MECHANISM — 4 SPEED (LATER VERSION) (SECTION 14)
Lever fixing to carrier

111

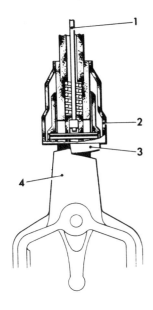

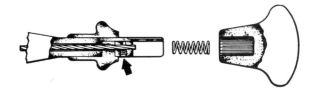

Fig 6.18 GEARCHANGE MECHANISM — 4 SPEED (LATER VERSION) (SECTION 14)
Reverse stop cable upper securing screw - arrowed

Fig 6.15 GEARCHANGE MECHANISM — 4 SPEED (LATER VERSION) (SECTION 14)
Reverse stop mechanism - lever cross section

1 Cable
2 Housing
3 Stepped abutment
4 Carrier

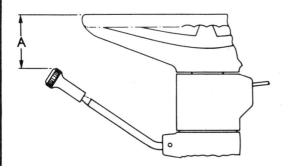

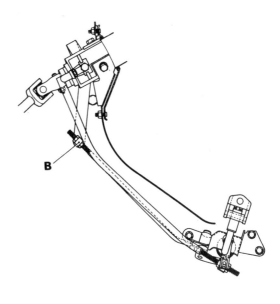

Fig 6.19 GEARCHANGE MECHANISM — 3 SPEED (SECTION 15)
Lever height A = 3.30 inches

Fig 6.20 GEARCHANGE MECHANISM — 3 SPEED (SECTION 15)
Lever height adjuster 'B'

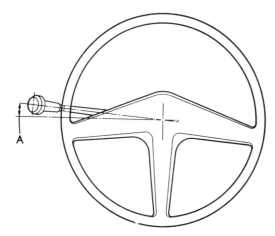

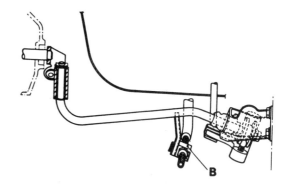

Fig 6.21 GEARCHANGE MECHANISM — 3 SPEED (SECTION 15)
Lever radial position A = 5º

Fig 6.22 GEARCHANGE MECHANISM — 3 SPEED (SECTION 15)
Lever radial position adjuster 'B'

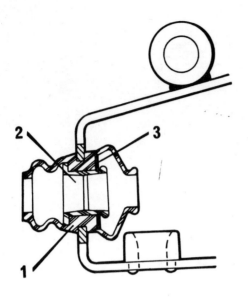

Fig 6.23 GEARCHANGE MECHANISM — 3 SPEED
Cross shaft bracket mounting cross section (Section 15)
1 Boot   3 Washer
2 Bush

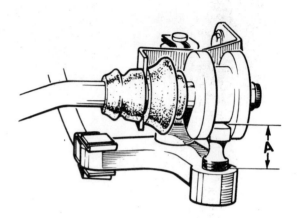

Fig 6.24 GEARCHANGE MECHANISM — 3 SPEED
Cross shaft collar and bell crank pin (Section 15)
A = .50 inch

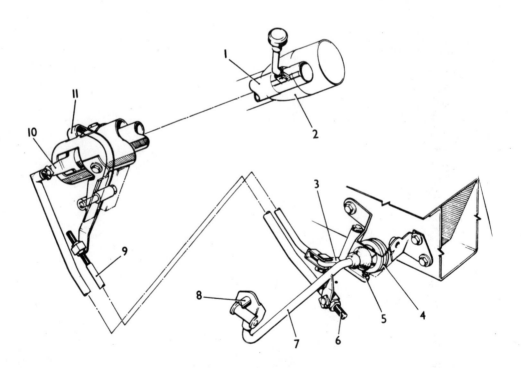

Fig 6.25 GEARCHANGE MECHANISM — 3 SPEED (SECTION 15)
Diagrammatic layout

1 Control tube	4 Grooved collar	7 Cross shaft	10 Control lever
2 Steering column housing	5 Cross shaft operating pin	8 Gearbox cross shaft	11 Selector lever
3 Bell crank lever	6 Control rod	9 Selector rod	

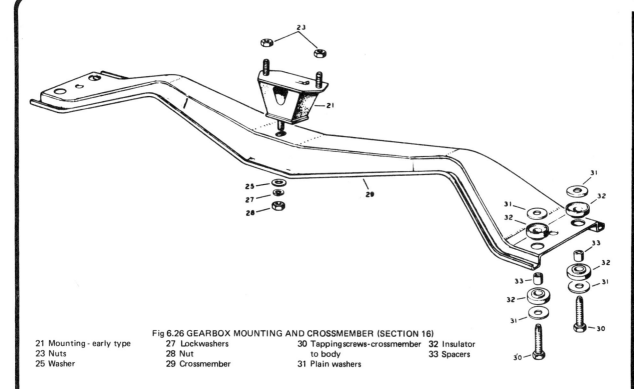

Fig 6.26 GEARBOX MOUNTING AND CROSSMEMBER (SECTION 16)

21 Mounting - early type	27 Lockwashers	30 Tapping screws - crossmember	32 Insulator
23 Nuts	28 Nut	to body	33 Spacers
25 Washer	29 Crossmember	31 Plain washers	

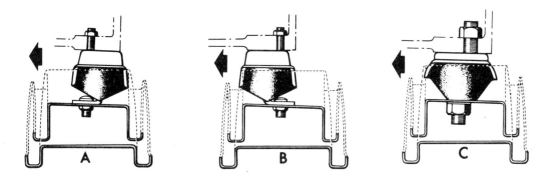

Fig 6.27 GEARBOX MOUNTING ON CROSSMEMBER (LATER TYPE) (SECTION 16)
A 4 speed gearbox   B 3 speed gearbox   C 4 speed with overdrive and automatic
Arrows point to front of car
NB When fitting new type mounting in place of old, elongate centre hole in crossmember .40 inch to rear

17 Overdrive - general description and operating principles

Overdrive units are fitted as standard on the VX 4/90 and as an optional extra on all those with 4 speed gearboxes.

The purpose of the overdrive unit is to provide a higher gear for sustained cruising speed. This results in lower engine revolutions, improved fuel consumption and less noise. For anyone who uses motorways regularly they would be a particularly attractive feature.

The overdrive unit is set to operate on 3rd and top gears only. If left engaged when 2nd gear is selected it will automatically disengage. It will, however, automatically re-engage when changing from 2nd to 3rd if it is not switched out. It would be superfluous to have it on the lower gears and the higher operating speeds would reduce its useful working life unnecessarily. If reverse were to be engaged with overdrive selected, the unit would lock solid and/or disintegrate.

The unit is a completely separate item attached to the rear of the conventional gearbox. It comprises a planetary gear train - sun gear, planet gears in a carrier and annulus with internal toothed ring.

The operation of the unit is controlled by a double faced cone clutch. In one position the clutch locks the whole gear set to the annulus thus providing straight through drive. In the other position the clutch locks the sun gear so causing the planet gears and carrier to revolve round the sun gear. This, in turn, means that the annulus and output shaft rotate more quickly than the input shaft which drives the planet gear carrier. The one way clutch permits the differential in shaft speeds and acts as a drive lock on the over-run allowing engine braking.

In direct drive the clutch is held in engagement with the annulus by coil springs reacting against the casing.

When acting in the other position the clutch is held against the stationary brake ring by pistons operated by oil pressure. This oil pressure is developed by a mechanical pump in permanent operation. It is driven from a cam fitted to gearbox mainshaft. When direct drive is being used the oil pressure is maintained at 20 lb/sq in. — the residual pressure. Excess pressure bleeds off through a spill port. When the overdrive switch is operated a solenoid plunger operates a valve which in turn operates the relief valve to effectively increase the system pressure to 300—340 lb/sq in. Under this pressure the cone clutch operating pistons move and force the clutch against the brake ring and stop it rotating.

The fractional time lag which occurs in the pressure system build up enables the overdrive to be engaged smoothly at all speed conditions.

18 Overdrive - precautions

1 Overdrive units are robust and well engineered and provided they are not abused will last as long as the rest of the transmission without trouble.

2 If there are any indications that some part of the system is not functioning properly then checks should be immediate. If left, serious damage will result with more expensive repairs resulting.

3 Do not engage the overdrive when accelerating fiercely. It will function but it imposes unnecessary strain.

4 Remember that it should only operate on 3rd and 4th gears. If it should start operating on 1st and 2nd (if tried) something is wrong with the inhibitor switch circuit. This means that reverse might be engaged with overdrive accidentally in operation. The unit could be ruined.

5 Be a little more particular about the gearbox oil level. Oil cleanliness is more important also as any metal particles can upset the pressure system. There is an oil filter incorporated in the unit.

6 If the overdrive does not disengage the car must not be reversed — either under its own power or otherwise. Damage would result. (The same applies in rare circumstances such as coming to a halt going up hill with overdrive engaged and then letting it run back).

7 Overdrive should not engage at all with the ignition switched off.

Fig 6.28 LAYCOCK TYPE J OVERDRIVE — COMPONENTS

1 Annulus assembly	46 Locking nut
2 Ball bearing	47 Tab washer
3 Circlip	48 Driving gear
4 Clutch spring	49 Pinion
5 Dashpot plug	50 Connection
6 'O' ring	51 Sump
7 Dashpot sleeve	52 Setscrew
8 'O' ring	53 Spring washer
9 Dashpot piston assembly	54 Gasket
10 Main casing	55 Steel rollers
11 Adaptor stud	56 Thrust bearing housing
12 Adaptor stud	57 Thrust bearing
13 Rear casing stud	58 Circlip
14 Rear casing stud	59 Solenoid valve
15 Screw	60 'O' ring
16 Gasket	61 Copper washer
17 Gasket	62 Pressure filter
18 Relief valve plug	63 Plug
19 Relief valve spring	64 Washer
20 Valve ball	65 Suction filter
21 Breather	66 Bridge piece nut
22 Washer	67 Bridge piece
23 Plug	68 Tab washer
24 Operating piston	69 Brake ring
25 'O' ring	70 Gasket
26 Planet carrier	71 Spring washer
27 Pump body	72 Copper washer
28 'O' ring	73 Nut
29 Pump plug	74 Sunwheel
30 'O' ring	75 Circlip
31 Pump plunger	76 Oil thrower
32 Non-return valve	77 Clip
33 Relief valve body	78 Freewheel cage
34 'O' ring	79 Freewheel inner
35 Relief valve piston	80 Spring
36 Piston spring	81 Thrust washer
37 Rear casing	82 Woodruff key
38 Rear casing weir	83 Cam (as gearbox mainshaft)
39 Oil seal	84 Spring ring
40 Welch plug	85 Circlip
41 Sliding clutch	86 Adaptor
42 Circlip	87 Gasket
43 Speedo bearing	88 Nut
44 Oil seal	89 Lockwasher
45 'O' ring	

Fig 6.29 Overdrive - removal of sump and suction filter screen

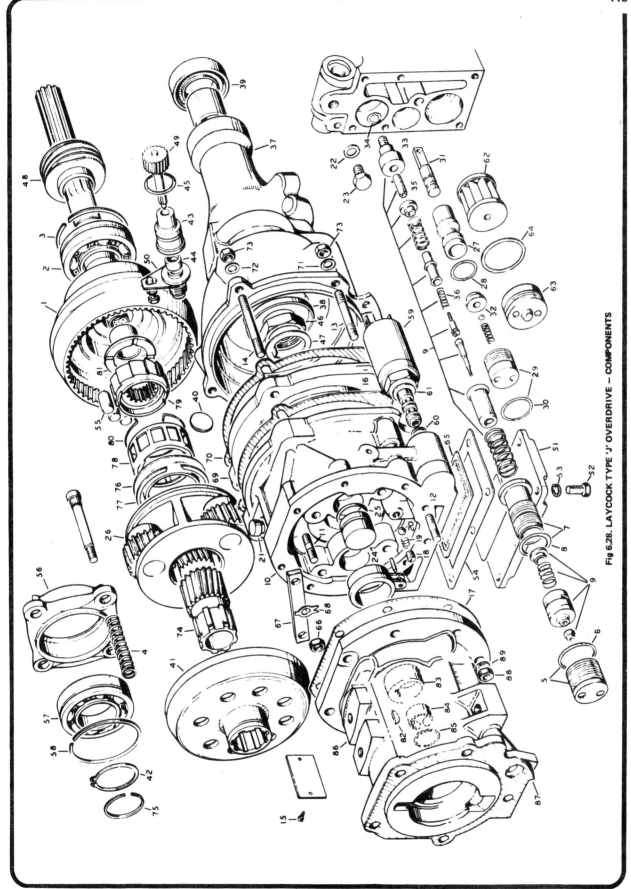

Fig 6.28. LAYCOCK TYPE 'J' OVERDRIVE – COMPONENTS

19 Overdrive - maintenance

If it works satisfactorily leave it alone. The only possible exception to this is the cleaning of the oil filter.

As Vauxhall routine servicing procedures no longer provide for periodic changing of the gearbox oil (it will presumably last as long as the gearbox!) it is possible that the filter will gradually become choked. (If there was nothing in the oil to choke it there would be no point in fitting a filter).

Access to the filter for cleaning is dealt with in the next Section.

20 Overdrive - fault diagnosis and checks

In general overdrive faults are best left for correction by mechanics who have experience with them.

Certain faults can be traced and rectified by owners without removing the unit from the car.

Remember at all times that after long periods of operation the overdrive oil can be hot enough to burn the skin.

1 Overdrive does not engage
a) Check oil level
b) Check electrical feed to solenoid
c) Check solenoid and valve
d) Check oil filter for blockage
e) Remove unit for overhaul

2 Overdrive does not disengage (do not use in this state)
a) Check for closed circuit on electrical feed to solenoid valve
b) Check that solenoid valve is not seized
c) Check relief valve for sticking parts and blocked control orifice
d) Remove unit for overhaul.

3 Overdrive slips when engaging
a) Check oil level
b) Check solenoid valve for correct operation
c) Check oil filter for blockage
d) Check pump non-return valve
e) Remove unit for overhaul

4 Overdrive disengagement slow - free wheeling on overrun
a) Check solenoid valve for correct operation
b) Check relief valve for sticking parts and blocked control orifice
c) Remove unit for overhaul

21 Overdrive - checks procedure

a) Electrical feed to solenoid

Remove the two leads from the solenoid and connect them to a voltmeter or 12 volt bulb. Put gear lever in neutral in the 3rd/top plane and switch on ignition. Do not start the engine. When overdrive is on the voltage should be 12 (bulb lights).

If no reading check the fuse (No 2), overdrive switch and inhibitor switch.

b) Inhibitor switch

The inhibitor switch is mounted on a bracket held by the gearbox to overdrive adaptor bolts (Fig 6.33). It is operated by the movement of the gearchange linkage and can be adjusted by movement in the slotted bracket.

Proceed with the connections as described in Check a) and then move the gear lever from side to side in the neutral position. In the 1st/2nd gear plane there should be no voltage whereas in the 3rd/4th gear position there should be. If the terminals of the inhibitor switch are bridged an indication will be obtained as to whether the fault lies in the switch or elsewhere.

c) Solenoid valve

If the overdrive does not disengage disconnect both leads from the solenoid and do Check a). If voltage is present then there is a closed circuit somewhere.

With the electrical feed to the solenoid on, switching it on and off should move the solenoid and this is audible.

To remove the solenoid and valve unscrew it from the casing using a proper spanner on the hexagon shoulder next to the casing. Do not grip it by the cylindrical section or you will ruin it.

If the solenoid is defective a new unit must be fitted.

d) Oil filter

1 The overdrive unit has a sump plate which can be removed by unscrewing the bolts for access to the oil filter, relief valve and oil pump (Fig 6.29). Beware of hot oil. Do not damage the suction filter screen (this is not the main filter).

2 Three plugs each with two holes in will now be visible. The two holes are for a suitable unscrewing tool to be fitted. Make one up. Do not try tapping them round with a punch.

3 The plug securing the filter is the largest one. When removed the filter can be taken out (Fig 6.30).

4 Wash the element in paraffin and fit a new aluminium sealing washer when replacing the plug. Stake it into position after tightening to 16 lb ft.

e) Pump non-return valve and body and relief valve and control orifice

The pump plug is the centre one. If it is the owner's wish to remove either of the two assemblies he may, but apart from flushing them in paraffin we can only recommend total renewal of the items if there is sure evidence of malfunction. Figs 6.31 and 6.32 give explanatory sectional drawings.

22 Overdrive unit - removal and replacement

1 It is most important that the overdrive is in 'free' state before removal. If it was in a drive situation the splines on the uni-directional clutch and planet carrier will be loaded on to the gearbox output shaft and prevent the unit from being drawn off. So drive the car in 3rd or top in overdrive and whilst in gear depress the clutch and disengage the overdrive. Do not use the overdrive again before removal.

2 Drain the oil from the gearbox and overdrive sump. Take off the propeller shaft as described in Chapter 7 and disconnect the leads to the overdrive solenoid.

3 Undo the nuts securing it to the overdrive adaptor (Fig 6.33).

4 Draw the unit off the gearbox.

5 Replacement is a reversal of the removal procedure. It helps if the high point of the eccentric on the gearbox shaft (which drives the overdrive pump) is facing downwards when the unit is fitted. (Fig 6.34).

6 If you are unable to measure exactly the three pints of oil needed for refilling the transmission make sure that you check the level after the overdrive unit has been used.

23 Automatic transmission - description

1 The Victor FD has been offered with automatic transmission as an optional extra since inception of the range in 1967. It is only fitted to the 1975 cc engine. Until 1969 the Borg Warner Model 35 unit was fitted. Since then the GM version has been used.

Both units have the same operating principles but the driver's control has improved on the later model.

2 The automatic transmission replaces the conventional clutch and gearbox, and occupies the same space in the same way - being bolted onto the rear of the engine. It comprises two basic parts - the torque converter and the three speed epicyclic gearbox.

The torque converter is a form of oil operated turbine which transmits the engine power from a multi-bladed rotor (the pump)

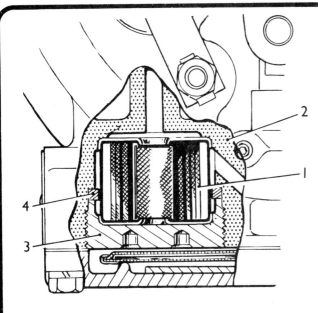

Fig 6.30 OVERDRIVE — CROSS SECTION OF PRESSURE
FILTER

1 Filter element   3 Threaded plug
2 Main casing   4 Aluminium washer

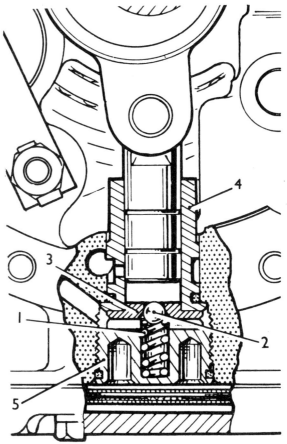

Fig 6.32 OVERDRIVE — CROSS SECTION OF OIL PUMP AND
NON—RETURN VALVE

1 Spring   4 Pump body
2 Non-return valve ball   5 Threaded plug
3 Valve seating

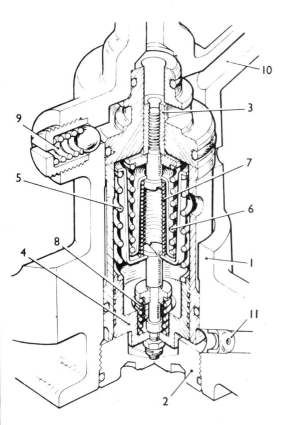

Fig 6.31 OVERDRIVE — CROSS SECTION OF PRESSURE
RELIEF VALVE AND CONTROL ORIFICE

1 Main casing
2 Threaded plug
3 Relief valve
4 Dashpot
5 Dashpot spring
6 Relief valve spring
7 Residual pressure spring
8 Supplementary dashpot
    spring
9 Spill port
10 Mainshaft lubrication pass-
    age
11 Control orifice

Fig 6.33 Overdrive - mounting studs (arrowed)

directly connected to the crankshaft to another multi-bladed rotor (the turbine) directly connected to the input shaft of the transmission. At low engine revolutions, the oil driven by the pump has little force imparted to it, so the turbine does not move. When the pump speed increases, so the force of the oil is transferred to the turbine.

An intermediate multi-bladed rotor (the stator) regulates the flow of oil back to the pump after it has done its work through the turbine.

The gearbox consists of a ravignaux planetary gear set in constant mesh and the selection of the gears is by braking one or more of the components of this gear set.

This braking is effected by one of the three servo operated multi-plate clutches and a band - literally a brake band, which can be applied to the outer ring gear of the set. The automatic operation of three clutches and the low speed band is the complicated part, involving a servo/hydraulic pump system controlled by road speed, inlet manifold vacuum, and the position of the accelerator.

3 The capabilities of the automatic transmission are different from the manual system and in order that those unfamiliar with them may understand the difference, a full description of the functions at starting, parking and stopping, in all of the five or six selector positions is given below:

'P'. Park. In this position with the engine either stopped or running, no gears are 'engaged' and the gearbox output shaft is mechanically locked, which in effect means that the propeller shaft and rear axle are also locked. The car cannot be moved, therefore. The engine may be started in this position. In order to select the 'P' position, the selector lever button must be fully depressed. Do not select 'P' if the car is moving. Damage will result.

'N'. Neutral. The conditions for neutral are the same as for 'P' except that the gearbox output shaft is not mechanically locked. The car will, therefore, roll with the engine either running or stopped.

'R'. Reverse. The button on the selector lever must be partially depressed to engage 'R'. In this position reverse gear is 'engaged'. If the engine is not running, it cannot be started unless the selector lever is moved to 'P' or 'N'. With the brakes applied, the car will not move. With the brakes off, increase in engine speed will move the car backwards. When the engine speed is decreased, the engine will act as a brake through the transmission. If the car is standing with the brakes off, it may roll at low engine speed in either direction. Reverse should not normally be selected whilst the car is moving.

'D'. Drive. The selector position for normal driving requirements. In this position first gear is initially 'engaged' but, at low engine speed with the brakes off, the car may roll in either direction. The engine cannot be started in this position. With the engine speed increased, the car will move forward in low gear.

When the speed and load conditions are right, the transmission will automatically move to second gear 'engagement' and then subsequently to top gear. When speed decreases, the gears will automatically shift back down as far as first, again according to speed and load situations.

The engine does not act as a brake or over-run in any of the three speeds in the 'D' position.

'L'. Lock-up (Borg Warner versions only). In this position the transmission stays in 1st gear and provides engine braking. If 'L' is selected whilst in the 'D' range and the car is moving in excess of 5 mph, the transmission will immediately shift down to second gear and lock there. If the speed reduces further to below 5 mph it will shift down to 1st and stay there. Increased speed will not move it back again to 2nd gear.

'L' range should not be selected when the vehicle is exceeding 55 mph, for the reasons given in the subsequent paragraphs.

'I'. Intermediate. To select this position the lever button must be partially depressed. When selected, the automatic transmission will operate exactly as in 'D' except that it will not move up out of 2nd. It should not be used in excess of 60 mph.

It is possible to change to 'I' when the vehicle is moving. It will immediately put the vehicle in 2nd gear until speed or throttle position may cause it to change down to first. The intermediate range is normally used in traffic or on uphill sections where one would tend to get a lot of changing going on between 2nd and top if in the 'D' position. Although there is no over-run braking in 1st gear, there is on 2nd gear in the 'I' position.

'L'. Low. To select this position, the selector lever button is fully depressed. This position should not be selected above 35 mph. It would normally be used to provide engine braking on steep downhill sections of road, or to avoid unnecessary changing between 1st and 2nd in dense traffic or on continuous slow uphill climbs.

As implied, the engine acts as a brake on over-run in this range.

Some points to bear in mind in the operation of automatic transmission are:
a) It is possible to obtain a quick change down to provide instant acceleration by depressing the accelerator fully. This change will not take place, however, if the vehicle is already in excess of the maximum speed of the gear below.
b) Where continuous engine braking on over-run is wanted, 'L' or 'I' ranges must be selected. It follows, therefore, that when shifting into these ranges when on the move, engine braking will take place if the car speed is high. On slippery surfaces the possibility of skids occurring must, therefore, be considered due to the sudden braking effect on the rear wheels.
c) It is not possible to push or tow start the car.
d) If the car is to be towed for any reason, the speed must be kept below 30 mph and the selector be put in 'N'. Not more than 30 miles should be covered. If there is a suspected fault in the transmission, the car should not be towed at all unless the propeller shaft is disconnected or the driving wheels revised to prevent the transmission being turned.
e) Cars fitted with automatic transmission are also fitted with automatic chokes on the carburettor so that the engine speed is suitably governed until it is warmed up. There will be a tendency to a faster tickover and subsequent 'creep' when in any of the driving ranges until the engine is fully warm. Engine tuning and smooth running is much more significant where automatic transmission is fitted.
f) Transmission fluid normally heats up in use. Severe or abusive use, or failure to keep cooling areas clean, can cause overheating and damage.

24 Automatic transmission - fluid level

1 The total capacity of the system is 11 pints for the Borg Warner and 9 pints for the GM unit. A dipstick is provided in the filler pipe which is located on the right hand side and projects into the engine compartment at the rear of the engine (Fig 6.38).
2 To check the fluid level, the engine and transmission should be fully warmed up to normal working temperature. With the car stationary on level ground, engine ticking over at idling speed and the selector lever in 'P' or 'N', remove the dipstick, clean it off, replace and remove again to note the level. The level must be kept between the 'Full' and 'Add' marks. From 'Add' to 'Full' calls for 1 pint. Do not overfill or foaming and loss of fluid may occur. Use only the proper fluid for topping up the transmission (Castrol TQ Dexron 'R') and under no circumstances should additives of any kind be mixed with it.
3 It is generally best to check the level after a normal run. If otherwise, it is difficult to judge the correct working temperature. If starting from cold, then it will be necessary to select a drive range, apply brakes (driver in the driving seat for safety) and run the engine at a fast idle for no more than two minutes.

Fig 6.34 Overdrive - position of high point of eccentric (arrowed) before replacement of unit

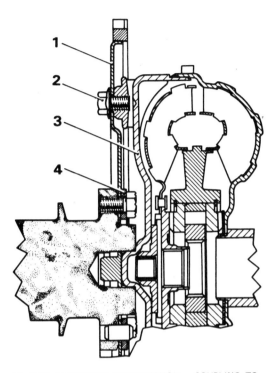

Fig 6.35 AUTOMATIC TRANSMISSION — COUPLING TO ENGINE FLEXPLATE

1 Flexplate   3 Torque converter
2 Flexplate to converter bolts   4 Distance plate

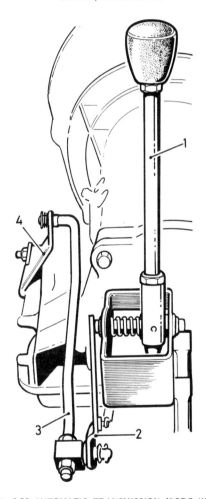

Fig 6.36 AUTOMATIC TRANSMISSION (BORG WARNER)
Selector lever details

1 Selector lever   3 Control rod
2 Selector lower lever   4 Front selector lever

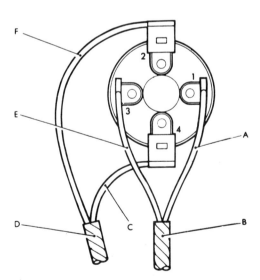

Fig 6.37 AUTOMATIC TRANSMISSION (BORG WARNER)
Starter inhibitor switch connections

1 and 3 Starter inhibitor ter-   2 and 4 Reverse lamp terminals
minals

A   White/yellow   D   Reverse lamp harness
B   Inhibitor switch harness   E   White/red
C   Green/brown   F   Green

25 Automatic transmission - adjustments and attention

1 Automatic transmission systems are sophisticated and complicated, and require specialist tools, experience and skill if they are to be properly set up. As they tend to be the exception rather than the rule on anything other than larger vehicles, it follows that the availability of the tools and frequency of experienced mechanics is rare. Non-professional experience is rarer still. Consequently the owner is not advised to tamper with his unit himself.

2 A cross section of the selector lever mechanism and starter inhibitor switch is given so that adjustment can be made to ensure that the operation of the selector lever button and the safety start cut-out are correct. It should not be possible to start the engine when the selector lever is in the 'D', 'I', 'L' or 'R' positions. Similarly it should only be possible to select 'L' or 'P' when the selector button is fully depressed, and 'I' and 'R' when it is partially depressed.

3 Details are given in the next Section on how to remove the transmission unit but, it must be emphasised that, full testing can only be carried out when it is installed. Thus removal and replacement should only be carried out when it is known that the unit is beyond repair in its installed position.

4 The test which the owner may carry out, if he suspects that there is either slip or otherwise, is the stall test. However, it will be necessary for a tachometer to be fitted to the engine. With the transmission fully warmed up, apply the brakes fully (chock the wheels too for safety), engage a drive range and press the accelerator to the floor. The engine speed should settle at 1550 rpm on BW units or 2100—2150 rpm for GM versions on later cars. Do not maintain this test for more than 10 seconds or overheating will result. If the engine rpm are too high then the torque converter oil supply should be suspect, and then the low band servo in the transmission itself. If the rpm are too low then the engine is not delivering full power or the torque converter unit is faulty.

5 The lower part of the torque converter housing is fitted with a perforated metal cover to permit cooling air into the housing. It is important to keep this clean as any restriction could result in overheating and loss of efficiency and damage.

26 Automatic transmission - removal and replacement

1 Before making any attempt to remove the transmission, make sure your reasons are valid. In other words get expert diagnosis first if transmission malfunctioning is the reason.

2 If you are removing the engine from a car with automatic transmission, the two should be separated at the flexplate which connects the crankshaft to the torque converter. Do not try and separate the torque converter from the gearbox.

3 All the normal precautions for gearbox removal as described in Section 2 should be taken. It must be remembered that they are heavier than conventional gearboxes - approximately 110 lbs and, therefore, adequate support must be provided.

4 Proceed to remove the crossmember support as described in Section 2 after having first slackened the transmission brace bolts at the sump bracket, and moving the starter as far forward as possible to clear the starter teeth on the flexplate rim.

5 If an oil cooler is fitted it will be necessary to drain the oil out so that the cooler tubes may be disconnected from the transmission. Make sure the unions are perfectly clean first and seal the holes suitably to stop dirt entering. The combined filler/dipstick tube must be removed taking the same precautions.

6 The three bolts which hold the flexplate to the torque converter are accessible as soon as the semicircular sheet steel plate across the bottom half of the casing has been removed. These three bolts must be removed before the main housing bolts securing the transmission to the engine are undone, otherwise, a strain could be put on the flexplate which would distort.

7 Once the flexplate bolts are removed, the casing bolts can come out with the whole unit properly supported. The transmission is then drawn a little to the rear and lowered in the normal way.

8 If the flexplate is to be renewed, it may be unbolted from the crankshaft flange. Seal the bolts on replacement as for the flywheel.

9 When replacing the transmission, proceed in the reverse order of removal. Line up the painted balance marks on torque converter and flexplate. When tightening the transmission brace, tighten the bolts on the torque converter housing first and then those on the sump bracket.

Fault Finding Chart - Gearbox

NOTE: It is sometimes difficult to decide whether it is worthwhile removing and dismantling the gearbox for a fault which may be nothing more than a minor irritant. Gearboxes which howl, or where the synchromesh can be 'beaten' by a quick gear change, may continue to perform for a long time in this state. A worn gearbox usually needs a complete rebuild to eliminate noise because the various gears, if re-aligned on new bearings will continue to howl when different wearing surfaces are presented to each other.

The decision to overhaul, therefore, must be considered with regard to time and money available, relative to the degree of noise or malfunction that the driver has to suffer.

Symptom	Reason/s	Remedy
Ineffective synchromesh	Worn baulk rings or synchro hubs	Dismantle and renew.
Jumps out of one or more gears (on drive or over-run)	Weak detent springs or worn selector forks or worn gears	Dismantle and renew. (Detent balls and springs can be renewed without dismantling the gearbox).
Noisy, rough, whining and vibration	Worn bearings and/or laygear thrust washers (initially) resulting in extended wear generally due to play and backlash	Dismantle and renew.
Noisy and difficult engagement of gears	Clutch fault	Examine clutch operation.

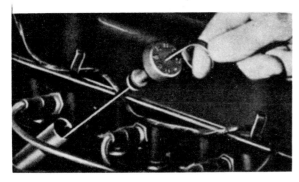

Fig 6.38 Automatic transmission - fluid level dipstick

WARM OIL. FULL — ADD 1 PINT

Fig.6.39. Automatic transmission G.M. starter inhibitor and reverse lamp switch

1 Neutral cam
2 Park cam
3 Switch roller upper
4 Red/white connector (starter inhibitor)
5 Yellow/white connector (starter inhibitor)
6 Green/brown connector reverse lamp
7 Green connector/reverse lamp

Position switch so that cams (1 and 2) operate switch lever in neutral and park positions.

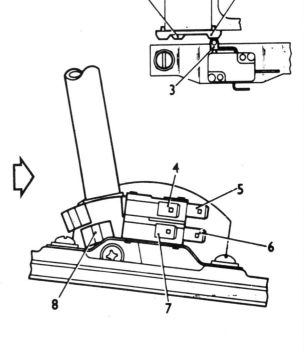

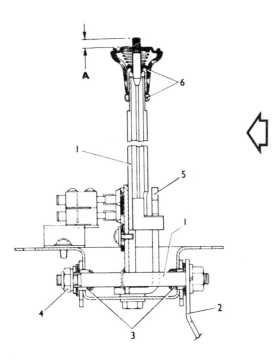

Fig 6.40 AUTOMATIC TRANSMISSION (GM) — SELECTOR LEVER LATERAL CROSS SECTION

1 Selector lever and pivot shaft
2 Lower lever
3 Pivot shaft bushes
4 Pivot shaft locking nut
5 Selector plate
6 Locking ring and grip

Dimension A = .24 inch with plunger up and selector lever in 'P' position

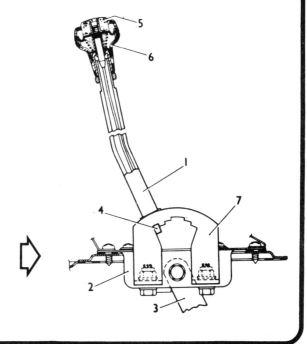

Fig 6.41 AUTOMATIC TRANSMISSION (GM) — SELECTOR LEVER LONGITUDINAL CROSS SECTION

1 Selector lever
2 Housing
3 Lower lever
4 Plunger pawl
5 Push button
6 Grip
7 Selector plate

Chapter 7 Propeller shaft and universal joints

Contents

Specifications

Propeller shaft

Make...	Hardy Spicer or BRD
Type...	Tubular

Universal joints

Make...	Hardy Spicer or BRD
Type...	Tubular
No of rollers each bearing	34

Sliding sleeve

Diameter	1.3735–1.3750 in
Clearance in rear cover bush	.002–.005 in

Torque wrench settings

Coupling flange bolts...	18 lb ft

1 General description

The drive from the gearbox to the rear axle is via the propeller shaft which is, in fact, a tube. Due to the variety of angles caused by the up and down motion of the rear axle in relation to the gearbox, universal joints are fitted to each end of the shaft to convey the drive through the constantly varying angles. As the movement also increases and decreases the distance between the rear axle and the gearbox, the forward end of the propeller shaft is a splined sleeve which is a sliding fit over the rear of the gearbox splined mainshaft. The splined sleeve runs in an oil seal in the gearbox mainshaft rear cover, and is supported with the mainshaft on the gearbox rear bearing. The splines are lubricated by oil in the rear cover coming from the gearbox.

The universal joints each comprise a four way trunnion, or 'spider', each leg of which runs in a needle roller bearing race, pre-packed with grease and fitted into the bearing journal yokes of the sliding sleeve and propeller shaft and flange.

2 Propeller shaft - removal, inspection and replacement

1 Jack up the rear of the car and support it on stands.
2 The rear of the shaft is connected to the rear axle pinion by a flange held by four nuts and bolts. Mark the position of both flanges relative to each other, and then undo the bolts.
3 Move the propeller shaft forward to disengage it from the pinion flange and then lower it to the ground.
4 Draw the other end of the propeller shaft, that is the splined sleeve, out of the rear of the gearbox extension cover and the shaft is then clear for removal.
5 Place a receptacle under the gearbox rear cover opening to catch any oil which will certainly come out if the gearbox is tilted.

6 If the propeller shaft is removed for inspection, first examine the bore and counterbore of the two flanges which mate at the rear. If they are damaged in any way, or a slack fit, it could mean that the propeller shaft is running off centre at the flange and causing vibration in the drive. If nothing obvious is wrong, and the universal joints are in good order, it is permissible to reconnect the flanges with one turned through 180° relative to the other. This may stop the vibration.
7 The replacement of the shaft is a reversal of the removal procedure. Ensure that the sliding sleeve is inserted into the gearbox end cover with care, and is perfectly clean, so as not to cause damage to, or failure of, the oil seal in the cover.
8 The flanges should be mated according to the position marks (unless a 180° turn is being done as mentioned in paragraph 6).
9 The four bolts should be fitted with the heads towards the universal joint.

3 Universal joints - inspection, removal and replacement

1 Preliminary inspection of the universal joints can be carried out with the propeller shaft on the car.
2 Grasp each side of the universal joint, and with a twisting action determine whether there is any play or slackness in the joint. Also try an up and down rocking motion of the same purpose. If there is any sign whatsoever of play, the joints need replacement.
3 Remove the propeller shaft as described in the previous section.
4 Clean away all dirt from the ends of the bearings on the yokes so that the circlips may be removed using a pair of contracting circlip pliers. If they are very tight, tap the end of the bearing race (inside the circlip) with a drift and hammer to relieve the pressure.
5 Once the circlips are removed, tap the universal joints at the yoke with a soft hammer and the bearings and races will come out of the

housing and can be removed easily.

6 If they are obstinate they can be gripped in a self locking wrench for final removal provided they are to be replaced.

7 Once the bearings are removed from each opposite journal the trunnion can be easily disengaged.

8 Replacement of the new trunnions and needle rollers and races is a reversal of the removal procedure.

9 Keep the grease seals on the inner ends of each trunnion as dry as possible

10 Place the needles in each race and fill the race $1/3$rd full with grease prior to placing it over the trunnion, and tap each one home with a brass drift. Any grease exuding from the fourth bearing journal after three have been fitted should be removed before fitting the fourth race.

11 Replace the circlips ensuring they seat neatly in the retaining grooves.

12 In cases of extreme wear or neglect, it is conceivable that the bearing housings in the propeller shaft, sliding sleeve or rear flange have worn so much that the bearing races are a slack fit in them. In such cases it will be necessary to replace the item affected as well. Check also that the sliding sleeve splines are in good condition and not a sloppy fit in the gearbox mainshaft.

13 Replace the propeller shaft as described in Section 3.

4 Universal joint renewal - later models

1 On some cars the universal joint bearings are not held in position by circlips, but by staking the edge of the yoke over the retaining disc. If you have the misfortune to own a car with this arrangement, which needs universal joint renewal, you may find it necessary to renew the propeller shaft as well. Without proper press equipment it will be virtually impossible to stake any new needle roller bearing assemblies tightly into position.

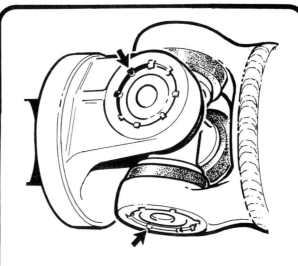

Fig 7.1 UNIVERSAL JOINTS
Showing staking used instead of circlips for needle bearing retention

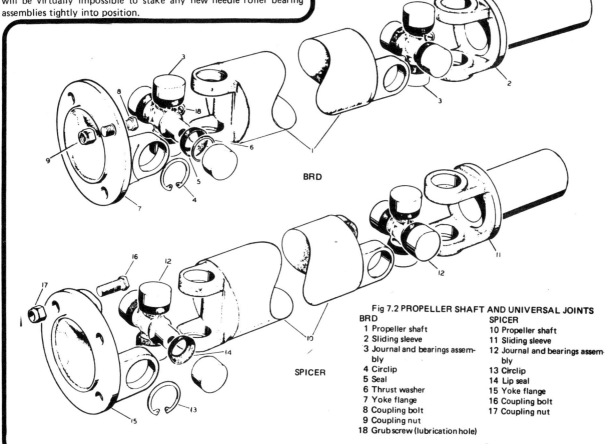

BRD

SPICER

Fig 7.2 PROPELLER SHAFT AND UNIVERSAL JOINTS

BRD
1 Propeller shaft
2 Sliding sleeve
3 Journal and bearings assembly
4 Circlip
5 Seal
6 Thrust washer
7 Yoke flange
8 Coupling bolt
9 Coupling nut
18 Grub screw (lubrication hole)

SPICER
10 Propeller shaft
11 Sliding sleeve
12 Journal and bearings assembly
13 Circlip
14 Lip seal
15 Yoke flange
16 Coupling bolt
17 Coupling nut

Chapter 8 Rear axle

Contents

Specifications

Type	Semi-floating hypoid

Ratios:

1599 cc saloon)	
1975 cc saloon)	10:39 (3.9:1)
1975 estate)	
1599 cc estate)	
early 1599 cc saloons)	8:33 (4.125:1)
Oil capacity	2.5 pints (Imp)

Pinion

Bearing pre-load - new	10—15 lb in
used	8—12 lb in
Shim thicknesses available	.003, .005 and .010 in

Differential

Side bearing pre-load - new	3 lb
- used	1 lb
Pinion shaft diameter	.6242—.6248 in
Pinion fit on shaft...	.0015—.0060 in
Bearing spacer thicknesses available	.100 and .101 in
Bearing shim thicknesses available...	.003 in
Differential case maximum run-out	.001 in

Crownwheel

Maximum run-out...	.002 in
Backlash to pinion teeth...	.006—.008 in (early)
	.005—.007 in (later)

Torque wrench settings

Differential side bearing cap bolts...	24 lb ft
Crown wheel bolts	38 lb ft
Half shaft bearing retainer nuts	12 lb ft
Pinion/Coupling flange nut	75 lb ft
Flange/propeller shaft bolts...	18 lb ft

---

1 General description

The rear axle is of the semi-floating type with a hypoid final drive, the pinion is overhung and contained in an extension to the axle housing.

The rear axle casing assembly is located to the rear body members by means of four arms, two each side. These are longitudinal and their attachment points consist of steel bolts in rubber mounting bushes to hangers which are an integral part of the axle casing. A transverse Panhard rod provides lateral axle location.

To control pinion to side gear backlash, thrust washers are used against spherical faces on the differential pinions and graded spacers are assembled to the side gears. The whole crown wheel and pinion unit is supported in the axle housing by two taper roller bearings secured by caps and bolts. The pinion runs in two pre-loaded taper roller bearings. The pinion is held in correct location to the crown wheel by shims between the front face of the rear bearing outer race and the abutment face in the axle housing.

An oil seal is pressed into the end of the pinion housing.

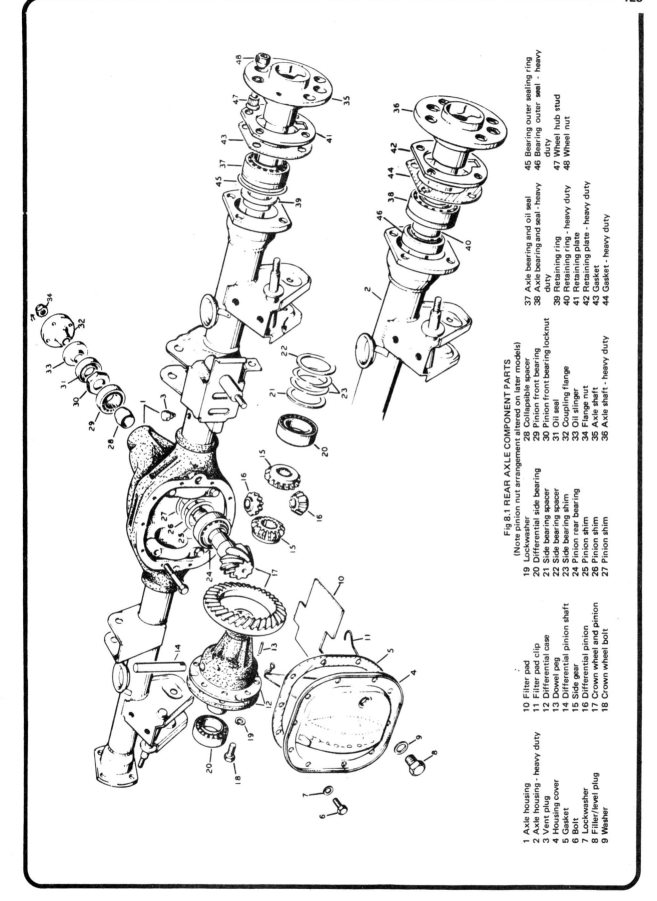

Fig 8.1 REAR AXLE COMPONENT PARTS
(Note pinion nut arrangement altered on later models)

1 Axle housing
2 Axle housing - heavy duty
3 Vent plug
4 Housing cover
5 Gasket
6 Bolt
7 Lockwasher
8 Filler/level plug
9 Washer
10 Filter pad
11 Filter pad clip
12 Differential case
13 Dowel peg
14 Differential pinion shaft
15 Side gear
16 Differential pinion
17 Crown wheel and pinion
18 Crown wheel bolt
19 Lockwasher
20 Differential side bearing
21 Side bearing spacer
22 Side bearing spacer
23 Side bearing shim
24 Pinion rear bearing
25 Pinion shim
26 Pinion shim
27 Pinion shim
28 Collapsible spacer
29 Pinion front bearing
30 Pinion front bearing locknut
31 Oil seal
32 Coupling flange
33 Oil slinger
34 Flange nut
35 Axle shaft
36 Axle shaft - heavy duty
37 Axle bearing and oil seal
38 Axle bearing and seal - heavy duty
39 Retaining ring
40 Retaining ring - heavy duty
41 Retaining plate
42 Retaining plate - heavy duty
43 Gasket
44 Gasket - heavy duty
45 Bearing outer sealing ring
46 Bearing outer seal - heavy duty
47 Wheel hub stud
48 Wheel nut

2 Rear axle - removal and replacement

1 Remove the hub caps and loosen the wheel nuts.
2 Raise and support the rear of the vehicle body, and remove the wheels. The easiest way to do this is to jack the car under the centre of the differential unit.
3 When it is sufficiently high, stands should be placed under the side frame body members just forward of the lower suspension arms (see Fig 8.2).
4 The front wheels should be chocked also to prevent any inadvertent movement. Under no circumstances should makeshift supports be used when doing work of this nature under the car.
5 Next, mark and disconnect the propeller shaft at the pinion flange as described in Chapter 7.
6 When the shaft is disconnected tie it in position to one side rather than lower it which would possibly impose a strain and cause damage to the gearbox extension housing bush and oil seal. If wished, the propeller shaft may be removed from the gearbox (see Chapter 7). Oil will not drain out of the gearbox provided the rear of the car is several inches higher than the front.
7 Disconnect the handbrake cable clevis pin from the end of the cable where it joins the equaliser assembly on the rear axle bracket. For details refer to Chapter 9.
8 Disconnect the lower end of the flexible hydraulic fluid pipe where it is attached to a bracket on the rear axle.
9 Detach the lower end of each rear telescopic damper from the axle bracket by removing the two nuts and driving out the stud and bushes. For details see Chapter 11.
10 Remove the nuts and bolts from the lower arm rear mountings on the axle and then do the same with the shorter upper arms where they locate to the brackets on the top of the axle.
11 Disconnect the transverse Panhard rod from the axle bracket.
12 The whole axle assembly is now free and by pushing the hydraulic dampers out of the way it can be drawn out straight back from under the car.

3 Halfshafts - removal and replacement

1 Remove the hub caps, and loosen the wheel nuts.
2 Raise and support the side of the axle from which the halfshaft will be removed. Remove the wheel. NOTE: If both halfshafts are to be removed and the vehicle is raised level, oil may run out of the axle tubes. Precautions must be taken to prevent it running over the brake linings and the best way would be to remove the shoes as described in Chapter 9.
3 Release the handbrake. Undo the bolts which hold the brake drum to the halfshaft flange and remove the drum.
4 Remove the nuts securing the halfshaft bearing retaining plate. This must be done through one of the holes in the halfshaft flange. As each bolt is undone and removed, the flange must be rotated through 90° to the next bolt. Take care not to lose the four lock-washers.
5 The shaft can now be withdrawn and inspected. If the bearing is a tight fit in the housing a slide hammer will be required to fix to the flange to draw the axle out (Fig 8.4).
6 Carefully inspect the differential engagement splines for wear, and also the bearing and oil seal. If the oil seal shows any signs of failure it should be replaced. If the oil seal is to be replaced, the bearing will also have to be renewed because the oil seal is integral with the bearing.
7 Replacement of the halfshaft is a straightforward reversal of the removal procedure. See that the 'O' ring on the outside of the bearing is seated in its groove. However, before replacement ensure that the oil drain hole in the brake backplate is clear, coat the halfshaft, from bearing and bearing circumference oil seal to splines, with oil. Also coat with oil the bearing bore in the axle halfshaft tube; this will allow easy replacement. The bearing retainer plate nuts should be tightened to 18 lb/ft with clean dry threads. Remember to adjust the brakes as described in Chapter 9.2.

4 Halfshaft bearings and oil seals - removal and replacement

If it is decided, after inspection, to renew the bearing and oil seal the procedure is as follows:
1 Slacken the bearing retainer ring by nicking it with a chisel. The retainer and bearing can be removed as one. As you will probably not have the correct pullers to remove the bearing, and the bearing is to be discarded, the following method of removal can be employed:

a) Clamp the bearing in a vice so that the halfshaft is parallel with the jaws.
b) Now using a hide hammer or mallet on the splined end of the halfshaft drive it back through the bearing and retainer. NOTE: A piece of wood MUST be interposed between the hammer and halfshaft.

2 Oil the new bearing journal and push the bearing down the halfshaft as far as it will go by hand. Ensure that the integral oil seal is facing towards the splines. Now drive the bearing right home against the shaft shoulder using a piece of steel tubing of a suitable length and diameter. Note that the tubing must only contact the bearing inner race, not the bearings, oil seal or outer race.
4 The bearing retainer can be driven home by the same method as the bearing, ensuring that retaining ring collar faces the bearing. On estate cars the ring should be heated first and when in position against the bearing allowed to cool naturally.
5 Halfshaft replacement is described in Section 3.

5 Pinion oil seal - removal and replacement

If oil is leaking from the axle casing where the pinion emerges it will mean that the oil seal needs renewal.
1 Raise the car, support it on stands and disconnect the propeller shaft as described in Chapter 7.
2 The pinion flange nut will now be exposed and, where it is staked into the slot in the pinion, should be tapped back.
3 In order to hold the flange when undoing the nut it will be necessary to make up a piece of flat bar with two holes at one end which can be bolted to the flange. This can then be held firm while the socket wrench turns the nut which, is initially, a very tight fit.
4 Before pulling the flange off the pinion splines mark the positions of flange to pinion so that it may be replaced in the same position.
5 Next prise the mud slinger disc off the end of the shaft which will expose the oil seal.
6 On later models the nut holding the pinion also maintains the pre-load of the pinion bearings. It will be seen that the nut is staked into a groove in the pinion flange and when the nut is removed this staking will break away. As the nut has to be tightened to exactly the same position afterwards, it will be necessary to grind another slot in the shaft to provide a staking position. If the nut is not tightened properly the bearing pre-load will be incorrect and rapid wear and noise will occur.

On later models the mud slinger is pressed on to the flange rather than the shaft.
7 The oil seal may then be literally dug out of the housing with a pointed punch and a hammer (see Fig 8.3).
8 A new seal should be installed with the lip facing into the casing. Oil the seal lip and the pinion first and then carefully tap it home. It is important that it is not driven too far in otherwise the seal lip will contact the threads on the pinion shaft. On early models two types of seal were used and care must be taken to ensure that the projection of the seal from the housing is correct (Fig 8.5).
9 Replace the mud slinger so that its forward face is also positioned correctly depending on which type of seal is fitted (see Fig 8.5).
10 On later models with the seal which bears on the pinion flange rather than the shaft the seal can be driven fully home. The position of the dust shield on the flange should be as shown in Fig 8.6.

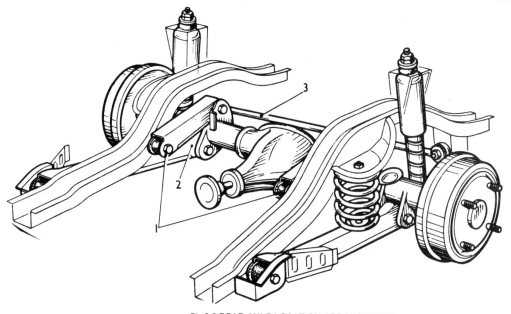

Fig 8.2 REAR AXLE LOCATION ARRANGEMENT

1 Upper longitudinal arms
2 Lower longitudinal arms
3 Panhard rod

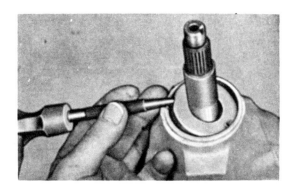

Fig 8.3 Pinion oil seal. Removal with a pointed punch

Fig 8.4 Halfshaft removal - use of slide hammer

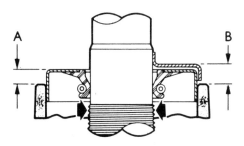

Fig 8.5 PINION SHAFT OIL SEAL (EARLY AXLES)
A = .19 inch or .26 inch depending on type of seal used
B = .36 inch or .42 inch depending on seal used

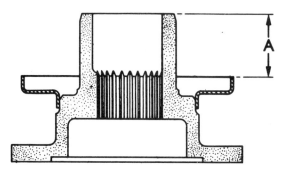

Fig 8.6 PINION SHAFT FLANGE (LATER AXLES)
Dust shield position. A = .70 inch

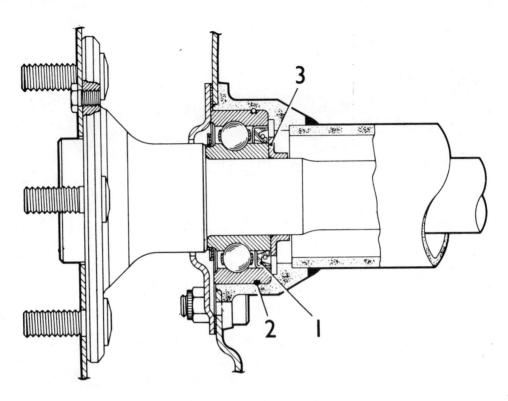

Fig 8.7 HALF SHAFT — CROSS SECTION OF BEARING AND HOUSING

1 Oil seal   2 'O' ring in outer race   3 Bearing retaining ring

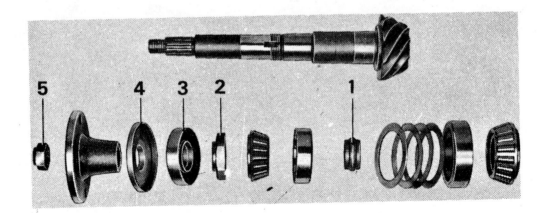

Fig 8.8 PINION AND BEARING COMPONENTS (EARLY VERSIONS

1 Compressible spacer   3 Oil seal   4 Dust shield   5 Flange nut
2 Pinion bearing nut
    (Note: On later versions the pinion nut (2) is in effect omitted - the flange nut (5) serving to do both functions)

EARLY VERSION

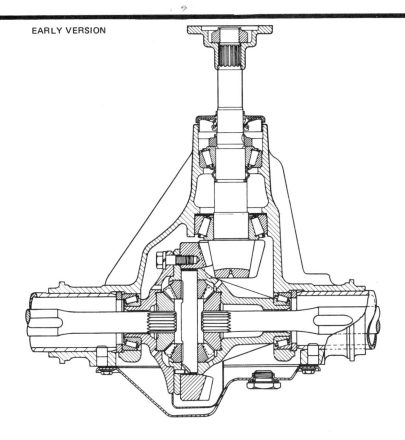

Fig 8.9 Differential and pinion. Plan cross sections to illustrate difference between pinion nuts and seal arrangement on early versions and later versions

LATER VERSION

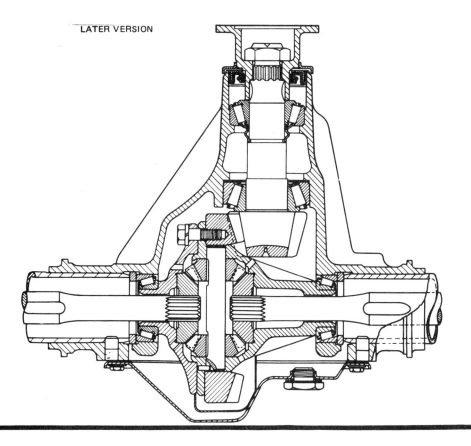

11 Replace the pinion flange to the pinion ensuring the location marks made line up. Then fit the flange nut and tighten it to the specified torque of 75 lb/ft. This will require use of the tool described in paragraph 3 once more. The nut on later models is tightened as described in paragraph 6.

12 Finally, stake the nut rim into the pinion slot and reconnect the propeller shaft.

6 Pinion, crown wheel and differential

1 This Chapter has so far shown how to replace bearings and oil seals for the halfshafts and the pinion oil seal, as these are considered to be within the average owner-drivers competence and facilities. We do not recommend that owners go into the more complex problems of pinion to crown wheel settings, differential gear settings, differential side bearing replacement, or pinion bearing replacement.

2 If, however, an owner feels he has the requisite tools and competence we give the procedures to be followed. We shall refer to the special tools needed as it is not considered either sensible to attempt, or feasible to carry out, this work without them.

3 Remove the rear axle from the car and the halfshafts from the axle as described in Sections 2 and 3.

4 Remove the rear cover plate from the axle casing and drain the oil.

5 Remove the bolts holding the differential side bearing caps and when removing the caps note the marks on the right hand cap and the casting to prevent inadvertent mixing up on replacement.

6 Place a bar under one of the differential case bolts and lever the casing assembly and crown wheel out of the housing.

7 Carefully remove the spacers and shims from each side of the housing and keep the bearing inner races on the bench noting which side they are from.

8 Remove the pinion flange (see Section 5).

9 Remove the pinion mud slinger and oil seal.

10 Remove the pinion nut using a holding tool (Z8307) the special wrench (Z8534).

11 Tap out the pinion and remove the front inner bearing, bearing washer and compressible spacer.

12 Press the outer races of the pinion bearings from the housing using the removers as shown in Fig 8.12.

13 Press the pinion rear bearing inner race from the shaft.

14 Dismantle the hypoid gear and differential by first removing the hypoid gear from the differential casing by removing the bolts. Tap the gear off from alternate sides using a soft mallet.

15 Punch out the pin which locates the differential pinion shaft, and remove the shaft.

16 The pinion can be lifted out with the hemispherical shaped thrust washers followed by the side gears and spacers.

17 If the side bearings are to be replaced, draw them off the differential case using a puller.

18 When new races are fitted ensure that they are pressed fully home to the shoulder on the casing.

19 Fit a new filter pad in the axle housing.

20 Examine the pinion shaft for wear at the oil seal land. If badly worn, a new pinion (and therefore crown wheel as well) will be required. If only lightly scored clean up the shaft with very fine emery cloth.

21 To reset the differential pinions and side gears in the differential casing, first dip all the components in oil to ensure initial lubrication when first put back into use.

22 Replace the pinions together with new thrust washers and the side gears, each with selected spacer.

23 Replace the pinion gear shaft, lining up the locating pin hole in the casing, but do not replace the retaining pin yet.

24 With a feeler gauge behind opposite sides of the sidegear spacers, check the clearance between each of them and the case, which should be .006 inch with no gear backlash evident.

25 Increase or decrease the spacer thickness accordingly. Spacers are available in seven thicknesses with a total range from .019—.033 inch inclusive. It is permissible for the spacers used on each side to be of

different thicknesses if necessary. When tolerances are correct fit a new shaft retaining pin and punch the end flush with the casing. As a final check the gears should turn by hand with the halfshafts inserted in the side gears.

26 Install the hypoid gear to the differential case by first warming the gear evenly (on a hot plate). It is best also to make up two guide studs that can be screwed into two opposite bolt holes in the gear. These will ensure that the register on the case fits into the gear, first time, squarely. Draw the gear on with the mounting bolts and new lockwashers and tighten to specified torque.

27 The lateral location of the differential case and hypoid gear assembly in the axle casing is controlled by spacers and shims. These also determine the side bearing pre-load and are available in two thicknesses of spacer, viz .100 inch and .101 inch and shims of .003 inch. These cover from .100 inch upwards, therefore, in steps of .001 inch, using two spacers for each bearing and the requisite shims (Fig 8.10).

28 Replace the differential case in the housing complete with side bearings, and then select four spacers and the appropriate number of shims which will remove all the end float between the bearing outer races and the ends of the axle housing tubes.

29 Remove the differential casing once more and then divide the spacers and shims equally into two lots, ie two spacers for each side with the necessary shims. Fit one lot on one side of the housing, ensuring that any shims are sandwiched between the spacers and that the spacer chamfers are facing outwards.

30 Add one extra shim of .003 inch to the second lot, arranging them in the same way, and placing these at the other end of the axle housing, fit the casing back into the housing once more. Some pressure will be needed to force the assembly in and care must be taken to ensure the side bearings do not tilt and jam.

31 Tap the axle housing lightly near the bearings and rotate the assembly so that the bearings will settle properly. Then replace the bearing caps in the correct sides and tighten the bolts to the specified torque.

32 The pre-load on the bearings can now be checked by measuring the torque resistance at the periphery of the crown wheel. This is simply done by tying a piece of string around the crown wheel and measuring the turning resistance with a spring balance. If the reading is outside the 'Specifications' given at the beginning of this Chapter, then the unit must be removed and the shim thicknesses adjusted accordingly (Fig 8.11).

33 Check that the run-out of the hypoid gear rear face does not exceed .002 inch on a clock gauge micrometer. If it does, it indicates that dirt or burrs may have affected it when being reassembled to the differential case.

34 Once the differential has been satisfactorily fitted and checked remove it once more, keeping the shims and spacers carefully for final assembly on their respective sides.

35 The pinion fitting is somewhat more complex and there are factors which determine the initial selection of pinion spacers and shims to control the pinion/crown wheel mesh. These are:

a) The pinion bearing correction - being the variance from the maximum of .9626 inch of the thickness of the pinion rear bearing - is determined by measuring the actual thickness of the rear pinion bearing on a special jig plate, with a micrometer.

b) The pinion meshing correction - being the variance from standard required in production assembly - is stamped on the nose of the pinion in single figures representing thousandths of an inch.

c) The axle housing correction - being the deviation from the nominal depth of the bearing abutment face in relation to the centre line of the crown wheel axis. This figure is stamped on the axle housing rear face at the top - the single figure representing thousandths of an inch.

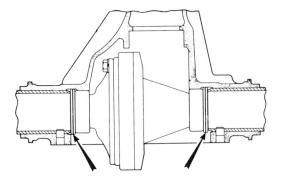

Fig 8.10 Differential side bearings - location of shims (arrowed) between spacers for pre-load application

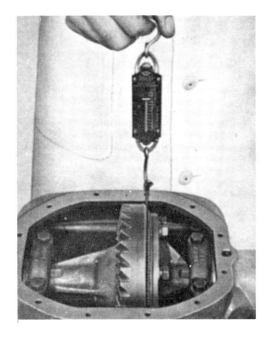

Fig 8.11 Side bearing pre-load check using a spring balance

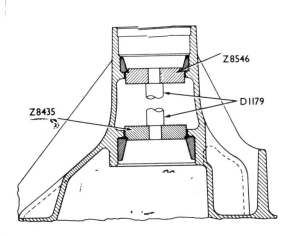

Fig 8.12 Pinion bearings. Outer race removal tools

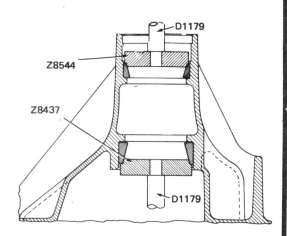

Fig 8.13 Pinion bearings. Outer race installation tools

36 The calculation of the pinion spacer/shims required is best indicated using an example:

Pinion rear bearing maximum thickness	.9626 inch
Pinion rear bearing actual thickness	.9591 inch
Difference (pinion bearing correction)	.0035 inch
Axle housing correction '3'	.0030 inch
Pinion meshing correction '5'	.0050 inch
Total shim thickness required	.0115 inch

Shims are available in three thicknesses (.003, .005 and .010 inch). The nearest thou is taken. So here one would have four shims of .003 inch (.012).

It is better to select the larger thickness in this case as this will reduce backlash fractionally, rather than increase it.

37 Having checked each shim and spacer with a micrometer the shims should be placed on the pinion rear bearing abutment face in the axle housing.

38 The pinion rear bearing outer race should then be pressed firmly into place in the housing using installer No Z8437 as shown in Fig 8.13 followed by the front bearing outer race using installer Z8544.

39 Having fitted the pinion rear bearing inner race to the shaft then fit a new compressible spacer and bearing washer over the shaft. Place the shaft into the axle housing. On later models a washer is used before the spacer and the spacer length is adjusted to compensate for it.

40 Next place the front bearing inner race over the shaft and, whilst supporting the end of the pinion, tap it home on the shaft using installer VR2053.

41 All is now set to apply the pinion bearing pre-load. Using a new pinion but lubricated with rear axle oil, tighten it until a positive

resistance is felt, indicating that all end float is taken up between the front bearing inner race, bearing washer and compressible spacer. On later models the oil seal and flange must first be replaced as the whole assembly is pre-loaded and held together with the one nut.

42 Using a torque pre-load gauge fitted to the pinion shaft the pinion nut should now be tightened gradually, (compressing the spacer as it does so) until the pre-load reading is within specification.

43 If the pre-load is exceeded it will be necessary to fit a new compressible spacer and start again.

44 The differential case/crown wheel assembly together with the selected shims should now be installed in the axle housing as previously described in paragraphs 30 and 31. If there is an odd number of shims the greater number should be put between the right hand pair of spacers.

45 Check the backlash between crown wheel and pinion. If incorrect then the shims can be moved from one side to the other, (fitting them always between the spacers) until it is correct. On no account alter the total number of shims and spacers originally selected, or the side bearing pre-load will be altered.

46 With the backlash correct, according to specification, the bearing caps can be replaced and tightened down to specified torque, after which backlash needs to be rechecked.

47 A final test for correct pinion/crown wheel location can be carried out by applying a load to the crown wheel and driving it by turning the pinion so that marks will be made on the teeth. Use engineers blue to emphasise the marks if necessary.

48 If the pinion is too far out (ie too far away from the crown wheel) the marks will be on the peaks of the crown wheel teeth, whereas if the pinion is too far in, they will be in the valleys (Fig 8.14).

49 Stake the nut into the pinion shaft slots and install the new oil seal, pinion shaft extension, extension shaft bearing and coupling flange as described in Section 5.

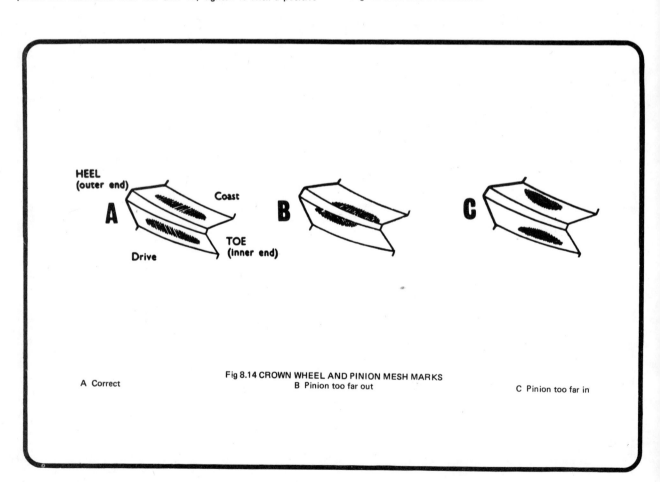

Fig 8.14 CROWN WHEEL AND PINION MESH MARKS

A Correct   B Pinion too far out   C Pinion too far in

Chapter 9 Braking system

Contents

Specifications

Make
    Drum ... ...   Girling
    Disc ... ...   Girling or Lockheed

Type ... ...   Drum brakes all round or with servo-assisted discs at front. Cable operated handbrake to rear wheels. Tandem master cylinder on left drive models and later right drive cars

Drums
    Internal diameter ... ...   9.00–9.005 in
    Maximum internal diameter   ... ...   9.06 in
    Maximum run-out of front drums (on hubs)... ... ...   .002 in
    Maximum run-out of rear drums (on axles) ... ...   .004 in

Discs
    Disc thickness (friction material) ... ...   .06 in (minimum)
    Disc run-out maximum ... ...   .004 in

Torque wrench settings
    Front brake flange plate to steering knuckle nuts ... ...   25 lb ft
    Disc brake caliper to steering knuckle bolts   ... ...   33 lb ft
    Lockheed brake caliper bolts ... ...   37 lb ft
    Master cylinder (single) reservoir adaptor   ... ...   22 lb ft
    Master cylinder (dual) tip valve nut (early type) ... ...   38 lb ft

1 General description

Since 1968 when the model was introduced there have been changes and developments to the braking systems fitted. Originally the 1599 cc models were fitted with conventional drum brakes, front drums fitted with two leading shoes. A single hydraulic master cylinder operated the system. The 1975 cc models were fitted with servo-assisted brakes - disc brakes being used on the front. Either Girling or Lockheed calipers may be fitted. Early left hand drive models also had a tandem master cylinder fitted (Girling). All later models were fitted with a tandem master cylinder (Lockheed) as standard equipment. This ensures that if a pressure failure occurs in the hydraulic system only half the system is put out of action which is divided between front and rear. For this unit a different type of

servo was incorporated for those models with disc brakes.

The handbrake consists of cable operated compensating pull rods to the rear wheels and the handle is of the twist and pull umbrella type.

All brake shoes are adjustable - those at the front being snail cams with square headed spindles projecting through the backplate. There is one adjuster to each shoe. The rear brake shoes are adjusted by a conical screw operated on the pair in each wheel. The screw head is square and projects from the backplate in the same way as for the front. Disc brake pads are self-adjusting.

The basic principles of operation of the hydraulic brake system are as follows:

The brake pedal, when depressed, operates the plunger of a pump containing hydraulic fluid (the master cylinder) and forces this fluid along small diameter pipes, both rigid and flexible, to a series of small cylinders located at each wheel. The hydraulic fluid pressure at these cylinders (wheel cylinders) forces their pistons outwards. These pistons are connected to the ends of the brake shoes which are then forced against the drums, thereby applying the brakes. When the brake pedal is released, the shoes are drawn off the drums by springs which link the pairs of shoes together inside each wheel drum.

With disc brakes the conventional drum is replaced by a disc, against each side of which pads of friction material are forced by hydraulic pressure from a caliper - rather like gripping a gramophone record between a thumb and fore finger.

As the pads wear, so the hydraulic piston which forces them against the disc advances further towards the disc and obviates the need for adjustment. There is no return spring of any sort for the brake pads so that when the hydraulic pressure is relieved, the frac-tional reverse movement of the pistons relieves the pads sufficiently to clear the disc surfaces. This automatic adjustment is the reason why an additional reservoir of hydraulic fluid is required. The rear wheel brakes and handbrake on models fitted with front disc brakes are identical to those fitted on standard models.

In addition to the disc brakes where fitted, a vacuum-servo unit is installed. This unit uses the vacuum of the inlet manifold of the engine to operate what is, in effect, another pump to apply pressure to the hydraulic system. This reduces the pressure required on the conventional brake pedal when operating the brakes.

2 Adjustment - drum brakes

1 If the pedal travel becomes noticeably excessive before the brakes operate, and presuming that the pedal pressure is still firm and hard when pressure is applied, then the brake shoes need adjustment. This will be necessary on average about every 2—3000 miles.
2 Adjust the front wheels first. Jack up the car so that one front wheel is just clear of the ground and spins freely.
3 Behind the brake backplate are two square headed adjusters, one at the top and the other at the bottom of the backplate. Turn the top one clockwise (see Fig 9.2) (using a square headed ring spanner pre-ferably, to prevent burring the screw head), until the shoe is locked tight on the drum. Then release the adjuster in the opposite direction for two notches (which can be felt when turning it). Spin the wheel to ensure the shoe is not binding on the drum. Repeat this process with the lower adjusting screw.
4 Lower the wheel to the ground and repeat the full adjustment process for the other front wheel.
5 Release the handbrake, block the front wheels and jack up the rear wheels in turn. The single adjuster also has a square head and is located at the bottom of the brake flange and towards the rear of the car. Turn the adjuster clockwise until the brake shoes lock the wheel, then reverse it two notches as for the front wheel adjusters. Turn the wheel to ensure that the shoes are not binding on the drum. The rear wheels will not spin quite so freely as the front ones because the dif-ferential gear and propeller shaft will be revolving with them, so do not confuse this turning resistance with brake drag. Repeat the adjustment process with the other rear wheel.
6 It is often possible that a little shoe rubbing can be detected even after the adjusters have been slackened off the required two notches. Provided the degree of drag in such instances is negligible, ignore it. The shoes will bed down into their new positions on the drums after a mile or two. If there is serious binding after the adjusters have been slackened off two or more notches it will be necessary to remove the drum and examine the shoes and drums further (see Section 4).

3 Adjustment - disc brakes

1 Disc brakes are fitted to the front wheels only and do not require adjustment.
2 Drum brakes are fitted to the rear wheels of all cars fitted with front disc brakes and adjustment should be carried out in accordance with Section 2.

Fig 9.1 DRUM BRAKES — COMPONENTS
 1 Backplate - front drum
 2 Bolt
 3 Bolt
 4 Bolt
 5 Lockwasher
 6 Nut
 7 Nut
 8 Lockwasher
 9 Lockwasher
10 Brake shoe
11 Lining
12 Rivet
14 Wheel cylinder assembly RH
15 Piston
17 Seal
19 Spring
21 Piston insert
22 Dust cover
23 Cylinder seating ring
24 Screw
25 Spring washer
26 Bleed screw
27 Shoe securing pin
28 Spring, securing pin
29 Securing pin cup
30 Bleed screw dust cover
31 Retractor spring
33 Backplate - rear drum
34 Bolt
35 Nut
36 Brake shoe
37 Lining
38 Wheel cylinder assembly
40 Piston
42 Seal
44 Dust cover
45 Dust cover clip
49 Shoe return spring
51 Shoe return spring
52 Shoe securing pin
53 Spring, securing pin
54 Lever assembly
55 Support plate
56 Support plate clip
57 Adjuster assembly
58 Nut
59 Lockwasher
60 Tappet
61 Cylinder retaining plate
62 Cylinder lock plate
63 Distance washer
64 Rubber dust seal
65 Rear drum
66 Securing bolt

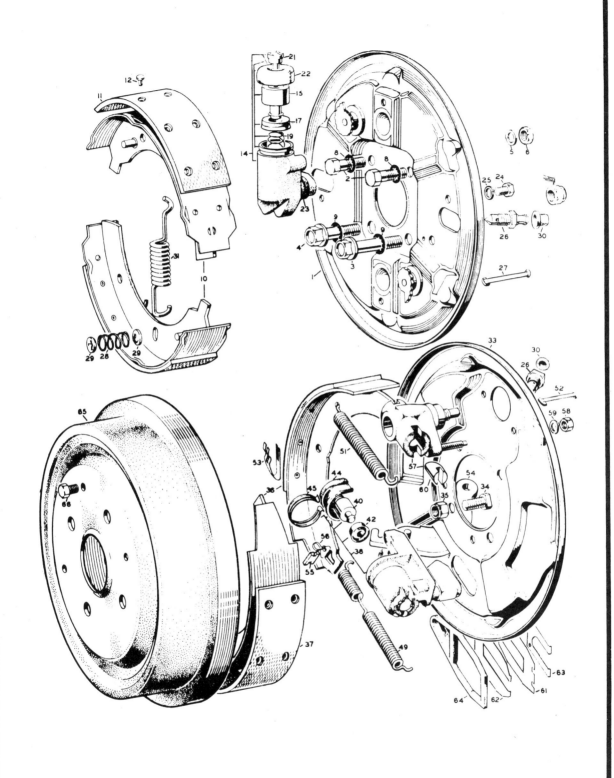

Fig 9.1. DRUM BRAKES – COMPONENTS

4 Drum brakes - removal, inspection and replacement of drums and shoes

1 If the brakes are inefficient, or the pedal travel excessive and the hydraulic system is showing no signs of leaks, first try adjusting the brakes. If little or no improvement results it will be necessary to examine the drums and shoes.

2 It is possible to attend to each wheel individually, so start with the front and remove the hub cap and slacken the wheel nuts. Then jack up the car and remove the nuts and wheel.

3 Next undo the two locating bolts which position the drum on the front hub. (The purpose of these bolts is to hold the drum tight in position when the wheel if off. The full load of the braking force applied to the drum is carried by the four wheel studs and the drum is only fully clamped when the wheel is on) (photo).

4 Now draw the drum off the studs. A light tap around the periphery with a soft mallet will help to start it moving if it tends to stick at the roots of the studs.

5 It is also possible that the drum, although loose on the studs, is restricted by the shoes inside from coming off. In this case slacken off the adjuster screws (Section 2), until the drum can be removed (photo).

6 Examine the friction surface on the interior of the drum (arrow, photo 4.5). Normally this should be completely smooth and bright. Remove any dust with a dry cloth and examine the surface for any score marks or blemishes. Very light hairline scores running around the surface area are not serious but indicate that the shoes may be wearing or heavy grit and dirt have got into the drum at some time. If there are signs of deep scoring the drum needs reconditioning or replacement. As reconditioning will probably cost as much as a new drum, and certainly more than a good secondhand one (obtained from car breakers without difficulty), it is not recommended. In theory a drum should not be renewed without replacing the front hub assembly also, but in practice the variations of concentricity which may occur with matched drums do not significantly affect the braking efficiency unless you are particularly unfortunate and have hub and drum tolerances at the extreme limits. You will not, however, be able to buy a **new** drum without the hub as well.

7 Examine the brake shoes for signs of oil contamination, deep scoring, or overall wear of the friction material. Deep scoring will be immediately apparent and will relate to any scoring in the drum. Oil contamination is evident where there are hard black shiny patches on the linings caused by the heat generated in braking which carbonises any oil that may have reached them. As a temporary measure, these areas can be rasped down but it is far better to replace the shoes. Normal wear can be judged by the depth of the rivet heads from the surface of the linings. If this is .025 inch (.65 mm) or less, the shoes should be renewed.

8 To remove the brake shoes, first of all slacken the two cam adjusters (front brakes) or cone adjuster (rear brakes) anticlockwise until the contracting movement of the shoes (pulled inwards by the springs) ceases. On the front brakes each shoe is held by a locating pin and spring in the centre of each shoe. With a pair of pliers turn the slotted washer on the pin so that it comes off the end of the pin. The spring and pin can then be removed. On the rear shoes the pin is held by a leaf spring clip instead.

9 Continuing with the rear brakes, release one of the shoes from the adjuster by levering it away with a screwdriver. Once this spring tension is released it will be quite easy to remove the shoes and springs.

10 With the front brakes it is much simpler to remove the front wheel hubs before trying to remove the shoes, as the return springs are hooked into the backplate. Shoe replacement is virtually impossible with the hubs fitted, so much time will be saved in the long run by turning to Chapter 11, and removing the hubs as detailed there.

11 With the hub removed, release the trailing end of a shoe from a cylinder slot with a screwdriver. Both shoes can then be easily lifted off. As soon as the shoes are removed make sure that the hydraulic cylinder pistons are prevented from coming out of the cylinders by tying wire or string around the slots to hold the pistons in.

12 Replacement of the shoes is a direct reversal of the removal procedure paying special attention to the following:

a) Ensure that the shoes and springs for the front brakes are reassembled exactly as shown in Fig 9.3.

b) Reassemble the rear brake shoes exactly as indicated in Fig 9.5. The spring next to the hydraulic cylinder should have the smallest number of coils towards the piston end of the cylinder. Ensure the cylinder slides freely in its slot in the backplate. Note also that the leading shoe of the rear brake (the upper one) has a support plate and clip at its leading end and these must be correctly fitted (Fig 9.4).

c) Handle the brake shoes with clean hands. Even a small oil or grease deposit could affect their performance.

d) Apply a thin film of grease (Duckhams KG20 Keenol) to the backplates where the edges of the shoes rub against them.

e) If any shoe requires replacement it means that all shoes at the front or all shoes at the rear (ie a minimum of four shoes) must be replaced together. Anything less can only lead to dangerous braking characteristics and uneconomical wear. Front and rear shoes are not interchangeable.

13 Replace the drums to the wheels from which they came and screw up the locating bolts.

14 Adjust the brakes as described in Section 3, and road test as soon as possible.

5 Handbrake - adjustment and repair

1 The handbrake is automatically adjusted each time the rear brake shoes are adjusted to the drums. With time, however, the operating cables may stretch and wear will develop in the brake rod clevis pins. When this happens it will be necessary to shorten the operating cable to take up the slack so that the handle does not have to be pulled too far in order to operate the brakes.

2 The adjustment is at the rear where the cable joins the lever attached to the equaliser assembly (Fig 9.6). If the locknut is loosened the threaded sleeve may be rotated and the cable tightened. The tightness should be gauged by ensuring that the clevis pins at the outer ends of the brake rods are not held so tightly that they cannot be revolved in positions.

3 The equaliser assembly mounted on a bracket on the rear axle swing is designed to ensure that the handbrake is applied equally on both drums (Fig 9.7). After long service wear will develop in the clevis pins, clevises and brackets to such an extent that rattles will develop, excessive backlash will be present and the strength of the assembly will be reduced. Such wear will be obvious and the pins, bushes and clevises should be renewed as required. Always keep the parts liberally greased.

4 The handle assembly (Fig 9.10) can be readily detached. First disconnect the clevis pin at the lower end which attaches the short cable inside the handle assembly to the front lever which is mounted on the engine mounting side rail inside the engine compartment (Fig 9.8). Then remove the large nut at the bottom of the tube which holds it to the lower dash panel nearby.

5 The upper end of the handle assembly is secured to the lower edge of the instrument panel by two bolts. These can be removed after the steering column finisher cover has been removed.

6 Once the assembly has been removed the handle can be withdrawn from the outer tube thus releasing the pawls and springs (Fig 9.9).

7 The long cable which runs from the front lever to the equaliser assembly at the rear may need renewal. After disconnecting both ends it can be withdrawn from the rear.

Note that on replacement it should pass **above** the gearbox support crossmember except on RHD models with automatic transmission when it should pass **below**.

6 Disc brakes - removal, inspection and replacement of pads

1 The thickness of the pads can be visually checked by jacking up the car and removing each front wheel, when the pads can be **seen**

4.3 Removing front drum brakes

4.5 Examining the friction surfaces

Fig.9.2. Adjusting front brake shoes — arrow shows second adjuster

Fig 9.3 Front brake shoes - assembled position (hub omitted from illustration for clarity

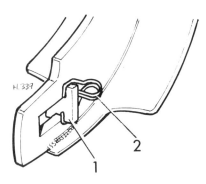

Fig 9.4 Rear brake leading shoe support plate (1) and clip (2)

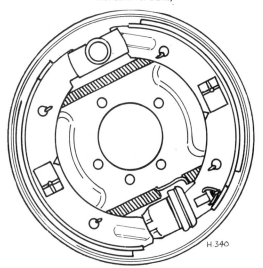

Fig 9.5 Rear brake shoes - assembled position (halfshaft flange omitted for clarity

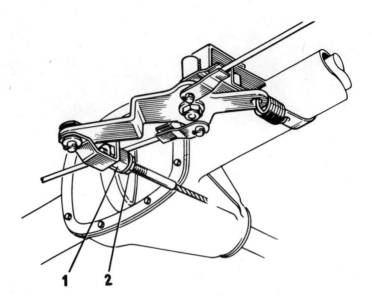

Fig 9.6 HANDBRAKE ADJUSTMENT
1 Threaded sleeve   2 Locknut

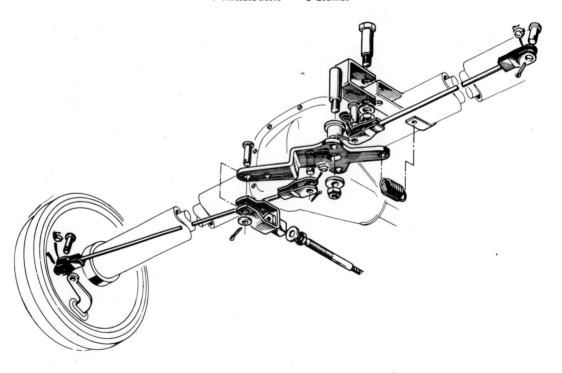

Fig 9.7 Handbrake - equaliser assembly components

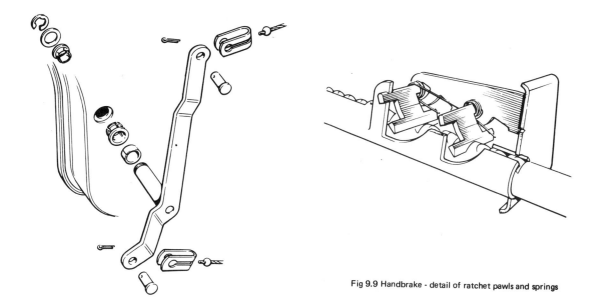

Fig 9.9 Handbrake - detail of ratchet pawls and springs

Fig 9.8 Handbrake - front lever components

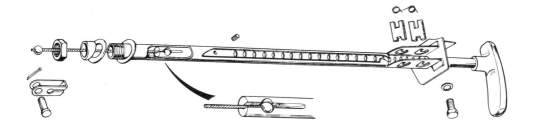

Fig 9.10 Handbrake - operating handle assembly

between the disc and caliper body. If the thickness of the friction material is less than .060 inch (1½ mm) they must be replaced. Sometimes the pads wear unevenly, but if one of a pair is under specification thickness, the pair should be renewed. As a general rule pads on both front wheels should be renewed even if only one needs it. Some cars are fitted with Lockheed disc brakes which can be identified by the fact that only the heads of the two attaching bolts are visible - unlike the Girling calipers where four bolt heads can be seen.

2 Remove the fluid reservoir cap and syphon out some fluid - say ¼ inch down. This will prevent the fluid overflowing when the level rises as the pistons are pushed back for fitting new pads.

3 To remove the pads, first pull the clips off the retaining pins and withdraw the pins. On Lockheed brakes the pins are split. The ends are spread to keep them in place. Behind the pins spring retaining plates are fitted (photos).

4 Apply pressure to the faces of the old pads with the fingers, so pressing the pistons behind them back into the caliper. Then lift out the pads and shims from the caliper body (photos).

5 Refit new pads and new shims also if the old ones show signs of distortion or deterioration. Make sure the shims are fitted with the arrow shaped hole in the top edge pointing in the direction of forward disc rotation. On Lockheed brakes the shims are symmetrical so it does not matter. Replace the locating pins and clips.

6 Depress the brake pedal two or three times to position the pistons and pads once more, and top up the fluid reservoir to the specified level.

7 Drum and disc brakes - hydraulic pipes, rigid and flexible - inspection, removal and replacement

1 Periodically, normally at safety check services, all brake pipes, pipe connections and unions should be completely and carefully examined.

2 First examine for signs of leakage where the pipe unions occur. Then examine the flexible hoses for signs of chafing and fraying and, of course, leakage. This is only a preliminary part of the flexible hose inspection, as exterior condition does not necessarily indicate the interior condition which will be considered later.

3 The steel pipes must be examined equally carefully. They must be cleaned off and examined for any signs of dents, or other percussive damage and rust and corrosion. Rust and corrosion should be scraped off and if the depth of pitting in the pipes is significant, they will need replacement. This is particularly likely in those areas underneath the car body and along the rear axle where the pipes are exposed to the full force of road and weather conditions.

4 If any section of pipe is to be taken off, first of all remove the fluid reservoir cap and line it with a piece of polythene film to make it air tight, and replace it. This will minimise the amount of fluid dripping out of the system, when pipes are removed.

5 Rigid pipe removal is usually quite straightforward. The unions at each end are undone and the pipe and union pulled out and the centre sections of the pipe removed from the body clips where necessary. Underneath the car, exposed unions can sometimes be very tight. As one can use only an open ended spanner and the unions are not large, burring of the flats is not uncommon when attempting to undo them. For this reason a self-locking grip wrench (Mole) is often the only way to remove a stubborn union.

6 Flexible hoses are always mounted at both ends in a rigid bracket attached to the body or a sub-assembly. To remove them it is necessary first of all to unscrew the pipe unions of the rigid pipes which go into them. Then, with a spanner on the hexagonal end of the flexible pipe union, the locknut and washer on the other side of the mounting bracket need to be removed. Here again exposure to the elements often tends to seize the locknut and in this case the use of penetrating oil or 'Plus-gas' is necessary. The mounting brackets, particularly on the bodyframe, are not very heavy gauge and care must be taken not to wrench them off. A self-grip wrench is often of use here as well. Use it on the pipe union in this instance as one is able to get a ring spanner on the locknut.

7 With the flexible hose removed, examine the internal bore. If it is blown through first, it should be possible to see through it. Any specks of rubber which come out, or signs of restriction in the bore, mean that the inner lining is breaking up and the pipe must be replaced.

8 Rigid pipes which need replacement can usually be purchased at any local garage where they have the pipe, unions and special tools to make them up. All they need to know is the total length of the pipe, and the type of flare used at each end with the union. This is very important as it is possible to have a convex flare at one end and a concave flare at the other (Fig 9.11).

9 Replacement of pipes is a straightforward reversal of the removal procedure. If the rigid pipes have been made up it is best to get all the sets (bends) in them before trying to install them. Also if there are any acute bends, ask your supplier to put these in for you on a tube bender. Otherwise you may kink the pipe and thereby restrict the bore area and fluid flow.

10 With the pipes replaced, remove the polythene film from the reservoir cap (paragraph 4), and bleed the system as described in Section 16. It is not necessary always to bleed at all four wheels. It depends which pipe has been removed. Obviously if the main one from the master cylinder is removed, air could have reached any line from the later distribution of pipes. If, however, a flexible hose at a front wheel is replaced, only that wheel needs to be bled.

8 Drum brakes - hydraulic wheel cylinders - inspection and repair

1 If it is suspected that one or more wheel cylinders is malfunctioning, jack up the suspect wheel and remove the brake drum.

2 Inspect for signs of fluid leakage around the wheel cylinder, and if there are any, proceed with instructions at paragraph 4.

3 Next get someone to very gently press the brake pedal a small distance. On rear brakes watch the wheel cylinder to see that the piston moves out a little. On no account allow it to come right out or you will have to reassemble it and bleed the system. Then release the pedal and ensure that the shoe springs force the piston back. On front brakes, block the shoe on each cylinder in turn with a piece of wood and see that the other one moves in and out as the pedal is depressed and released. Do not let the piston move too far out.

4 A wheel cylinder where there is leaking fluid or which does not move at all (ie with a seized piston) will have to be fitted with new seals at least.

5 Remove the brake shoes as described in Section 4 and seal the fluid reservoir cap.

6 Remove the rubber dust cover and clip from the end of the cylinder, and draw out the piston, on the inner end of which a seal will be fitted. On front brake cylinders only, draw out the spring behind the piston.

7 If the piston is seized in the cylinder it may be very difficult to remove, in which case it may be quicker in the long run to remove the cylinder from the wheel (see paragraphs 14—20).

8 Examine the bores of the wheel cylinders. Any sign of scoring or ridging in the walls where the piston seal travels means that the cylinder should be replaced.

9 If the cylinder is in good condition it will be necessary to replace only the seal on the piston. Pull the old one off and carefully fit a new one over the raised rim. The lip of the seal must face away from the centre of the piston.

10 Clean out the interior of the cylinder with a dry cloth and ensure the piston is quite clean. Then use a little brake fluid and lubricate the piston and seal before replacing the spring (front only) and piston in the cylinder. Be careful not to damage or turn over the seal lip on replacement.

11 If the old seal shows signs of swelling and deterioration, rather than just wear on the lip, it indicates that the hydraulic fluid in the system may have been contaminated. In such cases all fluid must be removed from the system and all seals replaced including those in the master cylinder. Flexible hose should be checked too.

6.3a Remove the clips off the retaining pads

6.3b Withdraw the retaining pins

6.3c Remove the spring retaining plates

6.4a Remove the pads using fingers

6.4b Remove the anti-squeal shims using pliers

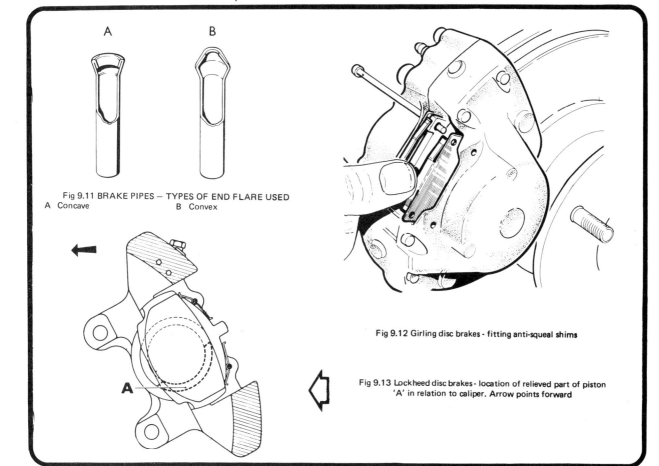

Fig 9.11 BRAKE PIPES — TYPES OF END FLARE USED
A Concave   B Convex

Fig 9.12 Girling disc brakes - fitting anti-squeal shims

Fig 9.13 Lockheed disc brakes - location of relieved part of piston 'A' in relation to caliper. Arrow points forward

142

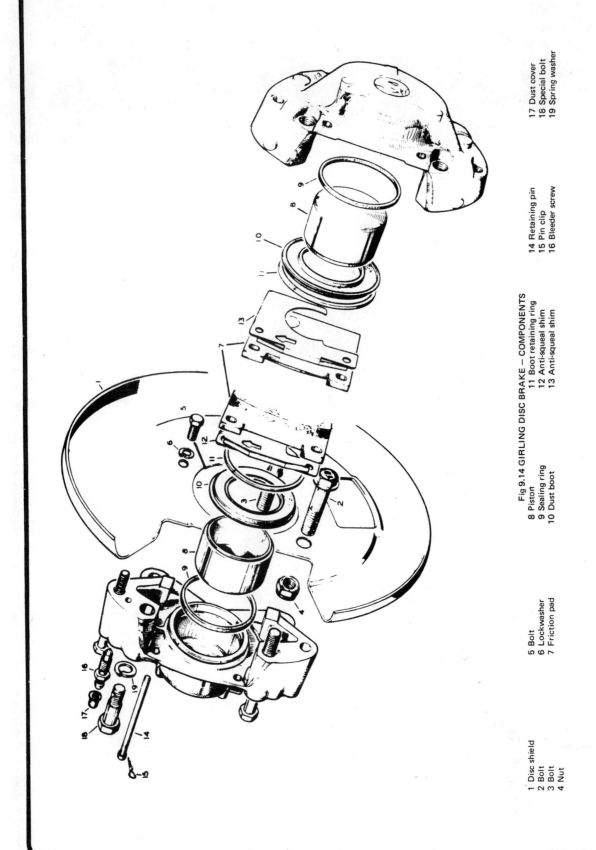

Fig 9.14 GIRLING DISC BRAKE — COMPONENTS

1 Disc shield
2 Bolt
3 Bolt
4 Nut

5 Bolt
6 Lockwasher
7 Friction pad

8 Piston
9 Sealing ring
10 Dust boot

11 Boot retaining ring
12 Anti-squeal shim
13 Anti-squeal shim

14 Retaining pin
15 Pin clip
16 Bleeder screw

17 Dust cover
18 Special bolt
19 Spring washer

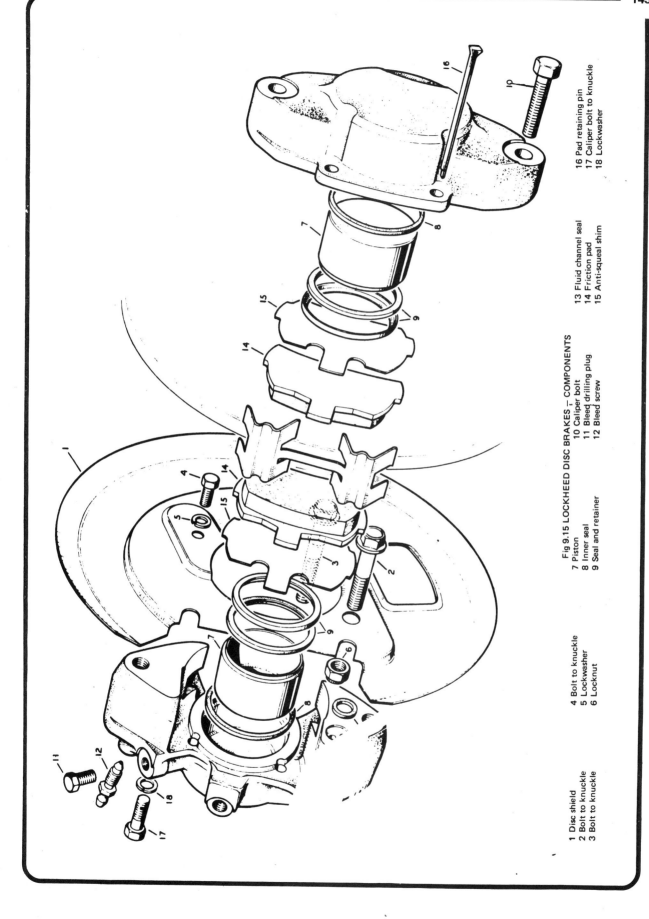

143

Fig 9.15 LOCKHEED DISC BRAKES – COMPONENTS

1 Disc shield	7 Piston	13 Fluid channel seal
2 Bolt to knuckle	8 Inner seal	14 Friction pad
3 Bolt to knuckle	9 Seal and retainer	15 Anti-squeal shim
4 Bolt to knuckle	10 Caliper bolt	16 Pad retaining pin
5 Lockwasher	11 Bleed drilling plug	17 Caliper bolt to knuckle
6 Locknut	12 Bleed screw	18 Lockwasher

12 Replace the guide clip (front) and dust cover.

13 Replace brake shoes and drums, remove the fluid reservoir cap seal and bleed the hydraulic system (Section 16).

14 If the cylinders are to be replaced, unscrew the unions of the hydraulic pipes on the brake backplate.

15 On front brakes, undo the two cylinder fixing bolts and washers and remove the cylinder and sealing ring. Replace the cylinder with a new sealing ring. Continue reassembly as from paragraph 9, using new piston seals always.

16 On rear brake cylinders, undo the pipe union behind the backplate and also remove the bleed screw.

17 Disconnect the handbrake cable from the lever by removing the clevis pin and then remove the dust cover.

18 Using a small screwdriver or spike, prise out the cylinder retaining plate followed by the spring plate and distance washer (Fig 9.1).

19 Lift out the cylinder assembly. Replacement is a reversal of the removal procedure. Continue reassembly as from paragraph 9, using new piston seals always.

20 Bleed the system (Section 16).

9 Disc brakes - caliper removal, inspection and replacement

1 If the caliper pistons are suspected of malfunctioning jack up the car and remove the relevant wheel.

2 Examine for signs of fluid leaks and if these are apparent it will be necessary to remove the caliper and proceed as described from paragraph 4 onwards.

3 If there are no signs of leaking get someone to depress the brake pedal and watch how the two disc pads come up to the disc. One may move very slowly or not at all, in which case it will be necessary to remove the caliper and proceed further.

4 Remove disc pads and shims as described in Section 7.

5 Seal the reservoir cap with a piece of plastic film.

6 Undo the hydraulic pipe union from the body of the caliper and draw back the pipe.

7 Undo the two bolts holding the caliper to the steering knuckle plate. Do NOT undo the bolts which clamp the two halves of the caliper together.

8 Lift the caliper off the disc.

9 Clean the exterior of the caliper assembly and then ease each rubber piston cover out of the grooves in the piston and the caliper body, and remove them.

10 It may be possible to pull the pistons out of their bores, but if not, it will be necessary to blow them out with pressure from an air pump hose attached to the hydraulic fluid inlet port. Support one piston while the other is blown out and then block the empty cylinder with a cloth while the other comes out. If one piston moves very slowly remove this one before the other. If one piston does not move at all it will have seized in the cylinder. Use a hydraulic cleaning fluid or methylated spirits to soak it for some time in an attempt to free it. If harsher measures are needed try to confine any damage to the piston, and not the caliper body.

11 With the pistons removed, the fluid seal rings may be eased out of the piston grooves with a small screwdriver. Make sure that the piston and groove are not damaged. Examine the bores and pistons for signs of scoring or scuffing. If severe, it is unlikely that a proper fluid seal will be possible and a new caliper assembly may be required. The part of the piston on the pad side of the seal groove may be cleaned up with steel wool if necessary. Take care to leave no traces of steel wool anywhere. Clean the cylinder bores also, using hydraulic cleaning fluid if possible, or methylated spirits otherwise.

12 Reassembly is an exact reversal of the dismantling process, taking care with the following in particular:

13 Ensure that the new fluid seal is seated properly in its groove.

14 The caliper mounting bolts have a nylon locking insert in the threads. If this is the third time of removal, then the bolts should be renewed. Tighten the bolts to the specified torque of 33 lb/ft. Replace the pads, as described in Section 6, remove the reservoir cap seal and bleed the system.

15 Some cars are fitted with disc brakes made by Lockheed (Fig 9.15). These are basically the same in operating principle. Two particular items to be noted on reassembly are the piston dust seal and the piston itself. The grooved rubber dust seal is located in a recess in the mouth of the cylinder bore and is kept there by a retaining ring. The piston has a cut-away portion on its outer edge, and this must face down and rearwards (as shown in Fig 9.13) when the piston is pressed back into the cylinder. Care must be taken when refitting the dust seal and retainer to ensure that they go in square and undistorted.

10 Disc brakes, disc run-out check

1 If the disc does not run true then it will tend to push the disc pads aside and force the pistons further into the caliper. This will increase the brake pedal travel necessary to apply the brakes, apart from impairing brake efficiency and the life of the pads.

2 To check the disc run-out (trueness), jack up the car and remove the wheel. Ensure the hub bearing has no free float in it.

3 Set a clock gauge micrometer on a firm stand up to a friction face of the disc near the outside edge so that a reading above .004 inch is registered on the gauge.

4 Spin the hub and if the gauge registers more than $\pm$ .004 inch the disc is warped and needs replacement.

11 Drum and disc brakes - hydraulic master cylinder

1 Unless there are obvious signs of leakage any defects in the master cylinder are usually the last to be detected in a hydraulic system.

2 Before assuming that a fault in the system is in the master cylinder, the pipes and wheel cylinders should all be checked and examined as described in Sections 7, 8 and 9.

3 To remove the master cylinder, first disconnect the pipe at the four-way connector which comes from it. On disc brake models detach the pipe from the servo unit.

4 Drain the master cylinder by pumping the brake pedal and collect the fluid at the end of the disconnected pipe. Then remove the pipe by undoing the union at the master cylinder end.

5 Remove the clevis pin from the brake pedal which attaches the pushrod from the master cylinder.

6 Remove the bolts and nuts which hold the master cylinder to the pedal support bracket and lift it out.

7 To dismantle the cylinder, first ease off the rubber dust cover from the end of the cylinder to expose the circlip.

8 Unclip the circlip from inside the end of the cylinder body and withdraw the pushrod, circlip, retaining washer and dust cover, all together.

9 The piston and valve assembly should now be taken out, or shaken out. If it sticks, try forcing air through the outlet port of the cylinder.

10 To remove the spring from the piston, prise up the tab on the spring retainer which engages in a shoulder on the end of the piston. The spring, spring retainer and valve assembly can then be detached from the piston.

11 To remove the valve stem from the spring retainer, compress the spring and move the stem out of the slotted hole in the retainer.

12 Withdraw the valve stem from the valve spacer, taking care not to damage or lose the spring shim washer.

13 Remove the gland seal from the piston and the valve seal from the valve stem.

14 Clean all parts in hydraulic cleaning fluid or methylated spirits and examine the cylinder bore for signs of ridges and scores. If in doubt, renew the cylinder.

15 Both rubber seals should be renewed. Assemble the valve seal, shim washer and spacer to the stem as shown in Fig 9.17.

17 Assemble the valve stem to the spring and retainer, and then locate the retainer over the piston spigot.

18 Press the retainer tab into the piston recess.

19 Smear the outer end of the piston and the cylinder mouth with the special grease usually provided with the new seals (no other is to be used except castor oil based rubber grease) and insert the piston

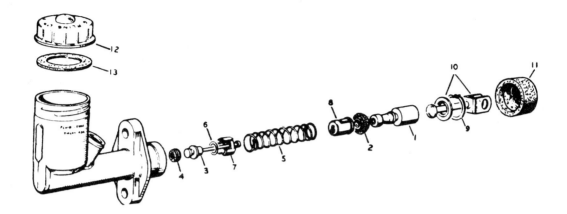

Fig 9.16 HYDRAULIC MASTER CYLINDER — COMPONENTS

1 Plunger	5 Plunger return spring	8 Return spring retainer	11 Dust cover
2 Seal - plunger gland	6 Spring washer	9 Circlip	12 Filler cap
3 Valve stem	7 Valve spacer	10 Push rod	13 Gasket
4 Seal, valve stem			

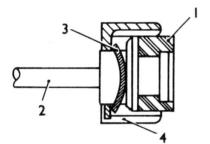

Fig 9.17 HYDRAULIC MASTER CYLINDER — DETAIL OF VALVE, SPACER AND SEAL ASSEMBLY

1 Seal	3 Spring washer
2 Valve stem	4 Valve spacer

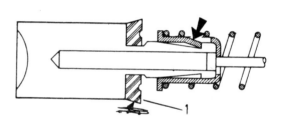

Fig 9.18 HYDRAULIC MASTER CYLINDER — DETAIL OF VALVE STEM AND PLUNGER ASSEMBLY

1 Plunger seal

Spring retainer tab (arrowed) is depressed into plunger recess

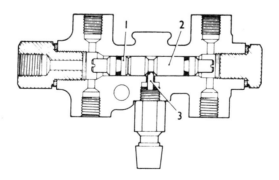

Fig 9.19 HYDRAULIC PRESSURE FAILURE ACTUATION SWITCH (USED IN CONJUNCTION WITH GIRLING TANDEM MASTER CYLINDERS ON EARLY MODELS)

1 Short piston	recess
2 Long piston with actuating	3 Switch plunger

and valve assembly into the cylinder bore with care.

20 Replace the pushrod assembly and engage the circlip in the cylinder mouth recess fully. Replace the dust cover.

21 The cylinder is replaced on the car in the reverse order of removal. Ensure that the brake pedal clevis pin is installed with the head between the clutch and brake pedals and that the bushes engage the clevis on the pushrod.

22 Reconnect the hydraulic pipe and bleed the system as detailed in Section 14.

12 Tandem master cylinders

1 Some early left hand drive models were fitted with Girling tandem master cylinders. All later models are fitted with tandem master cylinders from Lockheed. Should the hydraulic system fail on either the front or rear brakes, it means that the car may still be halted as the pressure in each system is independent of the other.

2 Figs 9.20 and 9.21 give a cross section and exploded view of the Girling cylinder. In order to remove the plungers for renewal of seals the reservoir must first be unbolted from the flange housing the tip valve and swung to one side. Do not try to remove the reservoir as it is held in its other location by a captive circlip in the body, and can only be detached with the possibility of damage. Once the tip valve retaining plug is removed the valve should be lifted out. The primary and secondary plungers may be removed after taking out the retaining circlip in the cylinder bore. In order to dismantle the secondary plunger assembly, the spring must be compressed in vice jaws to enable the retainer tag to be detached from the plunger. Similarly the spring must be compressed for reassembly.

3 The tip valve retainer plug must be tightened on reassembly to a torque of 38 lb/ft.

4 On some early cars fitted with tandem master cylinders a brake pressure warning lamp indicator is also installed, being a separate unit from the master cylinder (Fig 9.19). This will immediately indicate the loss of pressure in either half of the system when it occurs. Basically, the unit is a common piston held in position between opposing pressures in a cylinder. If there is any pressure difference the piston will move to one side, operate a plunger switch and light the warning lamp. The piston is, in fact, in two parts - the longer section incorporating the switch operating groove, and when dismantling, each part should be removed from its arm end of the cylinder. If this is not done the seals could be damaged when passing the switch orifice. In order to centralise the piston on reassembly, it will be necessary to bleed first the front and then rear brakes until the warning light goes out when the plunger is in the central position. For obvious reasons it is not spring loaded, being maintained in balance by the equal pressure of the front and rear hydraulic systems.

5 On later models the Lockheed tandem cylinder is fitted and thus is somewhat simpler (Fig 9.22). It can also incorporate (or not) the unequal pressure warning device inside the body of the unit.

6 Before removing the Lockheed model it should be noted that all pipe thread unions are metric where they join the master cylinder (10 mm). Such unions are coloured black.

7 Where a servo unit is fitted as well the master cylinder is bolted to the servo body. Care must be taken to avoid spilling fluid when removing the unit. It should be drained as soon as possible afterwards.

8 Pull off the fluid reservoir from the cylinder body by lifting it straight up.

9 To dismantle the cylinder, remove the circlip from the end of the bore. The primary piston may then be drawn out. On cars with a servo unit, a spring follows and behind this is the secondary piston.

10 Before the secondary piston can come out, the rubber seal and stop pin must be lifted out of the secondary inlet port. The pin is a loose fit, but the piston will need pushing forward a fraction against the spring to release it. The secondary piston and spring may then be tapped out.

11 Examine the cylinder bore for signs of scoring or other deterioration and, if in doubt, renew it. It is assumed that the seals on the pistons will be renewed anyway - it would be pointless not to do so.

12 When fitting new seals make sure that you do not get them muddled up. The front seals on the primary and secondary pistons are not the same. See that the lips of the seals on the primary piston both face **into** the cylinder, whereas those on the secondary piston face outwards from the centre of the piston (Fig 9.23).

13 The piston spring(s) have washers fitted at one end and these should go over the spigots on the ends of the pistons.

14 Some master cylinders are fitted with a pressure warning lamp device. This is a piston maintained in equilibrium by the two halves of the pressurised system. If the pressure of one half should drop, the piston moves and operates a switch.

To remove the piston assembly, undo the plug in the end of the master cylinder and also the actuator switch. The piston can then be tapped out (Fig 9.24).

15 Reassembly of the cylinder is a reversal of the removal procedure. Take care to fit the pistons correctly, and do not let the lips of the seals turn back when guiding them into the cylinder. The cylinder bores should be lubricated with fluid.

16 The fluid reservoir should be fitted after the stop pin and seal have first been put into the secondary piston inlet port, and the adaptor with 'O' ring into the primary inlet port. The seal which fits over the adaptor is best put into the reservoir aperture first. The seals and pipe on the reservoir should be well lubricated with fluid before pressing the reservoir into place (Fig 9.25).

17 Replace the unit to the mounting as appropriate and, when connecting up the outlet pipe unions, make sure that the rear brake connection goes to the single port at the end of the cylinder, the pipe from the left hand front brake to the upper of the two remaining ports, and pipe from right front brake to lower port.

18 Bleed the brake system and check for leaks at any of the unions.

13 Vacuum servo unit - general description

1 The vacuum servo unit is incorporated with a master cylinder and is operated directly from the brake pedal. It acts on all four wheels. When the pedal is depressed, suction from the induction manifold of the engine is applied to the piston inside the large cylindrical bowl of the servo unit. The piston then moves a plunger attached to its centre applying additional pressure to the hydraulic master cylinder piston. If the servo unit should fail to operate, pressure from the foot pedal is still applied to the system but, of course, the pedal pressure required will be more than it would be if the servo was functioning.

14 Vacuum servo units (early models) - examination, removal and replacement

1 The early models were so designed that any internal fault occurring requires the unit to be changed. There are certain checks which can be made.

The servo unit is equipped with a replacement air filter. The air filter is situated at the rear of the unit and is in the form of a disc round the pushrod. Pull the rubber dust cover away from the servo body and then the filter retainer out of the housing. The filter element may be cut in order to remove it and it is permissible to cut the new one in order to fit it over the pushrod. Replace the retainer and ensure the dust cover engages properly in the retaining flange.

2 The manifold suction pipe is fitted with a non-return valve where it connects with the servo unit. If any back pressure from the manifold occurred it could enter the servo unit and damage it. The non-return valve may be removed by turning it anticlockwise one quarter of a turn and lifting it out. When fitting a new valve always renew the 'O' sealing ring behind it. A modification was later made so that the non-return valve is retained by a rubber grommet and replaced by twisting and pushing it fully home.

2 The correct operation of the servo unit also depends on the movement of the pushrod. When correct, the nose of the pushrod should protrude between .095—.100 inch beyond the front face of the servo shell (Fig 9.26). Where a tandem master cylinder was fitted to these

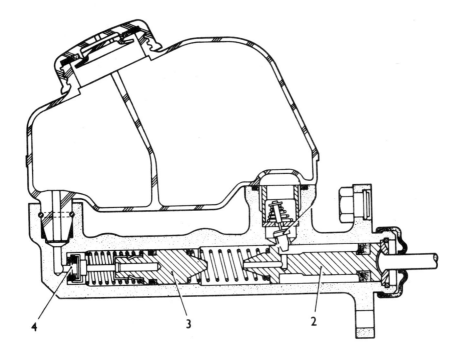

Fig 9.20 GIRLING TANDEM MASTER CYLINDER — CROSS SECTION

1 Tip valve   2 Primary plunger   3 Secondary plunger   4 Centre valve

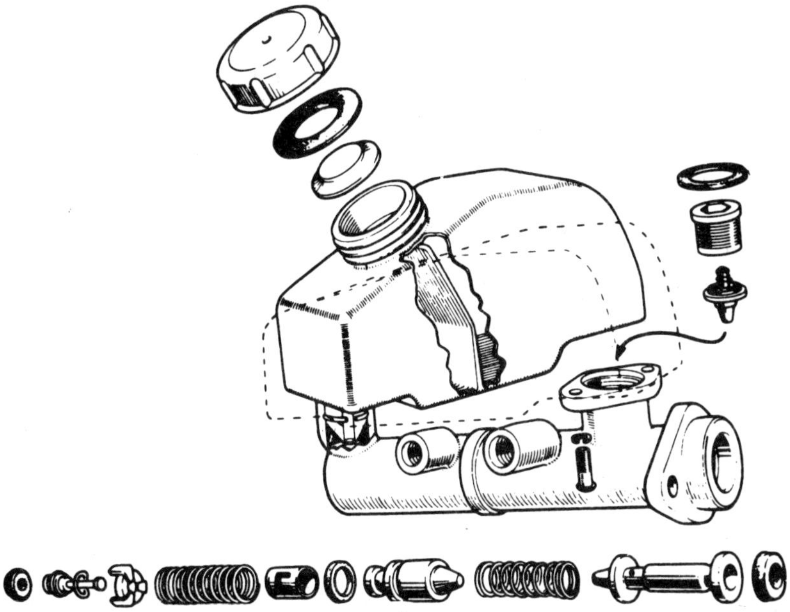

Fig 9.21 Girling tandem master cylinder - detail of components

early types the plunger should be recessed below the face by .011—.016 inch. This may be checked by first removing the master cylinder from the servo shell. Seal the cap of the fluid reservoir to prevent loss, disconnect the hydraulic pipe union and remove the two mounting nuts and washers. The pushrod sealing ring should be removed also after detaching the master cylinder. The protrusion of the pushrod as mentioned above should be measured with vacuum in the system - in other words with the engine running on tickover and the brakes 'off'. If the measurement is incorrect the servo unit needs renewal.

3 With the master cylinder detached as described in the previous paragraph, examine and renew the pushrod sealing ring if signs of deterioration are apparent.

4 To remove the servo unit, first remove the hydraulic master cylinder and disconnect the vacuum pipe from the non-return valve union. Remove the clevis pin attaching the pushrod to the brake pedal. Remove the nuts securing the servo bodyshell to the car. The whole unit may then be withdrawn. When replacing the servo, which is a direct reversal of the removal procedure, make sure that the pushrod grommet rubber pegs are properly engaged in the holes in the pedal support bracket.

15 Vacuum servo units (later models) - checking, dismantling, servicing and reassembly

1 The filter can be changed by drawing back the rubber boot from the end cover and withdrawing the retainer ring. The filter pad must be cut to remove it from the pushrod, as must the new one prior to fitting. Make sure the retainer is pressed back fully and the rubber boot properly engaged with five lugs on the end cover (Fig 9.28).

   To remove the unit, disconnect the vacuum pipe and the hydraulic pipes from the master cylinder and undo the mounting stud nuts.

2 Before beginning dismantling, obtain a complete repair kit which will contain the necessary seals and diaphragm needed to recondition the unit. If in any doubt, it may be preferable to obtain an exchange unit.

3 Having removed the unit from the car together with the master cylinder, attach the cover removal tool to the four mounting studs and clamp one leg of the tool in the vice. Undo the nuts securing the master cylinder and take it off. It is possible at this stage to check the setting of the servo pushrod. It is critical and needs careful measurement with a suitable straight edge or gauge. The correct projection is .408 inch and must be accurate to within .005 inch.

   If incorrect, proceed with dismantling in order to adjust it. Remove the rubber mounting and then fit the slave flange on the studs in its place and tighten the nuts to 11 lb/ft.

4 Release the cover removal tool from the vice and clamp the whole assembly instead, by gripping the slave flange in the vice.

5 Mark the relative positions of the shell and end cover and turn the cover removal tool anticlockwise whilst maintaining pressure, until the cover can be released and the spring pressure relieved.

6 Remove the return spring stop from the shell. Leave the pushrod where it is.

7 Remove the slave flange from the master cylinder mounting studs and carefully push out the master cylinder seal and seal retainer. Take off the cover removal tool, and the pushrod retainer can be prised out of the valve body to release the rod. Pull off the rubber boot and take the filter retainer out of the valve body. Then separate the filter pad and valve from the end cover.

8 The valve bearing, seal and retainer may be prised out of the end cover.

9 Remove the diaphragm from the valve body and by holding it with the key downwards, the valve rod and plunger assembly can be released when pressing the valve rod in. If this assembly is suspect it must be renewed.

10 Push out the reaction disc with a pencil from the valve body.

11 The pushrod adjuster can be turned if the stem is gripped in a vice near the head. One complete revolution represents approximately .035 inch. If the adjuster requires less than 5 lb/in. to turn it, it is too loose and a new one is required.

12 All parts should be cleaned with brake fluid and kept scrupulously clean and free from any bits of fluff that could come from certain types of cleaning cloth.

13 Where lubricant is necessary, use only Lockheed Disc Brake lubricant. Lubricate valve rod and plunger, check that it is seating centrally and insert assembly into the valve body.

14 Refit the key, using light pressure on the valve rod to secure it in the body.

15 Fit the new diaphragm to the valve body making sure the centre sits properly in its groove.

16 Lubricate the reaction disc and put it back in the valve bore using the pushrod to seat it.

17 To fit the new end cover seal, bearing and retainer, it is best to use a mandrel of the type illustrated (Fig 9.29). The lips of the seal should face away from the bearing ring and the flat side of the retainer goes in first.

18 Put the valve body into the end cover and put the filter over the forked end of the valve rod. Refit retainer and boot.

19 Fit the tool to the cover, once more, and the slave flange. Engage the spring stop in swollen end of the spring, and put it in the shell so that the recesses lock in position on the heads of the master cylinder mounting studs.

20 Lubricate the edge of the diaphragm where it will contact the lip of the shell and cover, and then line up the cover to the shell on the marks made previously. Dress the cover down carefully so as not to trap the diaphragm and turn it clockwise until it is up against the stops.

21 Remove the slave flange and insert the pushrod head into the valve body applying only enough pressure to seat it against the reaction disc.

22 Check the pushrod projection, as mentioned earlier, and if correct, press in the retainer using a piece of tube. Do not use excessive pressure. Then put the metal retainer in the shell over the pushrod, guarding against scratching the rod. Smear the rod with silicone grease and insert the rubber seal so that the pushrod adjuster and threads protrude. If this is not done properly, the shell could leak. It is most important also that the vent holes in the rubber seal are not blocked with any traces of dirt or lubricant, otherwise air might find its way into the master cylinder.

23 Before fitting the master cylinder in position, note the position of the vacuum hose connection which should be at 5 o'clock with the reservoir in the upright position. Press the master cylinder well home into its rubber seal before fitting the washers and nuts (Fig 9.27).

16 Hydraulic system - bleeding

1 The system should need bleeding only when some part of it has been dismantled which would allow air into the fluid circuit, or if the reservoir level has been allowed to drop so far that air has entered the master cylinder. If the vehicle has been standing unused for any length of time it is possible also that air bubbles may have developed in the system due to the air absorbing nature of hydraulic fluid. Bleed nipples are found on each of the front wheels and on the rear right wheel only. The line goes through the left hand rear cylinder on route to the right rear cylinder.

2 Ensure that a supply of clean non-aerated fluid of the correct specification is to hand in order to replenish the reservoir during the bleeding process. It is advisable, if not essential, to have someone available to help, as one person has to pump the brake pedal while the other attends to each wheel. The reservoir level has also to be continuously watched and replenished. Fluid bled out should not be re-used. A clean glass jar and a 9—12 inch length of $1/8$ inch internal diameter rubber tube that will fit tightly over the bleed nipples is also required.

3 For drum brakes the order of bleeding on the Victor is as follows: left hand rear, then left hand front, then right hand front. There is no bleed screw on the right hand rear brake

4 For disc brakes, the engine must not be running and the pedal should be operated three or four times to make sure that there is no residual vacuum in the servo unit. The order of bleeding is the same

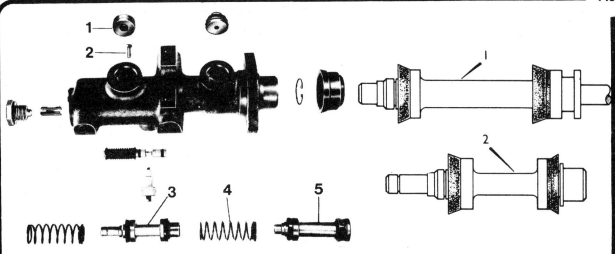

Fig 9.22 LOCKHEED TANDEM MASTER CYLINDER — DE-
TAIL OF COMPONENTS

1 Reservoir seal
2 Stop pin
3 Secondary piston
4 Return spring (omitted when servo assisted)
5 Primary piston

Fig 9.23 LOCKHEED TANDEM MASTER CYLINDER — DE-
TAIL OF SEAL ASSEMBLY TO PISTONS

1 Primary piston
2 Secondary piston

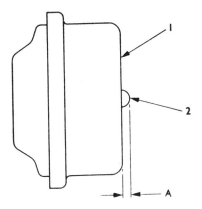

Fig 9.26 VACUUM SERVO UNIT (EARLY VERSIONS)
PUSHROD SETTING — ENGINE RUNNING, BRAKES OFF

1 Servo shell
2 Pushrod

A = .095—.100 inch (2.3—2.5 mm)

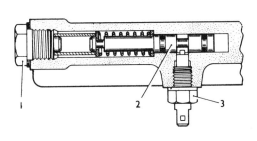

Fig 9.24 LOCKHEED TANDEM MASTER CYLINDER — CROSS
SECTION OF PRESSURE WARNING LAMP DEVICE

1 End plug
2 Actuator piston
3 Switch

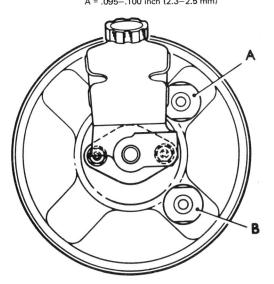

Fig 9.27 Master cylinder/servo unit showing correct position of
suction hose at point B. Point A is for 1600 cc engine

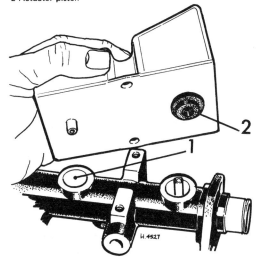

Fig 9.25 LOCKHEED TANDEM MASTER CYLINDER — FIT-
TING OF RESERVOIR TO BODY

1 Secondary piston inlet port seal
2 Primary piston inlet port adaptor seal

as that for drum brakes. The lengths of the runs to the front wheels are no greater, but the fluid capacity of the disc caliper cylinders is much larger.

5 Make sure the bleed nipple is clean and put a small quantity of fluid in the bottom of the jar. Fit the tube onto the nipple and place the other end in the jar under the surface of the fluid. Keep it under the surface throughout the bleeding operation.

6 Unscrew the bleed screw ½ turn and get your assistant to depress and release the brake pedal in short sharp bursts when you direct him. Short sharp jabs are better because they will force any air bubbles along the line with the fluid rather than pump the fluid past them. It is not essential to remove all the air first time. If the whole system has to be bled, attend to each wheel for three or four complete pedal strokes and then repeat the process. On the second time around operate the pedal sharply in the same way until no bubbles come out of the pipe into the jar. With the brake pedal in the fully depressed position the bleed screw should be tightened. Do not forget to keep the reservoir topped up throughout.

7 When all wheels have been bled satisfactorily re-adjust the shoes (Section 2).

8 If the reason for bleeding has been a repair to a pipe or cylinder near a wheel then it should be normally necessary to bleed only the wheel of the line in question - PROVIDED that no fluid has been allowed to drain out of the disconnected line. If in any doubt bleed the whole system.

9 Depress the brake pedal which should offer a firm resistance with no trace of 'sponginess'. The pedal near a wheel should not continue to go down under sustained pressure. If it does there is a leak, or the master cylinder seals are worn out.

17 Brake pedal and shaft - removal and replacement

1 If for any reason (such as worn out bushes) the brake pedal needs to be removed, follow the procedures as described for the clutch pedal in Chapter 5.

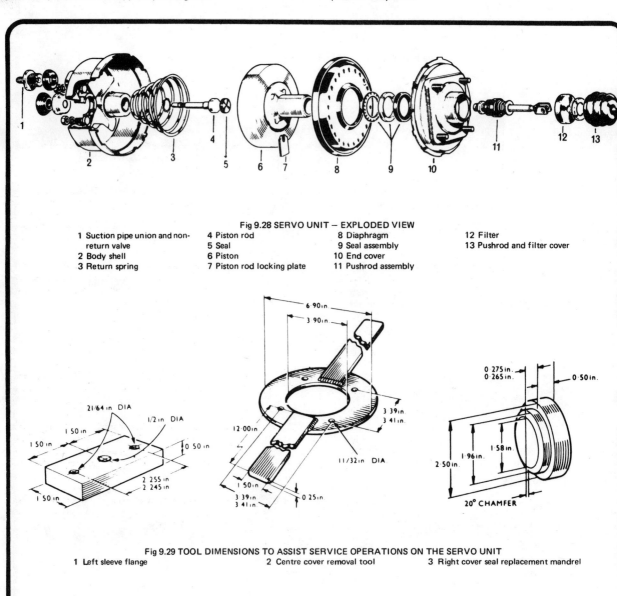

Fig 9.28 SERVO UNIT — EXPLODED VIEW

1 Suction pipe union and non-   4 Piston rod   8 Diaphragm   12 Filter
   return valve   5 Seal   9 Seal assembly   13 Pushrod and filter cover
2 Body shell   6 Piston   10 End cover
3 Return spring   7 Piston rod locking plate   11 Pushrod assembly

Fig 9.29 TOOL DIMENSIONS TO ASSIST SERVICE OPERATIONS ON THE SERVO UNIT

1 Left sleeve flange   2 Centre cover removal tool   3 Right cover seal replacement mandrel

Fault Finding Chart - Braking System

1 Uneven and incorrect tyre pressures.
2 Incorrect 'mix' of radial and cross-ply tyres.
3 Wear in the steering mechanism.
4 Defects in the suspension and dampers.
5 Misalignment of the body frame.

NOTE: For vehicles fitted with disc brakes at the front the references in the chart to front wheel shoe adjustments do not apply. The 'Reason/s' referring to hydraulic system faults or wear to the friction material of the linings still apply, however. Disc pads also come in different material and references to variations are also relevant.

Symptoms	Reason/s	Remedy
Pedal travels a long way before the brakes operate	Brake shoes set too far from the drums	Adjust the brake shoes to the drums.
Stopping ability poor, even though pedal pressure is firm	Linings and/or drums badly worn or scored	Dismantle, inspect and renew as required.
	Failure or one circuit in the dual hydraulic system (where fitted)	Check both circuits for hydraulic leaks and repair.
	One or more wheel hydraulic cylinders seized, resulting in some brake shoes not pressing against the drums (or pads against disc)	Dismantle and inspect wheel cylinders. Renew as necessary.
	Brake linings contaminated with oil	Renew linings and repair source of oil contamination.
	Wrong type of linings fitted (too hard)	Verify type of material which is correct for the car, and fit it.
	Brake shoes wrongly assembled	Check for correct assembly.
	Servo unit not functioning (disc brakes)	Check and repair as necessary.
Car veers to one side when the brakes are applied	Brake pads or linings on one side are contaminated with oil	Renew pads or linings and stop oil leak.
	Hydraulic wheel cylinder(s) on one side partially or fully seized	Inspect wheel cylinders for correct operation and renew as necessary.
	A mixture of lining materials fitted between sides	Standardise on types of linings fitted.
	Unequal wear between sides caused by partially seized wheel cylinders	Check wheel cylinders and renew linings and drums as required.
Pedal feels spongy when the brakes are applied	Air is present in the hydraulic system	Bleed the hydraulic system and check for any signs of leakage.
Pedal feels springy when the brakes are applied	Brake linings not bedded into the drums (after fitting new ones)	Allow time for new linings to bed in after which it will certainly be necessary to adjust the shoes to the drums as pedal travel will have increased.
	Master cylinder or brake backplate mounting bolts loose	Retighten mounting bolts.
	Severe wear in brake drums causing distortion when brakes are applied	Renew drums and linings.
Pedal travels right down with little or no resistance and brakes are virtually non-operative. (With dual braking systems this would be extraordinary as both systems would have to fail at the same time)	Leak in hydraulic systems resulting in lack of pressure for operating wheel cylinders	Examine the whole of the hydraulic system and locate and repair source of leaks. Test after repairing each and every leak source.
	If no signs of leakage are apparent, the master cylinder internal seals are failing to sustain pressure	Overhaul master cylinder. If indications are that seals have failed for reasons other than wear all the wheel cylinder seals should be checked also and the system completely replenished with the correct fluid.
Binding, juddering, overheating	One or a combination of causes given in the foregoing sections	Complete and systematic inspection of the whole braking system.

Chapter 10 Electrical system

Contents

Specifications

Battery

Standard	Exide 6 VTA Z9 BR or Lucas BH9 - 38 amp/hrs 20 hr rate
Heavy duty...	Exide 6 VTA 11 BR - 55 amp/hrs 20 hr rate
Earth	Negative

Generator ... ...   Lucas C40 L

Cut-in speed	1350 rpm max at 13 volts
Output	25 amps - 2275 rpm at 13.5 volts on .54 ohm resistance load
Field resistance	5.9 ohms
Minimum commutator diameter	1.430 in
Brush length minimum	.25 in
Brush spring tension	30 oz new brush , 15 oz minimum length
Fan belt tension	53 lb, equivalent to .36 inch depression midway between water pump and generator pulley with applied load of 10 lb

Regulator (Dynamo)

Type...	Lucas RB 340
Swamp resistor	53—57 ohms between tag ends prior to assembly
	13.25—14.25 ohms between centre tag and controller base after assembly
Field resistance	55—65 ohms
Voltage regulator - shunt winding resistance...	10.8—11.8 ohms at 20ºC
- open circuit settings	at 2000 rpm engine speed

Air temperature	Volts
10ºC	14.9—15.5
20ºC	14.7—15.3
30ºC	14.5—15.1
40ºC	14.3—14.9

- armature to core gap	.056—.060 in
Cut-out relay - shunt winding resistance	9.5—10.5 ohms
- cut-in voltage	12.6—13.4 volts
- reverse current	8 amps maximum
- armature to core gap	.035—.045 in
- moving contact follow through	contacts just touching with gap of .015 in between armature and core
Current regulator - load setting...	24—26 amps at 3000 rpm
- armature to core gap	.058 in

Alternators

Type...	Lucas 15ACR	17ACR	Delco-Remy DN460
Voltage	12	12	12
Output	28 amps	36 amps	28 and 35 amps
Field resistance (± 5%)	4.3 ohms	4.16 ohms	—
Brushes - minimum length	0.20 in	0.20 in	—
Brush spring pressure	7—10 oz	7—10 oz	—
Regulator (incorporated)	8 TR		

Starter motors

Make	Lucas			
Types	M35 G/I	M35 J/I	M35 G/PE	M35 J/PE
Brush length (minimum)	.30	.30	.30	.30
Brush spring tension new brushes	34—46 oz	28 oz*	25 oz	28 oz*
Commutator diameter minimum	1.281 in	—	1.422 in	—
Commutator thickness minimum	—	.080 in	—	.080 in
Armature shaft end float maximum	—	.010 in	—	.010 in
Pinion to thrust collar clearance	—	—	.005—.010 in	—
Solenoid switch test data series winding resistance	—	—	.40—.46 ohms	.21—.25 ohms
shunt winding resistance...	—	—	1.10—1.35 ohms	.9—1.1 ohms
Starter test data Free running current	45 amps at 9500 —11000 rpm	65 amps at 8000 —10000 rpm	70 amps at 7000 —10000 rpm	65 amps at 8000 —10000 rpm
Lock torque	10 lb ft at 420— 440 amps	7 lb ft at 350— 375 amps	7.2 lb ft at 336 amps	7 lb ft at 350— 375 amps

Windscreen wiper motors

Make	Delco-Remy
Stall torque at crank (single speed)	5 lb ft
Current consumption (light load) after 5—10 minutes...	1 amp (single speed)
	1.2 amps (low - 2 speed)
	2 amps (high - 2 speed)

Fuses

Fuse block containing 4 35 amp fuses is mounted on the inside of the dash panel and projects into the engine compartment where fuse replacements can be made. The four fuses cover the circuits not protected by the thermal circuit breaker.

No 1...	Windscreen wipers, cigarette lighter, radio
No 2...	Stop lamps, flasher indicator lamps, warning lamps, fuel and temperature gauges, heater fan, reverse lamps, overdrive
No 3...	Horn, interior light, map reading light
No 4...	Instrument lamps, rear lamps, number plate lamps, fog lamp, cigarette lighter lamp

Bulbs

Headlamps - inner...	37.5 watt sealed beam
- outer...	50/37.5 watt sealed beam
- France - both	45 pre-focus yellow
- Italy - inner	37.5 watt pre-focus
- outer	50/37.5 pre-focus
- other European - inner	37.5 watt pre-focus
- outer	45/40 pre-focus
Sidelamps	6 watt miniature centre contact
Tail/stop	6/21 watt small bayonet cap
Flasher bulbs	21 watt single centre contact

Number plate	6 watt miniature centre contact
Interior light	10 watt Festoon
Reverse light	21 watt Festoon
Boot interior	6 watt single centre contact
Fog lamp	55 watt quartz iodine
Indicator and warning lamps	1.5 watt wedge base capless
Instrument lamps...	5 watt wedge base capless
Auto transmission selector lamp	2 watt peanut
Cigarette lighter lamp	2.2 watt peanut

Torque Wrench Settings

Pre-engaged starter pivot pin locknut	15 lb ft
Wiper motor crank locknut	12 lb ft
Wiper motor thrust screw locknut...	12 lb in
Alternator through bolts	47 lb in

1 General description

The system is a conventional 12 volt, negative earth arrangement comprising a storage battery, generator - either dynamo with control box or alternator - and starter motor.

The generator is mounted on the left front of the engine and is driven by the V belt which also drives the fan from the crankshaft pulley.

The starter motor is mounted on the right of the engine into the clutch bellhousing and can be of the inertia or pre-engaged type.

The 12 volt battery supplies a steady amount of current for the ignition, lighting, and other electrical circuits, and provides a reserve of electricity when the current consumed by the electrical equipment exceeds that being produced by the dynamo or alternator.

The dynamo is of the two brush type and works in conjunction with the voltage regulator and cut-out. The dynamo is cooled by a multi-bladed fan mounted behind the dynamo pulley, which blows air through cooling holes in the dynamo end brackets. The output from the dynamo is controlled by the voltage regulator which ensures a high output if the battery is in a low state of charge or the demands from the electrical equipment high, and a low output if the battery is fully charged and there is little demand from the electrical equipment.

Where alternators are used the voltage and current control is incorporated in rectifier components in the alternator itself.

2 Battery - removal and replacement

1 Disconnect the negative (earth) lead from the battery terminal post and the positive lead similarly. The leads are held by either a clamp, which necessitates slackening the clamp bolt and nut, or by a screw driven through an all enclosing shroud (photo).

2 Remove the battery clamp and carefully lift the battery out of its compartment. Hold the battery vertical to ensure that none of the electrolyte is spilled.

3 Replacement is a direct reversal of this procedure. NOTE. Replace the positive lead before the earth (negative) lead and smear the terminals with petroleum jelly (vaseline) to prevent corrosion. NEVER use an ordinary grease as applied to other parts of the car.

3 Battery - maintenance and inspection

1 Normal weekly battery maintenance consists of checking the electrolyte level of each cell to ensure that the separators are covered by ¼ inch of electrolyte. If the level has fallen, top up the battery using distilled water only. Do not overfill. If a battery is overfilled or any electrolyte spilled, immediately wipe away the excess as electrolyte attacks and corrodes any metal it comes into contact with very rapidly.

2 As well as keeping the terminals clean and covered with petroleum jelly, the top of the battery, and especially the top of the cells, should be kept clean and dry. This helps prevent corrosion and ensures that the battery does not become partially discharged by leakage through dampness and dirt.

3 Once every three months, remove the battery and inspect the battery securing bolts, the battery clamp plate, tray and battery leads for corrosion (white fluffy deposits on the metal which are brittle to touch). If any corrosion is found, clean off the deposits with ammonia and paint over the clean metal with an anti-rust/anti-acid paint.

4 At the same time inspect the battery case for cracks. If a crack is found, clean and plug it with one of the proprietary compounds marketed by firms, such as Holts, for this purpose. If leakage through the crack has been excessive then it will be necessary to refill the appropriate cell with fresh electrolyte as detailed later. Cracks are frequently caused to the top of the battery cases by pouring in distilled water in the middle of winter AFTER instead of BEFORE a run. This gives the water no chance to mix with the electrolyte and so the former freezes and splits the battery case.

5 If topping up the battery becomes excessive and the case has been inspected for cracks that could cause leakage, but none are found, the battery is being overcharged and the voltage regulator will have to be checked and reset.

6 With the battery on the bench at the three monthly interval check, measure its specific gravity with a hydrometer to determine the state of charge and condition of the electrolyte. There should be very little variation between the different cells and if a variation in excess of .025 is present it will be due to either:

a) Loss of electrolyte from the battery at some time caused by spillage or a leak, resulting in a drop in the specific gravity of the electrolyte when the deficiency was replaced with distilled water instead of fresh electrolyte.

b) An internal short circuit caused by buckling of the plates or a similar malady pointing to the likelihood of total battery failure in the near future.

7 The specific gravity of the electrolyte for fully charged conditions at the electrolyte temperature indicated, is listed in Table A. The specific gravity of a fully discharged battery at different temperatures of the electrolyte is given in Table B.

Table A
Specific gravity - battery fully charged

1.268 at 100°F or	38°C	electrolyte temperature	
1.272 at 90°F or	32°C	''	''
1.276 at 80°F or	27°C	''	''
1.280 at 70°F or	21°C	''	''
1.284 at 60°F or	16°C	''	''
1.288 at 50°F or	10°C	''	''
1.292 at 40°F or	4°C	''	''
1.296 at 30°F or	-1.5°C	''	''

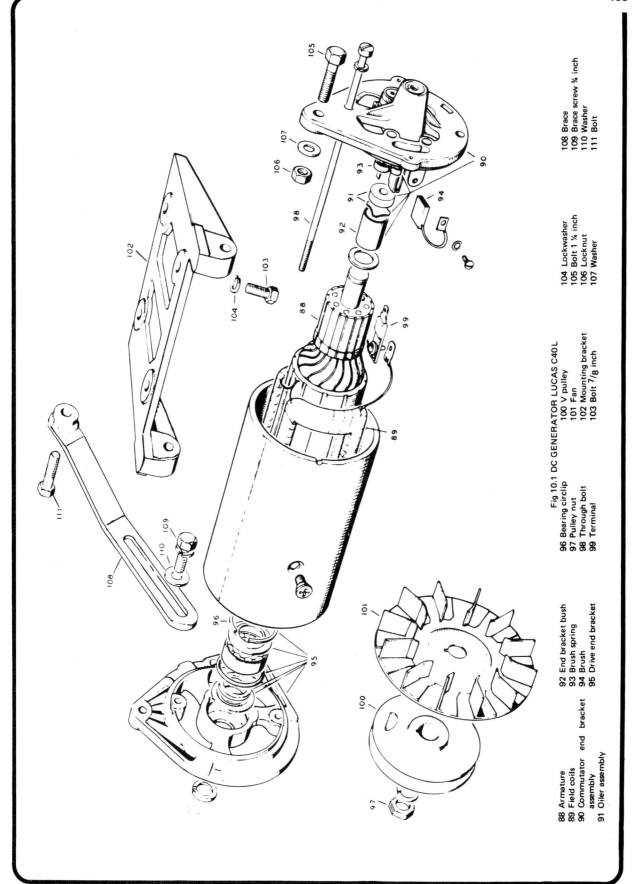

Fig 10.1 DC GENERATOR LUCAS C40L

88 Armature
89 Field coils
90 Commutator end bracket
   assembly
91 Oiler assembly

92 End bracket bush
93 Brush spring
94 Brush
95 Drive end bracket

96 Bearing circlip
97 Pulley nut
98 Through bolt
99 Terminal

100 V pulley
101 Fan
102 Mounting bracket
103 Bolt 7/8 inch

104 Lockwasher
105 Bolt 1 ¼ inch
106 Locknut
107 Washer

108 Brace
109 Brace screw ¾ inch
110 Washer
111 Bolt

Table B
Specific gravity - battery fully discharged
1.098 at 100°F or 38°C electrolyte temperature
1.102 at 90°F or 32°C   "   "
1.106 at 80°F or 27°C   "   "
1.110 at 70°F or 21°C   "   "
1.114 at 60°F or 16°C   "   "
1.118 at 50°F or 10°C   "   "
1.122 at 40°F or 4°C   "   "
1.126 at 30°F or -1.5°C   "   "

4 Battery electrolyte replenishment

1 If the battery is in a fully charged state and one of the cells maintains a specific gravity, reading which is .025 or more lower than the others, and a check of each cell has been made with a voltage meter to check for short circuits (a four to seven second test should give a steady reading of between 1.2 to 1.8 volts), then it is likely that electrolyte has been lost from the cell with the low reading at some time.

2 Top the cell up with a solution of 1 part sulphuric acid to 2.5 parts of water. If the cell is already fully topped up draw some electrolyte out of it with a pipette.

3 When mixing the sulphuric acid and water NEVER ADD WATER TO SULPHURIC ACID — always pour the acid slowly onto the water in a glass container. IF WATER IS ADDED TO SULPHURIC ACID IT WILL EXPLODE.

4 Continue to top up the cell with the freshly made electrolyte and then recharge the battery and check the hydrometer readings.

5 Battery charging

1 In winter time when heavy demand is placed upon the battery, such as when starting from cold, and much electrical equipment is continually in use, it is a good idea occasionally to have the battery fully charged from an external source at the rate of 3.5 to 4 amps.

2 Continue to charge the battery at this rate until no further rise in specific gravity is noted over a four hour period.

3 Alternatively, a trickle charger, charging at the rate of 1.5 amps can be safely used overnight.

4 Specially rapid 'boost' charges which are claimed to restore the power of the battery in 1 to 2 hours are most dangerous as they can cause serious damage to the battery plates through overheating.

5 While charging the battery note that the temperature of the electrolyte should never exceed 100°F.

6 Dynamo - testing in position

1 If, with the engine running, no charge comes from the dynamo, or the charge is very low, first check that the fan belt is in place and is not slipping. Then check that the leads from the control box to the dynamo are firmly attached and that one has not come loose from its terminal.

2 The lead from the 'D' terminal on the dynamo should be connected to the 'D' terminal on the control box, and similarly the 'F' terminals on the dynamo and control box should also be connected together. Check that this is so and that the leads have not been incorrectly fitted.

3 Make sure none of the electrical equipment (such as the lights or radio) is on, and then pull the leads off the dynamo terminals marked 'D' and 'F'.

4 Using a voltmeter (rated up to 20 volts) connect the positive lead to the output 'D' terminal of the generator and the negative lead to earth (see Fig 10.2). With the engine running at approximately 1500 rpm there should be a reading of 2—4 volts.

5 If there is no reading a possible cause may be a lack of residual magnetism in the field coil pole shoes. To rectify this, flash a lead

from the battery positive terminal to the field (F) terminal on the dynamo. If there is still no reading then check the brushes and brush connections.

6 If the output reading is satisfactory it will be necessary to check the field circuit. With the voltmeter still connected as before connect in addition an ammeter with its negative lead to the field (F) terminal and its positive lead to the 'D' terminal of the dynamo (see Fig 10.3).

7 Run the engine and increase the revolutions slowly until the voltmeter reads 12 volts. The ammeter should then read approximately 2 amps. It is also advisable to check this again when the generator has reached normal running temperature (after about fifteen minutes).

8 If the dynamo tests are satisfactory, any failure to charge the battery must be due to a break in the wiring or a fault in the voltage control/regulator unit.

7 Dynamo - removal and replacement

1 Slacken the two dynamo retaining bolts, and the bolt on the sliding link, and move the dynamo in towards the engine so that the fan belt can be removed.

2 Disconnect the two leads from the dynamo terminals.

3 Remove the sliding link bolt, and remove the two upper bolts. The dynamo is then free to be lifted away from the engine (photo).

4 Replacement is a reversal of the above procedure. Do not finally tighten the retaining bolts and the bolt on the sliding link until the fan belt has been tensioned correctly (see Chapter 2 for details).

8 Dynamo - dismantling and inspection

1 Mount the dynamo in a vice and unscrew and remove the two through bolts from the commutator end bracket (photo).

2 The end bracket may now be pulled off the armature. Take care not to damage or break the field coil wire attached to the smaller of the two terminal connectors. This connector will draw out of the end plate. Note also that there is a raised pip in the end plate which engages in a small recess in the dynamo casing. This ensures that the end plate is correctly lined up when replaced (photo).

3 Lift the two brush springs and draw the brushes out of the brush holders (photo).

4 Measure the brushes and, if worn down to $9/32$ inch or less, unscrew the screws holding the brush leads to the end bracket. Take off the brushes complete with leads. Old and new brushes are compared in the photograph.

5 Then pull the drive end bracket complete with armature out of the casing (photo).

6 Check the condition of the ball bearing in the drive end plate by firmly holding the plate and noting if there is visible side movement of the armature shaft in relation to the end plate. If play is present, the armature assembly must be separated from the end plate. If the bearing is sound there is no need to carry out the work described in the following two paragraphs.

7 Hold the armature in one hand (mount it carefully in a vice if preferred) and undo the nut holding the pulley wheel and fan in place. Pull off the pulley wheel and fan.

8 Remove the woodruff key from its slot in the armature shaft.

9 Place the drive end bracket across the open jaws of a vice with the armature downwards and gently tap the armature shaft from the bearing in the end plate with the aid of a suitable drift. Support the armature so that it does not fall to the ground.

10 Carefully inspect the armature and check it for open or short circuited windings. It is a good indication of an open circuited armature when the commutator segments are burnt. If the armature has short circuited the commutator segments will be very badly burnt, and the overheated armature windings badly discoloured. If open or short circuits are suspected substitute the suspect armature with a new one.

11 Check the resistance of the field coils. To do this, connect an ohmmeter between the field terminal and the yoke and note the read-

2.2 Disconnecting battery leads

7.3 Generator mounting lugs

8.1 Generator through bolts partly removed

8.2 Drawing off the end plate

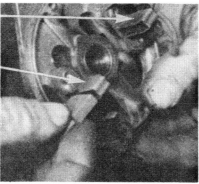

8.3 Carbon brushes - removal from brush holders (arrowed)

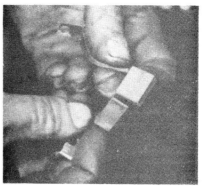

8.4 Carbon brushes - comparing worn and new

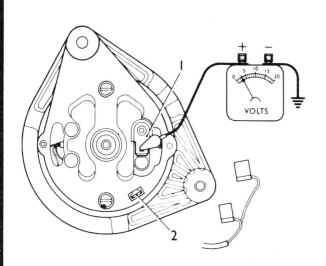

Fig 10.2 Dynamo voltage output test connections

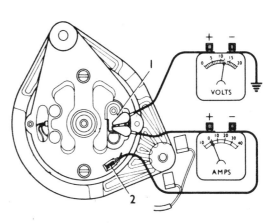

Fig 10.3 Dynamo field circuit test connections

ing on the ohmmeter which should be about 6 ohms. If the ohmmeter reading is infinity this indicates an open circuit in the field winding. If the ohmmeter reading is below 5 ohms this indicates that one of the field coils is faulty and must be replaced.

12 Field coil replacement involves the use of a wheel operated screwdriver, a soldering iron, caulking and riveting and this operation is considered to be beyond the scope of most owners. Therefore, if the field coils are at fault either purchase a rebuilt dynamo, or take the casing to an electrical engineering works for new field coils to be fitted.

13 Next check the condition of the commutator. If it is dirty and blackened, clean it with a petrol dampened rag. If the commutator is in good condition the surface will be smooth and quite free from pits or burnt areas, and the insulated segments clearly defined.

14 If, after the commutator has been cleaned, pits and burnt spots are still present, wrap a strip of glass paper round the commutator taking great care to move the commutator ¼ of a turn every ten rubs till it is thoroughly clean (photo).

15 In extreme cases of wear the commutator can be mounted in a lathe turning at high speed, a very fine cut may be taken off the commutator. Then polish the commutator with glass paper. If the commutator has worn so that the insulators between the segments are level with the top of the segments, then undercut the insulators to a depth of $1/32$ inch (.8 mm). This applies to fabricated commutators only. Do NOT undercut moulded commutators. The best tool to use for this purpose is half a hacksaw blade ground to a thickness of the insulator, and with the handle end of the blade covered in insulating tape to make it comfortable to hold.

16 Check the bush bearing in the commutator end bracket for wear by noting if the armature spindle rocks when placed in it. If worn, it must be renewed (photo).

17 The bush bearing can be removed by a suitable extractor or by screwing a $5/8$ inch tap four or five turns into the bush. The tap complete with bush is then pulled out of the end bracket.

18 NOTE: The bush bearing is made of a porous bronze material which needs to be saturated in engine oil before use. Oil can be forced through it, before installation, by blocking one end with a thumb, filling it with oil and squeezing it through the material by forcing a finger in at the other end. Otherwise, soak it in oil for several hours. If the oil is hot it will saturate the material more quickly.

19 Carefully fit the new bush into the end plate, pressing it in until the end of the bearing is flush with the inner side of the end plate. If available, press the bush in with a smooth shouldered mandrel the same diameter as the armature shaft.

---

9 Dynamo - repair and reassembly

1 The ball bearing fitted to the drive end bracket, is held by a circlip which is quite simply removed to release the bearing from the end plate.

2 Press out the bearing from the end bracket and remove the corrugated and felt washers from the bearing housing.

3 Thoroughly clean the bearing housing and the new bearing, and pack with high melting point grease.

4 Place the felt washer, retaining washer and pressure ring in the housing before the bearing.

5 Then fit the new bearing.

6 Gently tap the bearing into place with the aid of a suitable drift.

7 Replace the collar and circlip.

8 Locate the retaining cap over the armature shaft collar and refit the drive end bracket to the armature shaft. Do not try and force the bracket on but, with the aid of a suitable socket abutting the bearing, tap the bearing on gently, so pulling the end bracket down with it.

9 Slide the spacer up the shaft and refit the woodruff key.

10 Replace the fan and pulley wheel and then fit the spring washer and nut and tighten the latter. The drive bracket end of the dynamo is now fully assembled.

11 If the brushes are little worn and are to be used again then ensure that they are placed in the same holders from which they were removed. When refitting brushes, either new or old, check that they move freely in their holders. If either brush sticks, clean with a petrol moistened rag and if still stiff, lightly polish the sides of the brush with a very fine file until the brush moves quite freely in its holder.

12 Tighten the two retaining screws and washers which hold the wire leads in place, making sure that the tag ends are kept at 90° to the end bracket (photo).

13 It is far easier to slip the end piece with brushes over the commutator if the brushes are raised in their holders, as shown, and held in this position by the pressure of the springs resting against their flanks (photo).

14 Refit the armature to the casing and then the commutator end plate, and screw up the two through bolts.

15 Finally, hook the ends of the two springs off the flanks of the brushes and onto their heads so that the brushes are forced down into contact with the armature.

---

10 Control box - general description (dynamo only)

The control box consists of three main parts, the cut-out relay, the current regulator and the voltage regulator. The whole unit controls the dynamo output of the cars electrical equipment and the recharging requirement of the battery. The cut-out relay is basically an automatically operated switch which prevents current flowing the wrong way, from battery to dynamo, when the generator output is below 12 volts. The current regulator and voltage regulator work in conjunction to enable the generator to deliver its safe maximum output when necessary, and to reduce the current being delivered when the system or battery does not require it.

---

11 Control box - checks and adjustment (dynamo only)

1 If the generator and battery are both known to be in good condition yet the battery gives indications of inadequate or excessive charge it may be assumed that the reasons are a fault or maladjustment in the control box. If an adjustment is necessary, (as revealed by the tests) the cover of the control box must first be removed by drilling out the rivets which hold it in position. All adjustments must be carried out in the sequence given and quickly to prevent incorrect readings due to heating up of the appropriate coils. Use the special tool adjuster 54381742 as shown in Fig 10.12

---

12 Voltage regulator - checks and adjustment (dynamo only)

1 To check the voltage regulator, first disconnect the brown wire from the 'B' terminal on the control box and make sure it is not allowed to touch anything.

2 Then connect a voltmeter to the 'WL' terminal and earth as shown in Fig 10.4.

3 Start the engine and slowly increase revolutions to 2000 rpm. The voltage should reach between 14.3 to 15.5 volts according to air temperature as shown in the table in the specifications at the beginning of this Chapter. Unsteady fluctuations (more than .3 volts) may be due to dirty contacts. A steady reading outside the range can be adjusted by turning the cam arrowed in Fig 10.10. When the adjustment is completed, lower and raise the engine speed again to check the reading.

---

13 Cut-out - checks and adjustment (dynamo only)

1 Connect the voltmeter as for the voltage regulator check but with all connections to the cut-out box left as they are (Fig 10.5).

8.5 Generator drive end plate and armature being withdrawn

8.14 Generator commutator being cleaned with glass paper strip

8.16 Commutator end cover bush (arrowed)

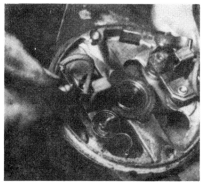

9.12 Replacing brush leads

9.13 Holding brushes out with the springs (arrowed)

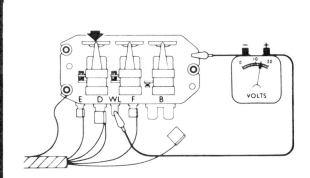

Fig 10.4 Voltage regulator check - test connections. Adjuster cam arrowed

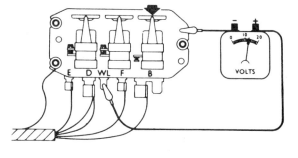

Fig 10.5 Cut-out check - test connection. Adjusting cam arrowed

2 Start the engine, and increase speed slowly. Check that the relay cuts in at between 12.6 and 13.4 volts. The cut-in is indicated by a flicker back of the voltmeter needle. If adjustment is required adjust the cam (arrowed) only when the engine is at idling speed. Then check by speeding the engine up.

3 Next disconnect the brown lead from terminal 'B' once more and connect an ammeter as shown in Fig 10.6, making sure that the loose tag does not touch anything.

4 Then switch on the headlamps, start the engine and increase the engine speed until a charge is indicated. Then gradually decrease engine speed and check that the discharge does not exceed 8 amps. If it does, bend the fixed contact (arrowed) back a little until it is correct.

14 Current regulator - checks and adjustment (dynamo only)

1 Having completed the checks in Sections 12 and 13 leave the ammeter connected as in check 13 and hold the voltage regulator contacts together with a clip (Fig 10.7, Item 1).

2 Start the engine and increase speed to 3000 rpm when the ammeter should give a steady reading of 24—26 amps. Adjust by turning the cam (Item 2) if necessary.

15 Control box contacts - cleaning

1 The cut-out contacts (Fig 10.8, Item 3) may be cleaned in position by drawing very fine glass paper (not emery) between them.

2 The voltage and current regulator contacts (Items 1 and 2) must be removed and faced up on fine carborundum (stone or paper) and then cleaned off with methylated spirits. Whenever contacts are cleaned in this way the setting checks must afterwards be made as described in the previous sections and the mechanical settings as described in the next section.

16 Control box - gap settings (dynamo only)

1 First check the gaps on the current and voltage regulators according to specifications. If adjustment is necessary, first turn the adjuster cams clockwise (Fig 10.10, Items 1 and 2) so that the locknut on the adjustable contact can be reached with a tubular spanner in order to slacken it. Then place the .058 inch feeler blade under the armature as far as the rivet heads allow, press the armature down and adjust the contact until they just touch. Recheck the armature core gap on release, and then tighten the locknut. The voltage and current regulator will need resetting afterwards as described in Sections 12 and 14.

2 The cut-out relay contacts should just touch with a .015 inch feeler blade between the armature and core and the armature pressed down (Fig 10.11). The contacts are adjusted by bending the fixed contact. The armature to core gap should be between .035 inch and .045 inch and this is adjusted by bending the armature back stop. After adjustments are completed the settings should be rechecked as described in Section 13.

3 If the control box has been removed from the car it should be replaced before securing the cover with new rivets or nuts and bolts as convenient. Make sure that the wire connections are all remade correctly as in Fig 10.9.

17 Alternators - general description

1 More and more cars are being fitted with alternators in place of the more well known dynamo and the Victor is no exception on the later models. The 15ACR Lucas is fitted to 1599 cc models and the 17ACR to 1975 cc models. They provide a higher output for lower weight and are able to cope with the full electrical loads at low revolutions.

Basically the alternator, as its name implies, generates alternating

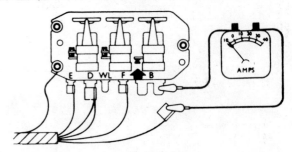

Fig 10.6 Cut-out check (2nd stage) - test connection. Fixed contact is arrowed

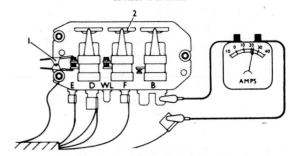

Fig 10.7 CURRENT REGULATOR CHECK — TEST CONNECTION
1 Contacts held closed   2 Adjusting cam

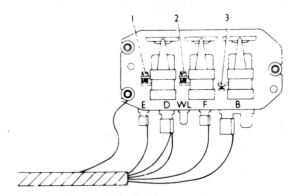

Fig 10.8 CONTROL BOX CONTACTS — CLEANING
1 Voltage regulator contacts   3 Cut-out relay contacts
2 Current regulator contacts

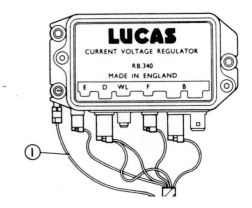

Fig 10.9 CONTROL BOX — WIRING CONNECTIONS
I Black   F Brown/green
E Black   B Brown
D Brown/yellow

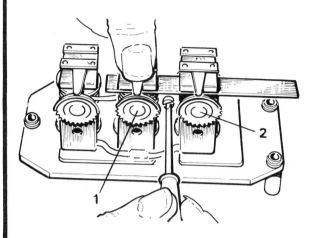

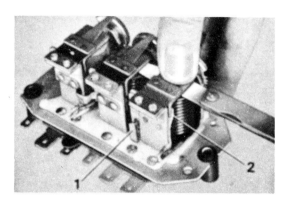

Fig 10.11 CONTROL BOX — AIR GAP SETTINGS
1 Fixed contact   2 Back stop

Fig 10.10 CONTROL BOX — MECHANICAL GAP SETTING
1 Current regulator cam   2 Voltage regulator cam

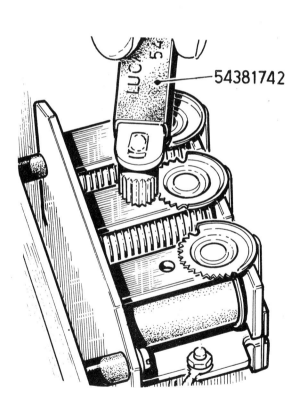

54381742

Fig 10.12 Using the special tool 54381742 to adjust control box settings

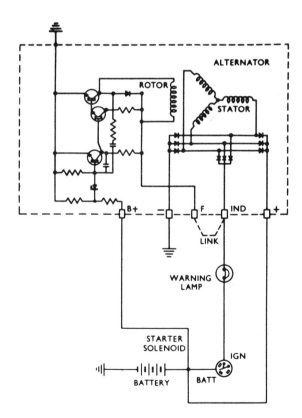

Fig 10.13 Alternator (Lucas 15/17ACR) system circuit diagram

current rather than direct current. This current is rectified (by diodes) into direct current so that it can be stored by the battery. The transistorised regulators are self-limiting in current output so they control only the voltage.

Apart from the renewal of the rotor slip ring brushes and rotor shaft bearings, there are not other parts which need periodic inspection. All other items are sealed assemblies and must be replaced if indications are that they are faulty.

18 Alternators - safety precautions

If there are indications that the charging system is malfunctioning in any way, care must be taken to diagnose faults properly, otherwise damage of a serious and expensive nature may occur to parts which are in fact quite serviceable.

The following basic requirements must be observed at all times, therefore, if damage is to be prevented.
1 ALL alternator systems use a NEGATIVE earth. Even the simple mistake of connecting a battery the wrong way round could burn out the alternator diodes in a few seconds.
2 Before disconnecting any wires in the system the engine and ignition circuits should be switched off. This will minimise accidental short circuits.
3 The alternator must NEVER be run with the output wire disconnected.
4 Always disconnect the battery from the car's electrical system if an outside charging source is being used.
5 Do not use test wire connections that could move accidentally and short circuit against nearby terminals. Short circuits will not blow fuses - they will blow diodes or transistors.
6 Always disconnect the battery cables and alternator output wires before any electric welding work is done on the car body.

19 Lucas 15ACR or 17ACR alternator systems - fault diagnosis

1 It is essential that when a fault occurs the correct procedure is followed to diagnose it. If it is not, the likelihood of damage is high. The safety precautions as described in Section 12 should always be observed.
2 No proper diagnosis is possible without an ammeter (0–100 amps range) a voltmeter (0–50 volts range) and a test lamp (12v 6 watt) being available. If you are unable to acquire these then leave the circuit checking to a competent electrician.
3 Check the obvious first, ie battery, battery terminals, fan belt tension and disconnected wires.
4 Follow the line of diagnosis as shown in Fig 10.14 and the accompanying table.

20 AC Delco alternators - fault diagnosis

Fault diagnosis procedure for this type are not readily translatable into 'Do-it-yourself' terms. If a fault develops it is recommended that proper checks are made by a service station which you know is equipped to deal with this make of alternator.

21 Alternators - removal, replacement and belt adjustment

1 Details of the procedure to be followed when removing, replacing and adjusting the alternator position are given in Chapter 2 being the same as for the dynamo.
2 The only points to note are that for alternators the rear mounting lug is fitted with a split sliding bush. This enables the bolts to be tightened without imposing any strain on the alloy mounting lugs. The front bolt should always be tightened first.
3 If the alternator is levered to tighten the fan belt avoid any strain against the fragile end casing.

Fig 10.14 Lucas 15/17ACR alternators fault diagnosis

1 Check fan belt(s) for tension and condition.
2 Disconnect main output connector and auxiliary connector. Install slave wire with a male Lucar terminal and a female Lucar terminal between alternator negative terminal and socket. Connect ammeter between alternator positive terminal and socket removed from this terminal. Reconnect auxiliary connector.

3 Remove rear cover from alternator. Re-install auxiliary connector, slave and ammeter wires. Bridge outer brush contact strip to ground. Adjust engine speed to give maximum output.

4 Install new or repair alternator.

5 Remove connector from field and sensing terminals (IND and B+). 'Switch On' but do not start engine.

6 Check for short circuit in wire between alternator indicator terminal and warning light bulb.

7 Connect voltmeter between battery positive and negative terminals; increase speed to approximately 1500 rpm. Voltmeter should read 14.1 to 14.5 volts, ammeter reading 7.5 amp maximum. Higher amperage which would probably give lower voltage readings could indicate need to recharge battery before continuing with test.

8 If fan belt tension and condition are satisfactory, faulty battery or overloaded system is indicated. Comparison should be made between electrical loading and alternator output. 15ACR: 28 amp. 17ACR: 36 amp.

9 Remove voltmeter from battery and connect it between battery sensing terminal on alternator (B+) and ground (this should be done without moving socket connector by inserting a probe in rear of connector to contact Lucas female blade terminal of brown 14/.012 wire).

10 Check battery terminals, ground strap connections, and wiring between battery and alternator for poor connection and resistive circuits.

11 Install new 8TR regulator.

12 Check wire from alternator B+ to starter solenoid for continuity.

13 Remove connector from alternator indicator socket and bridge double wires (brown/yellow 9/.012) in connector to ground.

14 Remove rear cover from alternator, re-install socket connectors. Disconnect yellow wire from field diode heat sink.

15 Reconnect yellow wire to field diode heat sink. Connect slave wire between outer brush contact strip and ground.

16 Disconnect slave wire from outer brush contact strip and connect between inner brush contact strip and ground.

17 Check connecting wire between indicator and field terminals in socket connector for continuity.

18 Check warning lamp bulb. Check bulb-holder for loose connection. Check wire (brown/yellow) between alternator indicator terminal, warning lamp bulb and key-start switch for continuity. Note: warning lamp bulb must be 12 volt 2.2 watt.

19 Check that charging system operates satisfactorily by connecting voltmeter across battery terminals and ammeter in series with alternator output circuit. Impose approximate 28 amp (15ACR) or 36 amp (17ACR) load on battery, start engine and increase engine speed until ammeter reads maximum charge, 28 amp and 36 amp respectively. Remove load from battery. Ammeter should then drop slowly back to show trickle charge. Voltmeter should show 14.1 to 14.5 volts

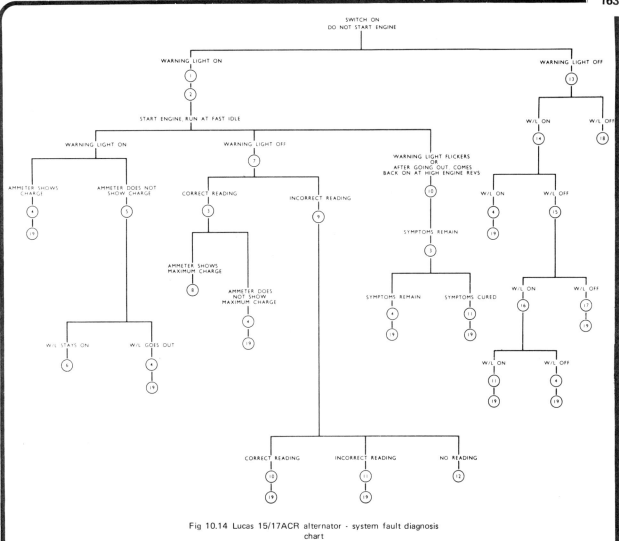

Fig 10.14 Lucas 15/17ACR alternator - system fault diagnosis
chart

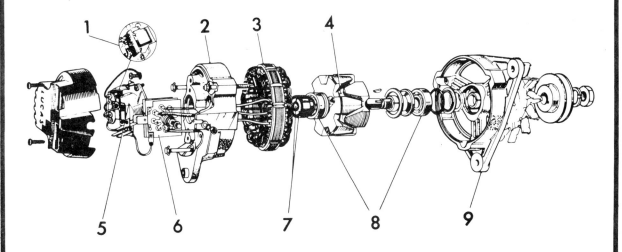

Fig 10.15 LUCAS 15ACR AND 17ACR ALTERNATORS — EXPLODED DRAWING

1 Regulator	4 Rotor	sink)	9 Drive end cover
2 Slip ring end cover	5 Brush housing	7 Slip rings
3 Stator	6 Rectifier (diodes and heat	8 Bearings

4 Electrical connections are through two multi-socket connectors

22 Alternators - dismantling and inspection

1 If tests indicate that the alternator is faulty it is possible that the slip ring brushes and slip rings may be the cause.

2 Alternators require the unsoldering of the stator connections to get at the brushes and slip ring and this is not recommended. If the diodes to which they are attached are overheated they could be damaged.

3 Therefore, we do not recommend dismantling as a general principle, as more damage could be caused to the system - not just the alternator, if a mistake is made.

4 When an alternator is diagnosed as unserviceable it should only be as a result of a thorough check of the complete system. If this is not done a new unit could be completely ruined immediately following installation if something is also at fault elsewhere.

23 Starter motors - testing in the car

1 If the starter motor fails to operate then check the condition of the battery by turning on the headlamps. If they glow brightly for several seconds and then gradually dim, the battery is in an uncharged condition.

2 If the headlamps glow brightly and continue to glow, and it is obvious that the battery is in good condition, then check the tightness of the battery wiring connections (and in particular the earth lead from the battery terminal to its connection on the bodyframe). Check the tightness of the connections at the relay switch and at the starter motor.

3 If the starter motor still fails to turn the fault lies in the wiring the solenoid switch or the motor itself. The following procedure will determine where the fault lies: (To prevent inadvertent starting of the engine remove the HT lead from the coil).

4 Connect a voltmeter (or 12 volt bulb) to the terminal on the solenoid to which the white/red wire is connected (Fig 10.16). If there is no reading (12 volts) when the starter switch is operated, there is a fault in the starter switch or white/red wire.

5 If the previous test is favourable connect voltmeter (or 12 volt bulb) to the two main terminals as shown in Fig 10.17. A 12 volt reading should be obtained (without touching the starter switch). If the starter switch is operated the reading should fall to zero (bulb goes out). If it does not the solenoid switch needs renewal.

6 The remaining terminal on the solenoid switch, to which the white/blue lead is attached, is the cold start feed to the coil which directs current to the coil only when the solenoid is operating. It can be tested by connecting a voltmeter (or 12v bulb) to the terminal, after disconnecting the lead, as shown in Fig 10.18. When the starter is operated there should be a 9v reading at least (bulb glows). If not there must be a fault in the internal solenoid connection.

7 On pre-engaged starters the solenoid switch is mounted directly on top of the starter motor. For these units the procedure is as follows:

8 Disconnect the white/red wire from the solenoid and connect the voltmeter (or bulb) from the wire to earth. When the key start switch is operated the voltage should read 12v. Otherwise the wiring or start switch is faulty (Fig 10.19).

9 Connect the voltmeter across the two main terminals of the solenoid and a 12v reading should be given. When the key start is operated the voltage should drop to zero. If ctherwise, the solenoid needs renewal (Fig 10.20).

10 To check the cold start feed to the coil, disconnect the white/blue wire from the 'IGN' terminal and connect the voltmeter from the terminal to earth. When the start switch is operated the reading should be at least 9 volts (Fig 10.21).

11 On either type of starter a solenoid fault confined to the non-functioning of the coil feed wire does not necessarily mean that the car will not start, although difficulty will certainly occur in cold weather or if the battery charge is low.

12 NOTE: When a new or reconditioned engine has been fitted it will be initially very stiff to turn. This could result in a very rapid discharge of the battery and slow turning of the engine before the engine has been successfully started. It is always advisable to have an additional battery available (in someone elses car perhaps) with a pair of jumper leads so that the extra power is available when it is really needed.

13 If the starter motor is the faulty item it must be removed from the car for inspection. Make sure that it is not merely jammed. This can be ascertained by putting a spanner on the square end of the shaft which protrudes. If it turns easily the starter is free. Otherwise use the spanner to turn the shaft in either direction until it is completely free. This latter facility applies only to inertia type starters.

24 Starter motor M35 G/I - removal and replacement

1 Disconnect the battery earth lead from the negative terminal.

2 Remove the cable from the starter terminal (see photo).

3 Remove the two bolts and lockwashers securing the starter motor to the clutch housing and lift out the starter and spacer plate.

4 Replacement is the reverse procedure of removal - do not forget the spacer plate (photos).

25 Starter motor M35 G/I - dismantling and reassembly

1 With the starter motor on the bench, loosen the screw on the cover band and slip the cover band off. With a piece of wire bent into the shape of a hook, lift back each of the brush springs in turn and check the movement of the brushes in their holders by pulling on the flexible connectors. If the brushes are so worn that their faces do not rest against the commutator, or if the ends of the brush leads are exposed on their working face, they must be renewed.

2 If any of the brushes tend to stick in their holders then wash them with a petrol moistened cloth and, if necessary, lightly polish the sides of the brush with a very fine file, until the brushes move quite freely in their holders.

3 If the surface of the commutator is dirty or blackened, clean it with a petrol dampened rag. Secure the starter motor in a vice and check it by connecting a heavy gauge cable between the starter motor terminal and a 12 volt battery.

4 Connect the cable from the other battery terminal to earth in the starter motor body. If the motor turns at high speed it is in good order.

5 If the starter motor still fails to function or if it is wished to renew the brushes, then it is necessary to further dismantle the motor.

6 Lift the brush springs with the wire hook and lift all four brushes out of their holders one at a time.

7 Remove the terminal nuts and washers from the terminal post on the commutator end bracket.

8 Unscrew the two through bolts which hold the end plates together and pull off the commutator end bracket. Also remove the driving end bracket which will come away complete with the armature.

9 At this stage if the brushes are to be renewed, their flexible connectors must be unsoldered and the flexible connectors of new brushes soldered in their place. Check that the new brushes move freely in their holders as detailed above. If cleaning the commutator with petrol fails to remove all the burnt areas and spots, then wrap a piece of glass paper round the commutator and rotate the armature.

10 If the commutator is very badly worn, remove the drive gear as detailed in the following section. Then mount the armature in a lathe and, with the lathe turning at high speed, take a very fine cut out of the commutator and finish the surface by polishing with glass paper. DO NOT UNDERCUT THE MICA INSULATORS BETWEEN THE COMMUTATOR SEGMENTS.

11 With the starter motor dismantled, test the four field coils for an

165

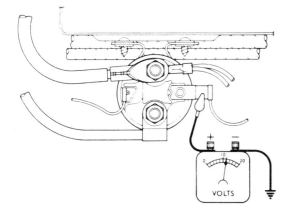

Fig 10.16 Starter motor (inertia). Connection for feed to solenoid check

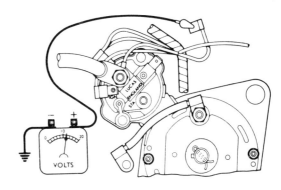

Fig 10.19 Starter motor (pre-engaged). Connection for feed to Solenoid check

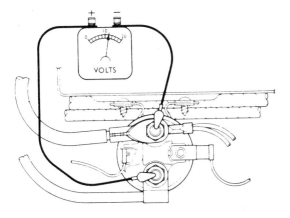

Fig 10.17 Starter motor (inertia). Connection for solenoid main contact check

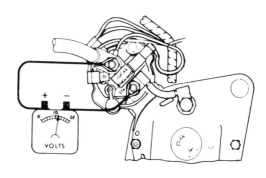

Fig 10.20 Starter motor (pre-engaged). Connection for solenoid main contact check

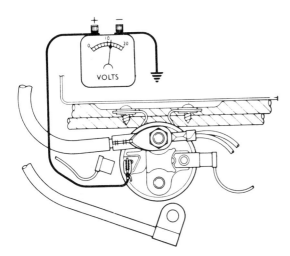

Fig 10.18 Starter motor (inertia). Connection for cold start feed to coil check

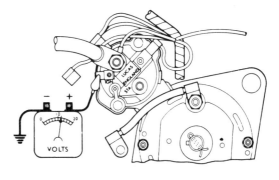

Fig 10.21 Starter motor (pre-engaged). Connection for cold start feed to coil check

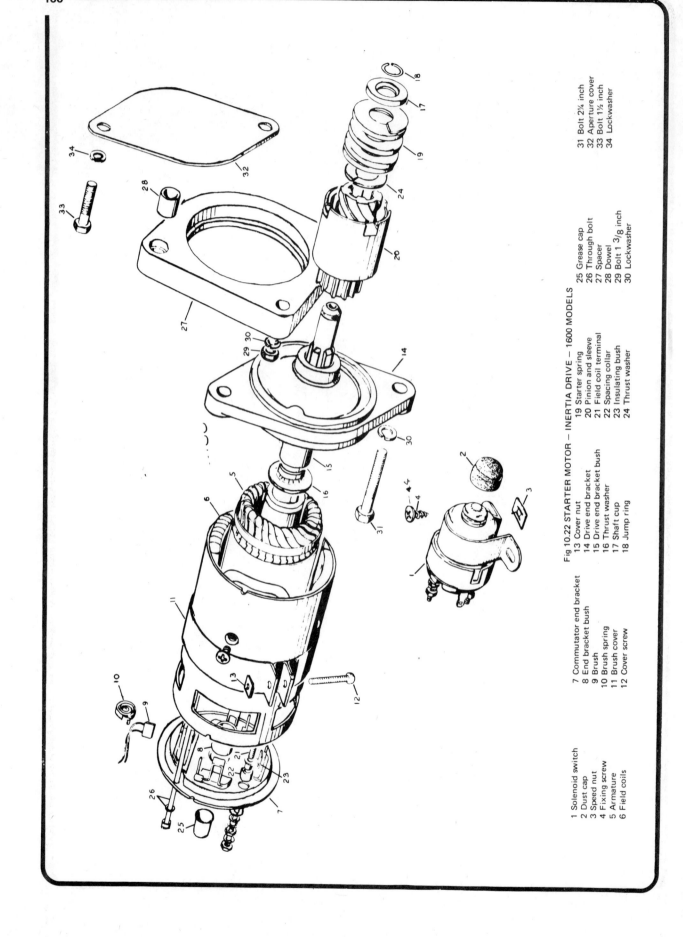

Fig 10.22 STARTER MOTOR – INERTIA DRIVE – 1600 MODELS

1 Solenoid switch
2 Dust cap
3 Speed nut
4 Fixing screw
5 Armature
6 Field coils

7 Commutator end bracket
8 End bracket bush
9 Brush
10 Brush spring
11 Brush cover
12 Cover screw

13 Cover nut
14 Drive end bracket
15 Drive end bracket bush
16 Thrust washer
17 Shaft cup
18 Jump ring

19 Starter spring
20 Pinion and sleeve
21 Field coil terminal
22 Spacing collar
23 Insulating bush
24 Thrust washer

25 Grease cap
26 Through bolt
27 Spacer
28 Dowel
29 Bolt 1 3/8 inch
30 Lockwasher

31 Bolt 2¼ inch
32 Aperture cover
33 Bolt 1½ inch
34 Lockwasher

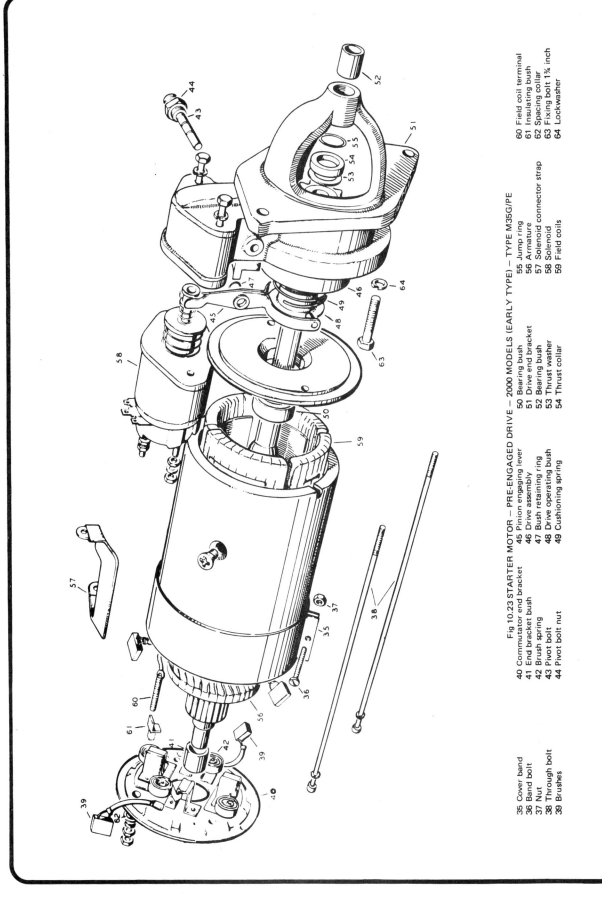

Fig 10.23 STARTER MOTOR – PRE-ENGAGED DRIVE – 2000 MODELS (EARLY TYPE) – TYPE M35G/PE

35 Cover band	45 Pinion engaging lever	55 Jump ring
36 Band bolt	46 Drive assembly	56 Armature
37 Nut	47 Bush retaining ring	57 Solenoid connector strap
38 Through bolt	48 Drive operating bush	58 Solenoid
39 Brushes	49 Cushioning spring	59 Field coils
40 Commutator end bracket	50 Bearing bush	60 Field coil terminal
41 End bracket bush	51 Drive end bracket	61 Insulating bush
42 Brush spring	52 Bearing bush	62 Spacing collar
43 Pivot bolt	53 Thrust washer	63 Fixing bolt 1¾ inch
44 Pivot bolt nut	54 Thrust collar	64 Lockwasher

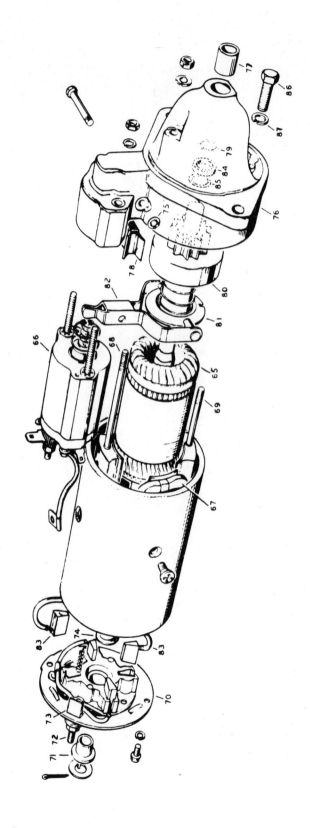

Fig 10.24 STARTER MOTOR – PRE-ENGAGED DRIVE – 2000 MODELS (LATER TYPE) – TYPE M35J/PE

65 Armature	72 Field terminal	80 Roller clutch drive
66 Solenoid	73 Terminal insulating bush	81 Bearing bush
67 Field coil	74 Thrust plate	82 Lever and pivot assembly
68 Pole piece and long stud	75 Pivot pin retaining clip	83 Brush
69 Pole piece and short stud	76 Drive end bracket	84 Thrust collar
70 Commutator end bracket	77 End bracket bush	85 Shim
71 Commutator end bracket bush	78 Grommet	86 Fixing bolt
	79 Jump ring	87 Lockwasher

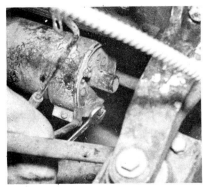

24.2 Remove the cable from the starter terminal

24.4a Replacing starter motor M35G/I - Do not forget the spacer

24.4b Starter M35G/I in position

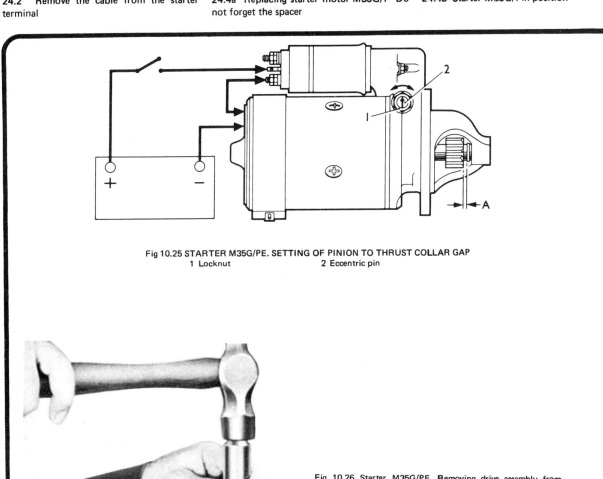

Fig 10.25 STARTER M35G/PE. SETTING OF PINION TO THRUST COLLAR GAP
1 Locknut   2 Eccentric pin

Fig 10.26 Starter M35G/PE. Removing drive assembly from armature shaft

open circuit. Connect a 12 volt battery with a 12 volt bulb in one of the leads between the field terminal post and the tapping point of the field coils to which the brushes are connected. An open circuit is proved by the bulb not lighting.

12 If the bulb lights, it does not necessarily mean that the field coils are in order, as there is a possibility that one of the coils will be earthing to the starter yoke or pole shoes. To check this, remove the lead from the brush connector and place it against a clean portion of the starter yoke. If the bulb lights, the field coils are earthing. Replacement of the field coils calls for the use of a wheel operated screwdriver, a soldering iron, caulking and riveting operations and is beyond the scope of the majority of owners. The starter yoke should be taken to a reputable electrical engineering works for new field coils to be fitted. Alternatively, purchase an exchange Lucas starter motor.

13 If the armature is damaged this will be evident after visual inspection. Look for signs of burning, discolouration and for conductors that have lifted away from the commutator. Reassembly is a straightforward reversal of the dismantling procedure.

26 Inertia starter pinion (M35 G/I and J/I) - dismantling and reassembly

1 The starter motor drive is of the outboard type. When the starter motor is operated the pinion moves into contact with the flywheel gear ring by moving in towards the starter motor.

2 If the engine kicks back, or the pinion fails to engage with the flywheel gear ring when the starter motor is actuated no undue strain is placed on the armature shaft, as the pinion sleeve disengages from the pinion and turns independently.

3 It is essential to obtain a press or clamp which can safely compress the heavy spring at the end of the shaft. Fig 10.27 shows the official tool (JWP 376) used by Vauxhall agents for this, but if one possesses a vice and a little ingenuity it can be done in other ways. As soon as the pressure is taken off the circlip it can be removed with a screwdriver. Then release the pressure on the spring.

4 Remove the spring collar and spring.

5 Slide the remaining parts with a rotary action off the armature shaft.

6 Reassembly is a straightforward reversal of the above procedure. NOTE: It is most important that the drive gear is completely free from oil, grease and dirt. With the drive gear removed, clean all the parts thoroughly in paraffin. UNDER NO CIRCUMSTANCES OIL THE DRIVE COMPONENTS. Lubrication of the drive components causes dust to adhere and results in sticking.

27 Starter motor armature shaft bushes - inspection, removal and replacement

1 With the starter motor stripped down check the condition of the bushes. They should be renewed when they are sufficiently worn to allow visible side movement of the armature shaft.

2 The old bushes are simply driven out with a suitable drift and the new bushes inserted by the same method. As the bearings are of the porous type it is essential that they are properly saturated with engine oil before fitting.

28 Starter (M35 J/I)

The M35 J/I starter is different from the G/I only insofar as an end face type commutator is used. In this respect it is almost identical to the M35 J/PE starter dealt with in the next sections.

29 Pre-engaged starter motors (M35 G/PE, M35 J/PE) - general description

1 Victors with the 1975 cc engine have pre-engaged starters. The motor part is the same as for inertia starters and both regular and end face commutators are used. The drive pinion engagement is by means of a solenoid actuator and starter switch mounted on the starter motor. The starter motor does not turn until the pinion is engaged with the flywheel ring gear. To provide for the possibility of overrun the pinion is driven through a one way roller clutch.

2 The M35 G/PE is the same as the M35 G/I models except for the pinion mechanism which is described in the next section. For motor details refer to Section 25.

30 Pre-engaged starter motors (M35 G/PE, M35 J/PE) - dismantling and reassembly

1 It will be necessary to dismantle the starter motor if checks indicate that failure to turn the engine is due to faults with it. After some time the brushes will also wear sufficiently to warrant renewal.

2 The solenoid may be removed after detaching the short connecting cable from the other main terminal and removing the two securing nuts. If this is all that needs replacing, a new one can be fitted over the existing plunger now.

3 To dismantle the motor further, remove the short bolts, or through bolts, which hold the commutator end bracket with the brush gear to the main yoke. Also remove the split pin, washers and shims from the end of the shaft. The end bracket may then be carefully removed. Do not lose the thrust washer which is located over the end of the shaft inside.

4 Next remove the bolts holding the drive end cover in position (if necessary) and the end cover complete with armature and shaft may be drawn out of the yoke. On 'G' versions the eccentric pivot pin must be taken out first (Fig 10.28).

5 On 'J' versions the pivot pin must be removed before the end cover can be separated from the armature.

6 To take the drive pinion and clutch assembly off the armature shaft it will be necessary to drive the thrust collar down the shaft with a piece of suitable tube and then remove the circlip which is exposed (Fig 10.26). If the driving gear assembly is worn the whole unit should be renewed. To check that the roller clutch is in good condition it should lock and take up the drive in one direction immediately it is turned. When turned in the opposite direction it should rotate smoothly and evenly. The whole clutch unit should also slide easily without excessive play along the splines of the armature shaft.

7 Examine the brushes to ensure that they are not less than the permitted minimum length of .30 inch (7.5 mm). If they need renewal, obtain first the new ones. Two will be supplied complete with their terminal post and the other two separately for soldering to the field coil end tags. On the M35 'J' starters which have an aluminium strip field winding, the old brushes should be cut off leaving a ¼ inch (7 mm) at least of the old copper wire to which the new brushes may be soldered. (You cannot solder aluminium!). Make sure the new brushes have sufficiently long leads and are in the proper position.

8 Clean up the face of the commutator with a petrol moistened rag. Light scoring may be cleaned up with fine glass paper. If there is deep scoring the commutator face may be skimmed in a lathe, provided it does not diminish in thickness below .080 inch (2 mm) (see Fig 10.29). Do not undercut the segment insulation.

9 If it is suspected that the insulation of the field coils is damaged it is recommended that the coils are removed, checked and repaired, by specialists with the proper equipment.

10 Check that the shaft is a good fit into each of the end plate bushes and renew the brushes if necessary.

11 Assembly is a procedure that must be carried out in sequence with attention to several points to ensure that it is correct.

12 First assemble the engagement lever to the solenoid plunger so that the chamfered corner faces the solenoid. Then make sure that

Fig 10.27 Starter (inertia). Spring compressor applied to release the circlip

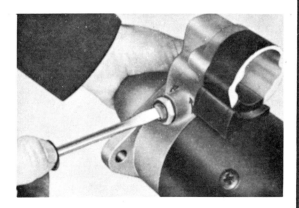

Fig 10.28 Starter M35G/PE. Removing eccentric pivot pin

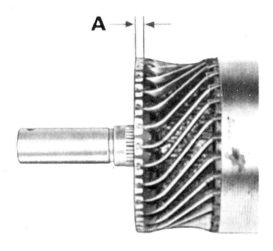

Fig 10.29 End face commutator. Dimension 'A' is minimum permissible thickness (.080 inch)

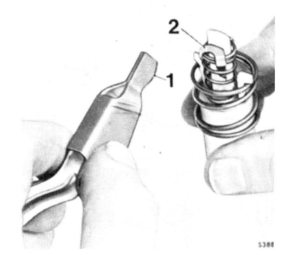

Fig 10.30 STARTER M35J/PE. ASSEMBLY OF SOLENOID PLUNGER AND ENGAGEMENT LEVER
1 Engagement lever   2 Retaining plate

the retaining plate is correct, relative to the lever (Fig 10.30).

13 Next fit the drive pinion and clutch assembly on the armature shaft, fit the engagement lever fork to the clutch and assemble the whole lot together to the drive end cover. Then fit a new lever pivot pin and peen over the end to prevent it coming out.

14 Replace the yoke, and then lightly screw up the end cover bolts (if fitted).

15 Next place the thrust washer over the commutator end of the shaft, fit all the brushes into their appropriate holders in the end cover and replace the end cover on to the shaft. Both end covers have locating pips to ensure they are fitted correctly to the yoke.

16 Replace the through bolts or end cover bolts as appropriate and tighten them up at both ends.

17 Replace the thrust washer and shims to the end of the shaft, install a split pin, and then measure the end float gap between the thrust washer and the end cover with a feeler gauge. It should be no more than .010 inch (.25 mm). Additional shims should be added to reduce the end float as required. This does not apply to 'G' models.

18 Next replace the rubber pad between the drive bracket (under the solenoid plunger housing) and the yoke, and refit the solenoid. Reconnect the short cable to the solenoid terminal.

19 Before replacing the starter in the car after reassembly it is a good idea to check that it is functioning properly by connecting it temporarily to the battery.

20 With 'G' models the actuating arm pivot pin has to be positioned so that the gap between the end of the pinion and the thrust collar is correct at .005—.010 inch (Fig 10.25). This measurement is made with the pinion thrown forward by the solenoid; so it will be necessary to connect a battery up to position it.

31 Fuses and thermal circuit breaker

1 The fuse block is mounted on the right hand side of the dash panel. The connectors to the fuse terminals, however, are fitted underneath. The thermal circuit breaker is incorporated in the light switch except on 2000 SL and VX 4/90 models. On these it is fitted underneath the instrument panel next to the glove box.

2 Four 35 amp fuses are used. They protect the circuits as listed in the specifications at the beginning of the Chapter.

3 If any of the fuses blow, check the circuits on that fuse to trace the fault, before renewing the fuse.

4 Headlamp and sidelamp circuits are protected by a thermal circuit breaker. This opens if the load exceeds 33 amps for ½ to 3 minutes. It can be tested by putting an ammeter and variable resistance in the circuit in series.

32 Flasher circuit - fault tracing and rectification

1 The flasher unit is located in a clip behind the centre panel of the facia which can be removed by undoing the securing screws.

2 If, when operated to either side, the warning lamp on the dashboard stays on but does not flash and there is no audible warning, then one or both signal bulbs are not working.

3 If the warning bulb does not light and the frequency of flashing is slightly reduced, then the warning bulb is defective.

4 Before assuming that anything else is wrong (other than blown bulbs) make quite sure that the bulb caps and sockets are perfectly clean and corrosion free. Water, which may seep in due to a leaking seal or cracked lens, could cause this sort of trouble. Do not forget to check the fuse also.

5 Where there is total failue , the simplest check is to substitute a known good flasher unit. Finally check the switch if no other check reveals anything wrong.

6 The combined dip, horn, headlamp flasher and turn signal switch is mounted on the steering column with a clamp. Access to it can be gained after removing the column shroud. If the wires for the flasher circuit are detached and bridged, the fault can be isolated to either switch or wiring.

33 Horn - fault tracing and rectification

1 If the horn works badly or fails completely, check the wiring leading to it for short circuits and loose connections. Check that the horn is firmly secured and that there is nothing lying on the horn body.

2 If the horn still does not work or operates incorrectly check the switch. This can be done by unscrewing the end cap on the combined switch. Bridge the two terminal blades and if the horn works check the contact piece inside the cap.

3 The horn adjusting screw is located in the back of the horn body. To adjust it turn it anticlockwise until nothing is heard then turn clockwise until the horn is just heard. Then turn another ¼ turn clockwise.

34 Headlamps and sidelamps

1 Headlamps fitted are either sealed beam units or pre-focus.

2 With sealed beam units the sidelamp bulb is carried in a holder integral with the connector and the light shines through a transparent area in the sealed beam unit reflector.

3 On pre-focus units (which have renewable main bulbs) the side lamp bulb holder is a push fit into the reflector.

4 On main beam all four lamps are in operation. On dip, the inner lamps go out and the outer ones change to the dip filament.

5 To gain access to the connectors at the back of the light unit first remove the plastic cover by squeezing the sides. On pre-focus units the bulb may then be removed after disengaging the clip.

6 Light units are removed from the front. First remove the radiator grille (see Chapter 12) and then slacken the three cross head screws (not the two plain screws which control the beam setting) (Fig 10.33). A small movement anticlockwise will enable the rim to be released.

7 Headlamp beam adjustment is best done with proper optical alignment equipment. However, if the lamps are seriously out, adjustment can be carried out on the two screws mentioned in the previous paragraph. The rear ends of these screws project into the engine compartment. Ideally, they are turned with a proper square section key. (If you wish to use the other ends of the screws it means taking the radiator grill off!).

8 The inner lamp should have a beam setting straight forward with ½° downward deflection. The outer lamps should be set when on dipped beams. They should then aim 2° down and 2° left (RHD) or 2° right (LHD).

35 Rear lamp clusters

1 Two makes or rear lamp are fitted, Lucas or Magnatex. Although similar in external appearance the components are different and are not interchangeable (except for bulbs and bulbholders).

2 Access to the units is from inside the boot (or rear corners of the compartment in estates). A cover, held by either knurled nuts (saloons) or screws (estates) is first removed.

3 Under the cover is the bulb bolt, also held by knurled nuts (2 or 4 depending on make) and after releasing these the bulbs are accessible.

4 To renew the lens remove the whole assembly from the body panel by undoing the four nuts on the rim studs. The two screws retaining the lens to the body are then accessible.

5 When replacing the units ensure that the sealing gaskets are in good condition and properly positioned and do not overtighten any of the nuts and screws.

36 Windscreen wipers - fault finding

1 If the wipers do not work when they are switched on first check the No 1 fuse. If this is sound then there is either an open circuit in the wiring or switch, the wiper motor is faulty, or the pivot spindles

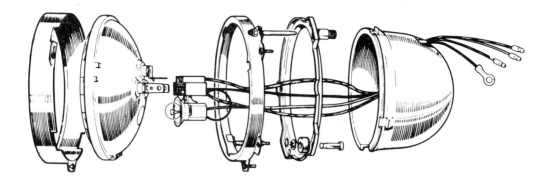

Fig 10.31 Headlamp assembly - (sealed beam unit)

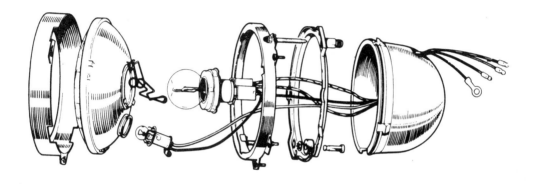

Fig 10.32 Headlamp assembly (pre-focus unit)

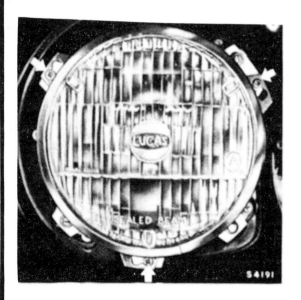

Fig 10.33 Headlamp unit removal screws (arrowed)

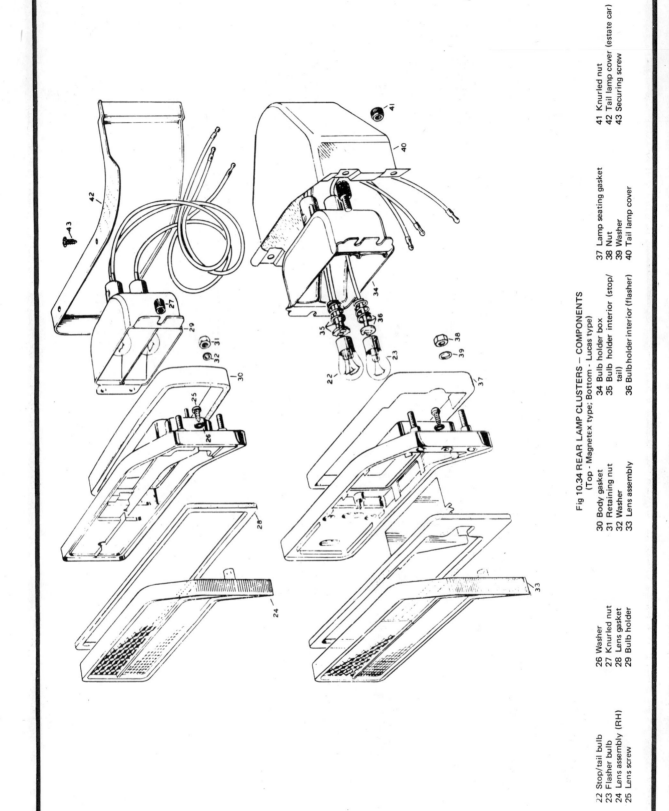

Fig 10.34 REAR LAMP CLUSTERS – COMPONENTS
(Top - Magnetex type; Bottom - Lucas type)

22 Stop/tail bulb	26 Washer	30 Body gasket	34 Bulb holder box	37 Lamp seating gasket	41 Knurled nut
23 Flasher bulb	27 Knurled nut	31 Retaining nut	35 Bulb holder interior (stop/tail)	38 Nut	42 Tail lamp cover (estate car)
24 Lens assembly (RH)	28 Lens gasket	32 Washer	36 Bulb holder interior (flasher)	39 Washer	43 Securing screw
25 Lens screw	29 Bulb holder	33 Lens assembly		40 Tail lamp cover	

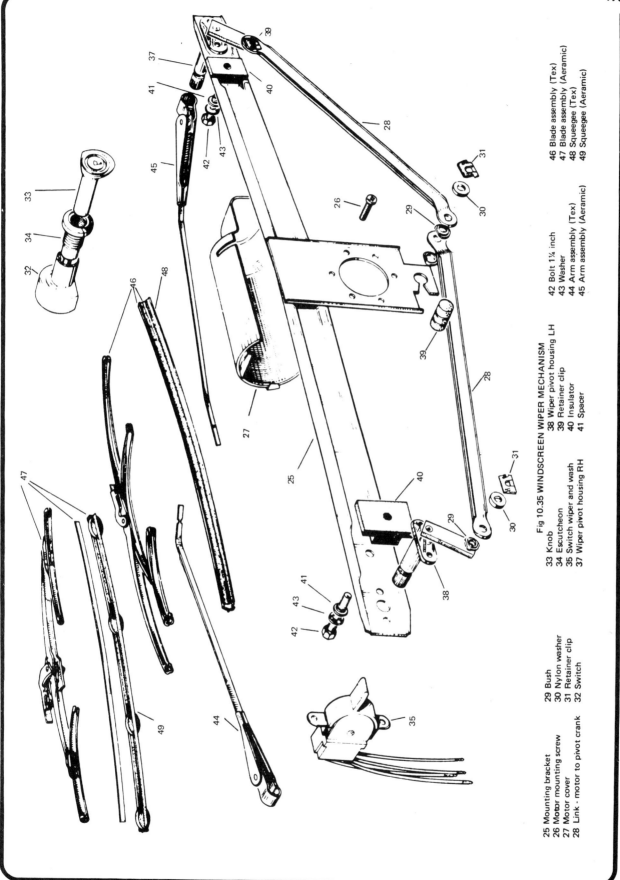

Fig 10.35 WINDSCREEN WIPER MECHANISM

25 Mounting bracket
26 Motor mounting screw
27 Motor cover
28 Link - motor to pivot crank

29 Bush
30 Nylon washer
31 Retainer clip
32 Switch

33 Knob
34 Escutcheon
35 Switch wiper and wash
37 Wiper pivot housing RH

38 Wiper pivot housing LH
39 Retainer clip
40 Insulator
41 Spacer

42 Bolt 1¼ inch
43 Washer
44 Arm assembly (Tex)
45 Arm assembly (Aeramic)

46 Blade assembly (Tex)
47 Blade assembly (Aeramic)
48 Squeegee (Tex)
49 Squeegee (Aeramic)

or linkages may be binding.

2 If the wipers work intermittently then suspect a short circuit in the motor. Alternatively, the armature shaft end float adjustment may be too tight or the wiper linkage may be binding.

3 Should the wipers not stop when they are turned off there must be a short circuit in the switch, wiring or park segment in the motor.

37 Windscreen washer - fault finding

1 If the windscreen washers do not work when pumped, first check that there is water in the washer reservoir and that the jets in the discharge nozzles are clear (poke them with a pin).

2 Examine the water pipe connections at all junctions to ensure they are firmly fitted.

3 If there is still no jet from the screen nozzles detach the pipes from the pump unit and remove the unit from the dashboard with the wiper switch.

4 In a bowl of water, submerge the inlet of the pump, operate it, and water should come from the outlet under reasonable pressure. Then operate the pump with the outlet only under water, when bubbles will come out. After a few strokes in this manner release the plunger and lift the outlet out of the water. If, on operating the pump again, some water comes from the unit then it means that the non-return valves inside are not functioning properly and the unit should be replaced. If the pump is satisfactory then the only possible faults can be in the suction and delivery pipes, unions or nozzles all of which must be carefully examined for splits, kinks, blockages or leaking connections.

5 On models fitted with two speed wipers the washer pump is electrically driven and is mounted on the ventilator panel under the bonnet on top of the water reservoir. Fig 10.36 gives an exploded picture of the pump assembly. It is possible to renew a worn impeller by removing the end cover, seal, distance piece and washer.

38 Windscreen wipers - removal and replacement

1 The windscreen wiper motor has to be removed complete with the wiper operating links and arms, which are held in a rigid frame and comprise the complete windscreen wiper assembly. The unit is located under the air intake grille at the lower centre outside edge of the windscreen (Fig 10.37).

2 Disconnect the battery and take off the windscreen wiper arms.

3 Remove the grille securing screws. Underneath the assembly will be seen to be held by two bolts and a rubber retaining plug. When those have been freed the assembly can be lifted up to disconnect the motor leads and then lifted out.

39 Windscreen wipers - dismantling, inspection and reassembly

1 Other than for normal wear, the bearings and gears in the motor should not deteriorate and if for any reason the motor should cease to function altogether, it is probably due to the wiper mechanism jamming or seizing which has overloaded the motor and burnt it out. In such instances the purchasing of either armature or field coils, and probably brushes as well, is hardly comparable to buying an exchange unit. If the motor ceases to function for no immediately obvious reason proceed as follows:

2 Remove the end frame by levering out the two retaining clips.

3 Remove the screw securing the terminal end cover to expose the drive gears.

4 The end frame and armature can be withdrawn together, care being taken to prevent loss of the nylon thrust bearing at the end of the worm shaft.

5 The brush plate and gear cover are a complete assembly and can be withdrawn together.

6 If any of the spindle brushes are worn, the cover complete (in which they are fitted) will need renewal, as they are not serviced (by Vauxhall) separately.

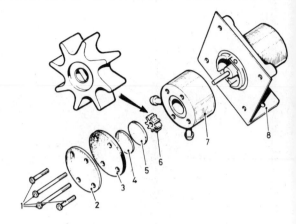

Fig 10.36 WINDSCREEN WASHER PUMP (ELECTRIC)
1 Cover bolts	5 Nylon washer
2 End cover	6 Impeller
3 Seal	7 Pump housing
4 Distance piece	8 Motor body

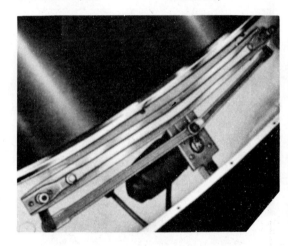

Fig 10.37 Windscreen wiper assembly - location

Fig 10.38 Instrument panel - location of instrument illumination bulb (arrowed)

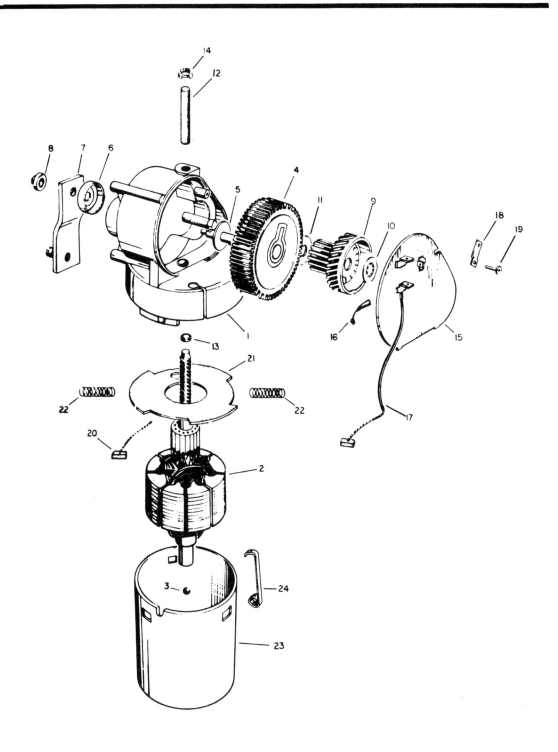

Fig 10.39 WINDSCREEN WIPER MOTOR

1 Housing and bearings
2 Armature
3 Thrust ball
4 Cross shaft and gear
5 Thrust washer
6 Water shield

7 Crank and pin
8 Locknut
9 Wormwheel and pinion
10 Retainer
11 Thrust washer
12 Thrust screw

13 Thrust bearing
14 Locknut
15 Cover assembly (single speed)
16 Brush and terminal
17 Brush and terminal (2 speed)
18 Terminal

19 Screw
20 Brush (single speed)
21 Brush plate
22 Brush spring
23 End frame
24 Frame clip

7 New carbon brushes may be fitted. One of them has to be soldered to the existing lead so when cutting the old lead leave sufficient length for soldering (Fig 10.40).

8 One of the most important features of reassembly is to make sure the end float in the armature and cross shafts is within specification. Excessive end float is what causes jamming and stiffness leading to overloading and a burnt out motor.

9 Make sure that the water shield and crank are assembled to the cross shaft so that the relative positions of the self-park segment and crank are correct as indicated in the illustration (Fig 10.43).

10 Before reassembly begins lubricate the armature end frame bush with engine oil and put anti-scuffing paste on the thrust ball recess in the shaft.

11 Hold back the carbon brushes by hooking the leads over the tags on the brush holders. Then they can be released through the clip holes in the end cover, after the end cover has been replaced.

12 When the motor is reassembled, test it with an ammeter in circuit if possible. Even though it runs, if the current used is above 1 amp then trouble may be expected because something is stiff and causing extra loading which the motor cannot take. While the motor is running, tap the end frame to help settle the bearings. If necessary adjust the end thrust screw but watch the loading on the ammeter whilst doing so to see that it does not increase more than .1 amp (Fig 10.41, 10.42).

13 Test that the self-park works also by re-arranging the wiring as mentioned in the connection illustration (Fig 10.41).

14 If any of the nylon bushes in the pivots and link arms are worn, they can be removed and renewed by simply snapping them out of position. The pivot assembly can be renewed also. Drill out the rivets and re-rivet new units in position. Refit the motor as shown in the illustration (Fig 10.44).

15 Two speed wipers are similar in construction - the difference being in the terminal plate and armature. The terminal plate also carries a thermal overload cut-out which protects the motor if the mechanism jams (Fig 10.45). Test connections for the two speed version are illustrated (Fig 10.42).

---

40 Instrument panel - Victor

---

1 There are many reasons which may require the owner to get access to the lamps, switches, speedometer head and instrument cluster.

   Where faulty gauges or warning lights are suspected make sure first that the sender units have been checked as appropriate (water temperature, fuel tank contents, oil pressure). These items are referred to in the relevant chapters.

2 Early Victors were equipped with two main units - speedometer comprising one and a cluster of warning lamps in the other (ignition, oil, main beam, temperature) together with a gauge for fuel. Three push/pull switches operated lights, wipers and fog lamps.

   Later models (Super, 2000 SL) were modified somewhat and the temperature warning lamp was replaced by a gauge. Instead of all switches being mounted on the instrument surround panel, the fog lamp and lighting switches (now changed to lever type) only were mounted on the surround and turn signal indication lights were incorporated in each one - fog (left) and lights (right). The wiper switch was mounted on a separate lower facia panel as was the choke pull.

3 To begin getting access for any reason first remove the instrument cluster surround which is held simply by screws. On later models the lower panel (on which the choke control and wiper switch are mounted) must be removed first. It is also secured by two screws.

4 The centre panel on the dashboard is covered by a trim panel which can be prised off. After removing the screws securing the panel access to the rear of the instrument clusters is possible. This is necessary to undo the speedometer cable from the back of the speedo head. The face level ventilator (passenger side) and long panel must come out on later models.

5 After the speedo cable the two instrument assemblies complete with the mounting panel can be brought out forwards. Access to the

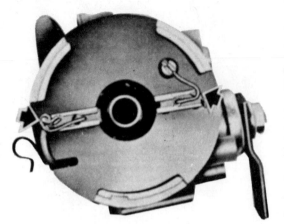

Fig 10.40 Windscreen wiper motor - terminal plate and carbon brushes (single speed motor)

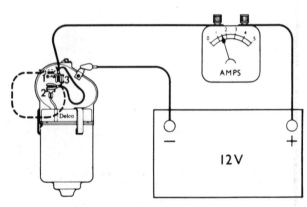

Fig 10.41 Windscreen wiper motor (single speed) running test. Connection of battery and ammeter. Continuous line shows connection for normal running. Dotted line from 2 to 1 shows additional lead connected to test self park

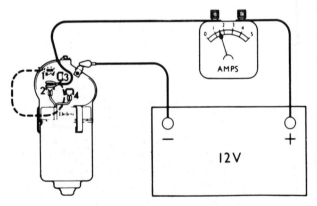

Fig 10.42 Windscreen wiper motor (2 speed) running test. Connection of battery and ammeter. Continuous line shows connection for low speed running. For high speed running move lead from terminal 2 to 4.
To check self park move supply lead to terminal 3 and add another lead (dotted line between terminals 1 and 2

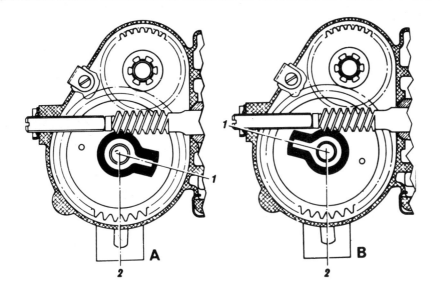

Fig 10.43 WINDSCREEN WIPER MOTOR – CORRECT POSITION OF PARKING SEGMENT (1) TO CRANK (2)
A Left hand drive   B Right hand drive

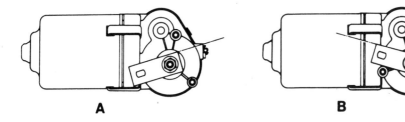

Fig 10.44 WINDSCREEN WIPER MOTOR, POSITION OF CRANK AT SELF PARK
(a) LHD   (b) RHD

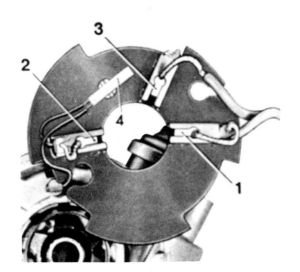

Fig 10.45 WINDSCREEN WIPER MOTOR (2 SPEED), ILLUS-
TRATION OF BRUSH PLATE
1 and 2 Slow speed brushes   4 Bi-metal strip safety cut-out
2 and 3 High speed brushes

instrument lights is then possible (Fig 10.38).

6 The connection bulbs in the rear of the instrument cluster is by means of a printed circuit and the capless warning lamps fit into holders which in turn are a push fit into the circuiting. Care must be taken to see that the two contact strips on the lamp holders match up with the copper conductors of the printed circuit when replaced (Fig 10.46).

7 To remove the fuel gauge from the cluster it will be necessary to pull out all the warning lamp bulb holders. Then squeeze the sides of the multi-socket connector to release it from the centre of the printed circuit. Then remove the clips securing the front glass and the instrument lamp lenses (Fig 10.55).

Two small screws on the face of the instrument are removed to enable the mask and lens to come out and the two nuts at the back are then removed.

8 Similarly the speedometer can be taken out after removing the appropriate clips and screws.

9 If a temperature gauge is fitted (later models) it comes out in the same fashion as the fuel gauge. Once all the warning lamps and gauges are released it will be found that the printed circuit can be taken away when the adhesive strip in the centre is removed.

11 Reassembly is a reversal of these procedures. Make sure the printed circuit tag is engaged by the stud of the fuel gauge (Fig 10.48) (and temperature gauge, if fitted). It should also engage over the peg in the speedo casing and be re-secured with adhesive tape (Fig 10.54).

12 The switches on early models may be removed after first taking off the instrument surround. The switch knobs are released by pressing in the plunger button with a suitable rod (Fig 10.47). Undo the locking ring and remove the switch from behind. On later models the lever type switches mounted on the surround can be levered out from the front (Fig 10.53).

41 Instrument panel (VX 4/90)

1 The VX 4/90 in the FD series was introduced at the same time as the Ventora II and the instrument panel is identical. The main panel is mounted similarly to the late model Victor but in place of the warning lamp cluster is a tachometer (impulse type). The 'lights on' main beam and turn signal warning lamps are mounted in push fit units each side of the main panel. The main light and wiper and washer switches are fitted on the centre console behind the gear lever.

2 Four separate instruments are installed centrally on the instrument panel. The whole assembly can be drawn back when the five screws are removed.

3 The carrier and instruments are then separated from the lower facia panel by removing another four screws (Fig 10.57).

42 Fuel and temperature gauges, oil and temperature warning lamps - testing

1 Early models had a fuel gauge and oil and temperature warning lights. The fuel gauge will need to be removed completely for testing and it is essential to check that the tank unit is functioning properly first (Chapter 3). It can be done with the instrument installed but you will need a square multi-socket connector and wires and it is not worth going to the trouble of getting hold of one. If the tank unit is satisfactory connect the gauge up with two jumper leads to the tank unit with a 12v battery in circuit. If it works then something is wrong with the wiring between the sender and the gauge. If it does not work a new gauge is needed.

2 The oil warning lamp should light when the ignition is on and the engine stopped. If the connection at the pressure sender switch is renewed and earthed the lamp should light. If it does not the wiring is faulty or the bulb is blown. This check is important as you must know if the oil pressure fails.

3 Normally the temperature warning lamp never glows at all under any circumstances unless the engine overheats. To check,

Fig 10.46 Instrument panel - location of warning lamps. Note relative position of contacts and printed circuit (arrowed)

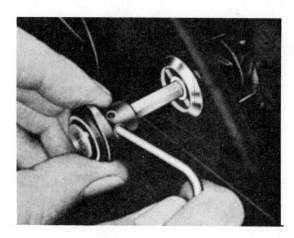

Fig 10.47 Switch knobs - removal

Fig 10.48 Fuel gauge - installation showing how one stud engages tag of printed circuit (arrowed)

Fig 10.49 Instrument panel - Victor

Fig 10.50 Instrument panel - later models (Super and 2000 SL)

Fig 10.51 Instrument panel VX 4/90

wire from the sender unit (screwed into the inlet manifold) and with the ignition switched on the warning bulb should light. This is also an important check to make regularly because if the bulb goes you will have no early warning of overheating.

4 Where a temperature gauge is fitted the instrument should be removed. It should then be connected in series with a 6 watt bulb and 12 volt battery and the needle should go right over to 'hot'.

43 Stop lamp switch

The stop lamp switch is mounted on the brake pedal bracket support and a plunger contact is operated when the pedal goes down. The mounting studs are in slots so the switch may be adjusted as required. The stop lights should come on after the pedal has moved ½ inch.

44 Reverse lamp switch

The reverse lamp switch is fitted on some later cars with four speed gearboxes. It fits onto the side of the gearbox at the left end of the cross shaft. The switch can be renewed by screwing it out and putting another in. There is no adjustment necessary. Make sure the sealing washer is sound.

45 Ignition switch

1 The standard ignition switch is mounted in the lower facia and access is gained through the centre panel aperture.

2 Remove the knob by depressing the locking plunger, undo the locking ring and remove the assembly from behind the panel. The connector can then be pulled off.

3 Where a steering column lock is also incorporated the whole unit is mounted on the steering column. Remove the steering wheel and column canopy and the lower covers through which the wiring harness passes. (The harness cannot be separated from the switch).

4 Remove the instrument head assembly so as to remove the multi-socket connection (see Section 40).

5 The mounting bolts must be drilled out to release the switch and lock assembly (Fig 10.52).

6 When fitting a new switch special break head bolts will be provided. Install everything and check that the lock and switch functions properly before tightening the bolts until the heads break off.

46 Switches - wiring connections

1 It is not indicated in the wiring diagrams how some switches are connected. It is always advisable to mark the terminals and leads anyway before removing switch connections. Use dabs of coloured paint or adhesive tape, self-adhesive labels or even pieces of coloured wool.

2 The following colour code and terminal numbers may prove useful on Super and 2000 SL models.

Lighting and fog lamp switches
   Terminal No 4 Red/brown
        "   No 7 Brown/blue
        "   No 8 Blue
Windscreen wiper switches
   Terminal No 1 Black/yellow
        "   No 2 Black/red
        "   No 3 Green
        "   No 4 (2 speed only) Blue

Fig 10.52 Ignition switch (steering column lock) - drilling out securing bolts

Fig 10.53 Instrument panel - switch removal (later models)

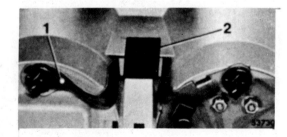

Fig 10.54 INSTRUMENT PANEL — PRINTED CIRCUIT
1 Locating peg on back of   cuit from fouling panel
  speedo   reinforcement
2 Adhesive tape to keep cir-

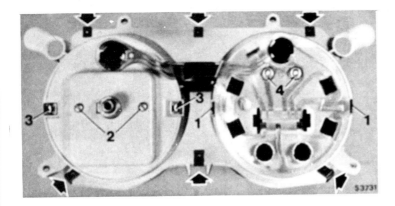

Fig 10.55 INSTRUMENT PANEL —
REAR VIEW
Arrows indicate front glass securing clips
1   Instrument lamp lens clips
2   Speedometer securing screws
3   Speedometer lamp lens slips
4   Fuel gauge securing nuts

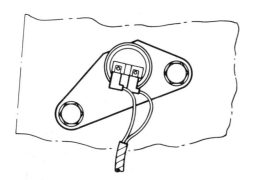

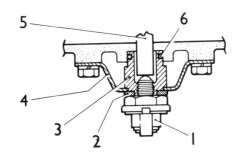

Fig 10.56 REVERSE LAMP SWITCH (4 SPEED GEARBOX ONLY) — LOCATION AND CROSS SECTION

1 Switch	3 Switch housing	5 Gearbox cross shaft	6 'O' ring
2 Sealing washer	4 Carrier plate		

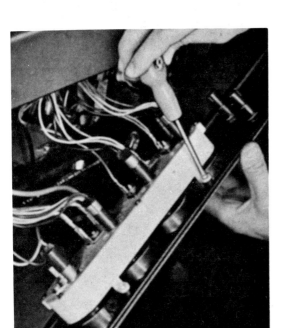

Fig 10.57 Instrument panel VX4/90 - removing carrier from facia

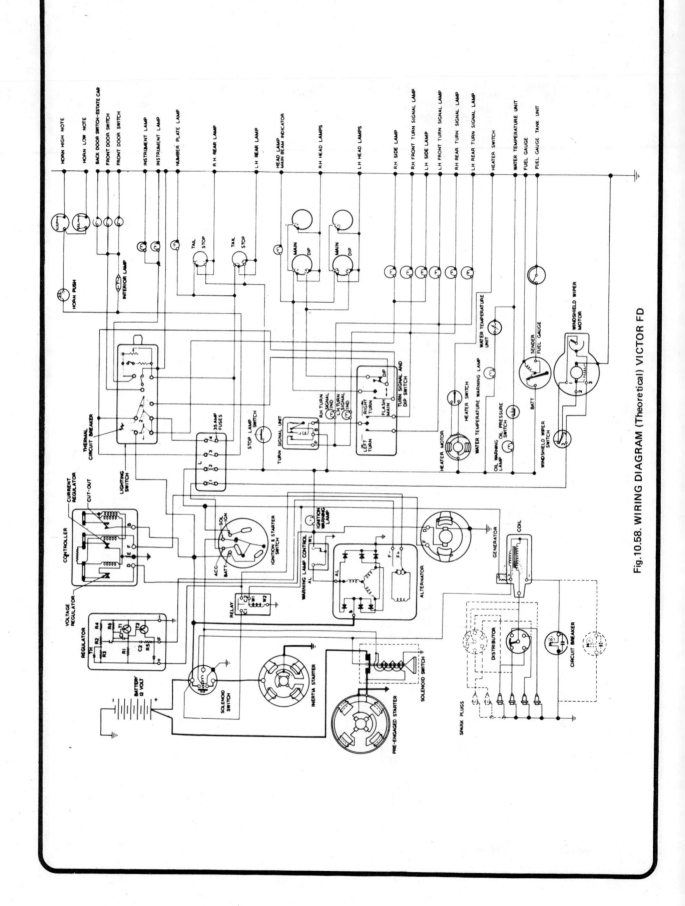

Fig. 10.58. WIRING DIAGRAM (Theoretical) VICTOR FD

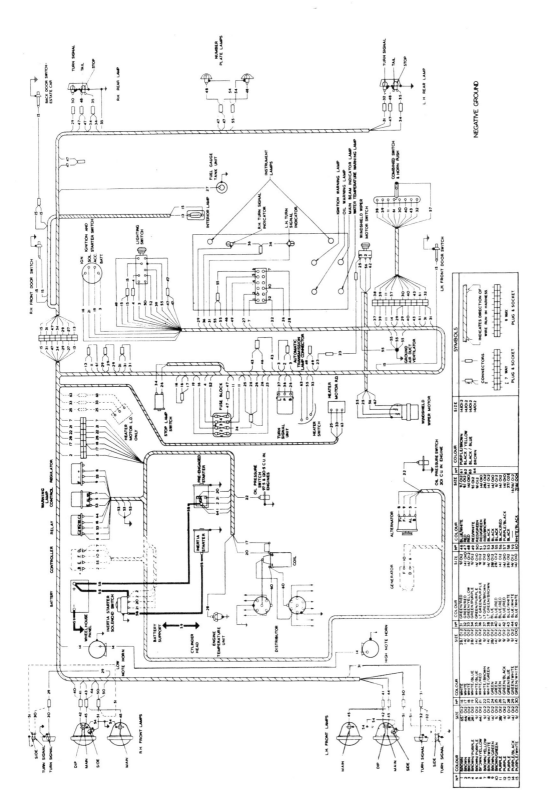

Fig. 10.59. WIRING DIAGRAM (Physical) VICTOR FD

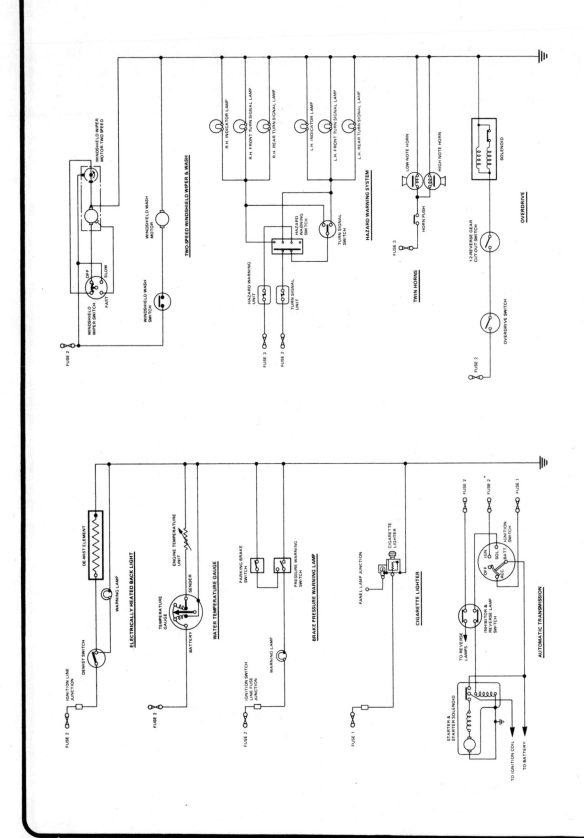

Fig.10.60. THEORETICAL WIRING DIAGRAM FOR OPTIONAL EQUIPMENT

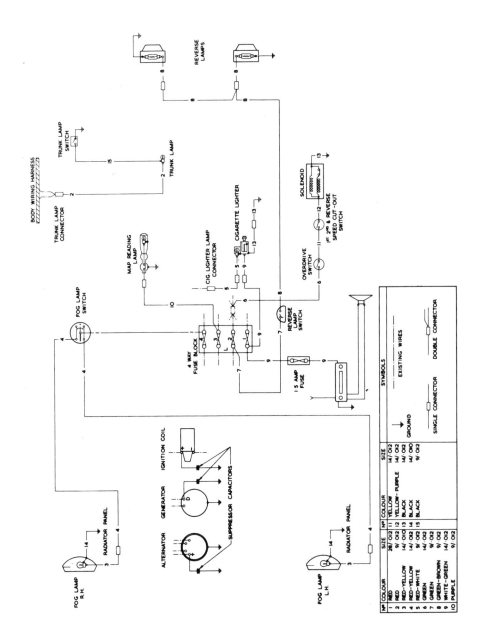

Fig. 10.61. ACCESSORY WIRING DIAGRAM

Chapter 11 Suspension, dampers and steering

Contents

Specifications

Front suspension

Type... ... ... Independent, coil springs with upper wishbone and single lower arm
Dampers positioned inside coil springs

Front end standing heights*

Tyres	Standard		Heavy duty	
	Saloon	Estate	Saloon	Estate
5.60 x 13	10.42—11.18 in		10.70—11.46 in	
6.2 x 13...	9.92—10.68 in		10.2 —10.96 in	
6.9 x 13...	10.52—11.28	10.40—11.16	10.80—11.56	10.70—11.46
165 x 13	9.88—10.64	9.76—10.52	10.16—10.92	10.06—10.82

*See text for checking procedures

Rear suspension

Type... ... ... Coil spring, 4 longitudinal arm with transverse Panhard rod

Rear end standing heights*

Tyres	Standard		Heavy duty	
	Saloon	Estate	Saloon	Estate
5.60 x 13	9.39—10.15		9.74—10.50	
6.2 x 13...	8.89—9.65		9.24—10.00	
6.9 x 13...	9.49—10.25	9.46—10.22	9.84—10.60	9.74—10.50
165 x 13	8.85—9.61	8.82—9.58	9.20—9.96	9.10—9.86

*See text for checking procedures

Steering

Make ... ... Burman or Cam gears
Type... ... ... Rack and pinion
Oil capacity ... ... ¼ pint (Imp)

Steering geometry

Front wheel alignment ... ... From .04 inch toe-in to .04 inch toe-out
Camber angle ... ... 0°—2° 30'
King pin inclination ... ... 5° 23'—8° 23'
Castor angle ... ... 2° 30'—4°
Toe-out on turns ... ... Outer wheel 19° from straight ahead with inner wheel at 20°

NOTE: Camber angle must be within 1° 30' between sides and castor angle within 1°

Dampers

Type... ... ... Telescopic double acting hydraulic front and rear

Wheels and tyres

Type...	Steel disc 4 stud fixing
Rims...	13 in to suit 5.60, 6.2, 6.9 and 165 tyre sections

Tyre pressures - all round

Normal operating - 5.60 and 165...	24 lb in^2
6.2...	22 lb in^2
6.9...	20 lb in^2
High speed or full load	
prolonged operating - 5.60 and 165...	28 lb in^2
6.2...	26 lb in^2
6.9 saloon...	24 lb in^2
6.9 estate...	26 lb in^2

Torque Wrench settings

	lb ft
Steering wheel nut	57 (early)
	45 (later models with serrated, flanged nut face)
	38 (later type VX 4/90)
Steering column mounting bracket bolts	17
Universal coupling cotter nut	7
Universal coupling pinch bolt nut	14
Flexible coupling to intermediate shaft nuts	12
Flexible coupling cotter nut	7
Steering gear to crossmember nuts	19
Track rod end to steering arm nut...	24
Panhard rod to underbody and axle	24
Rear spring upper and lower mounting	24
Rear suspension arm mountings	38
Front suspension control arm to lower arm nuts	38
Front suspension control arm rear nut	47
Front damper upper mounting...	38
Front damper lower mounting	57
Steering arm to knuckle nuts	25
Steering knuckle to suspension ball joint nuts	33 *
Wishbone fulcrum bolt nut	57
Lower arm fulcrum bolt nut - rubber bush	38
- steel sleeve bush	68
Front suspension crossmember to side rail mountings...	38

* If slotted turn onto split pin hole. Replacement upper joints tighten nut to **22 lb ft** only.

General description

The Victor suspension system is based on four coil springs, one at each wheel. At the front, the wheels are suspended independently on an upper wishbone and lower arm. The spring is fixed to the lower arm and passes through the wishbone to an upper anchorage on the end of the front crossmember.

The live rear axle is located by four parallel longitudinal arms, two long and two short. The longer arms trail from rubber bushed pivot pins on the frame side rails and attach to brackets by further rubber bushed pivot pins on the outer ends of the axle tubes. The shorter arms trail in the same way from the side rails to the axle tubes but are further inboard. Lateral stability is maintained by a transverse Panhard rod. The rear coil springs are positioned between the rear of the longitudinal arms and a fixture on the upper curve of side rail.

Telescopic dampers are mounted inside the coil spring at the front and are attached to the same members as the spring. At the rear they fix to brackets on the axle tube and to special mountings on the frame side rail.

The steering is rack and pinion of conventional design and the products of either of two manufactures is fitted, namely Burman or Cam Gears. These can be identified by the manufacturers name cast on to the bottom of the gear housing. The assembly, comprising a housing, rack and pinion, is supported in rubber mountings on the front of the axle crossmember. The rack is mounted in one end of the housing by a bush, and at the other by a spring loaded adjustable yoke which also maintains engagement with the pinion. The pinion is mounted between ball thrust bearings, the pre-loading of which is also adjustable. The inner ends of the steering tie rods are attached to the rack by adjustable ball joints. The outer ends are fixed to the steering knuckle by sealed ball joints.

The steering column is of the safety type. A lattice work section in the tube will collapse on impact and the shaft is telescopic, held in position by plastic injections for normal use. The steering column also incorporates a gear change tube whether or not floor change is fitted. This is in three telescopic sections held in position by plastic injections also which will collapse on impact.

2 Springs and dampers - inspection

1 With the tyre pressures correct, fuel tank full and the car standing on level smooth ground, bounce it up and down a few times and let it settle. Then measure the distance from the lower arm fulcrum bolt centre to the ground (Fig 11.6) and from the rear longitudinal arm front bolt centre to the ground (Fig 11.7).

Make sure that any measurement outside specification is not affected by another before deciding how many springs may need renewal. This can be done by raising the car to the correct height on blocks at the faulty location and rechecking the remainder.

2 Dampers may be checked by bouncing the car at each corner. Generally speaking the body will return to its normal position and stop after being depressed. If it rises and returns on a rebound the damper should be suspect. Examine also the damper mounting bushes

for any sign of looseness and the cylinders themselves for traces of hydraulic fluid leaks. If there is any sign of the latter, the unit must be renewed. Static tests of dampers are not entirely conclusive and further indications of damper failure are noticeable pitching; (bonnet going up and down when the car is braked and stopped sharply) excessive rolling on fast bends; and a definite feeling of insecurity on corners, particularly if the road surface is uneven. If you are in doubt it is a good idea to drive over a roughish road and have someone follow you to watch how the wheels behave. Excessive up and down 'patter' of any wheel is usually quite obvious, and denotes a defective damper.

3 Front dampers - removal and replacement

All figures in text refer to Fig 11.1.

1 Removal of the dampers is made easier with the special Vauxhall tool to compress the spring, but is not essential.

2 Jack up the car so that the front wheel is clear of the ground by a few inches.

3 Undo the three nuts (38, 58) which hold the lower damper mounting plates to the lower suspension arm and also the nut (55) on the lower damper mounting bolt (52).

4 Place a block under the front wheel and then lower the car so that the brackets and lower damper mounting come clear of the arm. Remove the lower mounting pin and detach the bracket.

5 Remove the upper mounting bolt and nut (50, 51) and the damper may be withdrawn from below.

6 The damper mounting bushes may be renewed separately if required.

7 Reassembly is a reversal of the removal procedure but for convenience refit the lower mounting bushes and brackets loosely before reconnecting the top. Tight all nuts to the specified torques.

4 Front springs - removal and replacement

All figures in text refer to Fig 11.1.

1 Proceed as for front damper removal as described in Section 3 as far as paragraph 4 inclusive. Slacken also the nut (35) on the lower arm fulcrum pin (34). The coil spring is now held in compression by the lower steering joint (26) to the steering arm. Obviously the joint cannot be separated from the arm without taking measures to control the expansion of the spring when the lower arm is released. A spring retainer can be made using short lengths of iron rod with the ends bent over to form hooks. Three of these will hold the coils of the spring sufficiently to enable the lower arm to be disengaged.

2 Jack up the lower suspension arm and install the spring retainer. Support the car under the front crossmember in the centre.

3 Place a block of wood between the spring upper mounting and the upper wishbone to hold the wishbone up in position.

4 Disconnect the lower suspension arm ball joint as described in Section 5.

5 Lower the jack under the lower suspension arm until the spring is completely relaxed. The spring may then be detached.

6 Replacement is a reversal of this procedure, but the new spring will need to be compressed and retained before it can be fitted. Make sure that the spring locates correctly in the lower arm seat and that the tapers of the ball joint pin and steering knuckle are perfectly clean and dry before reconnection.

7 When the weight of the car is finally resting on the suspension, retighten the lower arm fulcrum bolt to the recommended torque.

5 Front suspension arm ball joints - removal and replacement

1 The front suspension ball joints will need renewal if they are worn beyond the acceptable limits. This wear is one of the items checked when MOT tests become necessary. The lower joint can be checked by jacking the car up so that the wheel hangs free and then placing another jack under the lower suspension arm and raising the arm so

Fig. 11.1 Front suspension - components

1	Front axle beam	35	Nut
2	Axle mounting bush	36	Suspension control rod
3	Axle mounting bolt	37	Control arm bolt
4	Nut	38	Nut
5	Spring washer	39	Rubber bush
6	Axle mounting bush	40	Insulator
7	Axle mounting bolt	41	Spacer
8	Nut	42	Washer
9	Spring washer	43	Locknut
10	Upper suspension arm	44	Nut
11	Bush	45	Spring
12	Upper ball joint bolt	46	Insulator
	(removal only)	47	Bump stop
13	Spring washer	48	Damper
14	Nut	49	Bush
15	Ball joint gaiter	50	Damper bolt
16	Retaining ring	51	Nut
17	Retaining ring	52	Bolt
18	Nut	53	Bush
19	Grease nipple	54	Spacer
20	Fulcrum bolt	55	Nut
21	Washer	56	Anchor bracket
22	Self-locking unit	57	Anchor bracket
23	Lower suspension arm	58	Self locking unit
24	Lower arm bush	59	Plain washer
25	Damper bracket bolt	60	Anti-roll bar
26	Lower suspension arm ball	61	Strap
	joint	62	Insulator
27	Gaiter	63	Bolt
28	Retaining ring	64	Lockwasher
29	Retaining ring	65	Bush
30	Nut	66	Cup
31	Circlip	67	Spacer
32	Special washer	68	Bolt
33	Grease nipple	69	Nut
34	Lower suspension arm pin	70	Washer

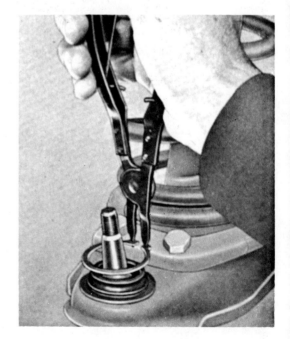

Fig. 11.2 Front lower suspension arm ball joint - Circlip removal

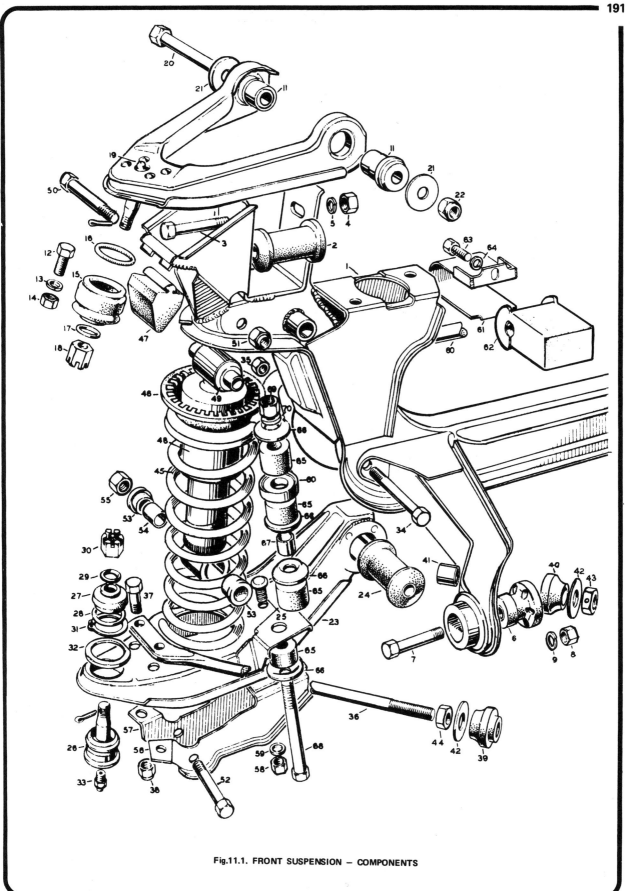

Fig.11.1. FRONT SUSPENSION – COMPONENTS

that movement in the joint can be detected. If there is any movement the joint must be renewed.

2 To remove the joint, first take off the nut from the pin located in the steering knuckle.

3 Separate the joint from the knuckle. This can only be done with surety by using a claw clamp. However, it is possible to drive through but only if the knuckle is firmly supported. The joint will almost certainly be damaged in the process. Another method is to strike the side of the knuckle where the pin goes through whilst holding the head of another hammer on the opposite. This has a squeezing out effect on the tapered pin.

The lower suspension arm will only move a limited way as it is held by the front damper.

4 The car should then be jacked up under the front crossmember, a block placed under the wheel, and the car lowered again until the lower ball joint is clear of the knuckle and can be got at for removal from the arm.

5 To remove the joint from the arm, first remove the circlip (Fig 11.2) and washer.

6 Using a piece of tube, drive the joint out of the arm (Fig 11.3). It may be necessary to put a block of wood under the arm to provide a firm support for this.

7 Drive in a new joint so that the splines engage in the arm. Then fit the special washer with the flat lined up (Fig 11.4) and the concave side upwards and replace the circlip.

8 Reconnect the pin to the steering knuckle ensuring that the mating surfaces of the taper are clean. Replace the nut.

9 The upper arm ball joint can be checked by jacking the car up and rocking the wheel whilst holding the joint to detect any play. If there is any play the joint must be renewed. This necessitates removal of the upper wishbone (see Section 6).

10 With the upper wishbone removed, the four rivets holding the joint must be drilled out without damaging the holes in the arm.

11 The holes in the arm must then be drilled out to $5/16$ inch. Use two ¼ inch bolts to hold the plate in position whilst drilling to ensure accurate alignment. The new joint will be supplied with the necessary mounting bolts. Install these with the heads uppermost and tighten the nuts to the specified torque of 22 lb ft.

12 Replace the arm as described in Section 6.

6 Front suspension arms - removal and replacement

Figures in the text refer to Fig 11.1.

1 The suspension arms will need to be removed if the bushes are worn. Also the upper suspension arm needs to be removed in order to renew the ball joint.

2 To remove the upper arm, jack up the suspension under the lower arm and then remove the upper ball joint from the steering knuckle. This entails removal of the nut and disengaging it as described in Section 5, paragraph 3.

3 Next remove the long fulcrum bolt (20) and nut (22), which hold the wishbone to the crossmember.

4 To renew the bushes (11) calls for care as the arms of the wishbone must not be distorted during the course of removing and replacing the bushes. It is best to get the old ones out by cutting through them.

5 New bushes should be lubricated and drawn in using a long nut and bolt together with a tubular spacer (on the inside of the arm) and large washers to ensure the bushes are drawn in square. Do not attempt to drive the bushes in with a hammer.

6 Replace the arm in the reverse order of removal but do not tighten the nut on the fulcrum bolt to the full torque until the weight of the car is resting on the suspension.

7 To remove the lower suspension arm proceed as for removal of the front spring as described in Section 4. Then remove the fulcrum bolt and the arm can be drawn away from the mounting brackets.

8 The single large bush needs careful treatment when removed otherwise the arm may be distorted. Do not try and drive it out - use a bolt, spacer and washers and draw it out. Note that there is a steel

sleeve on the outside of the rubber bush which must not be left behind.

9 The new bush should be lubricated on the outer steel sleeve. Make sure that it is drawn in from the side that will not let it foul the lip inside the housing in the arm. When installed the pin sleeve should project equally each side.

10 Replacement of the arm is in the reverse order of removal. Do not tighten the fulcrum bolt nut until the weight of the car is resting on the suspension.

7 Front suspension control rods - removal and replacement

All numbers refer to Fig 11.1.

1 The front suspension lower arms are stabilised fore and aft by a rod (36) which is bolted to their outer ends and located in rubber bushes (39) at the other end into the front crossmember support stays. The length of the rod is adjustable to achieve the correct degree of castor angle on the front wheels.

2 If the control rod bushes need renewal it will be necessary to remove the rod first.

3 Jack up the suspension under the lower arm and remove the two nuts and bolts (37, 38) securing the forward end to the suspension arm.

4 Slacken the two nuts (43, 44) noting the position of the inner one first in relation to the thread. Then remove the end one (43) followed by the washer (42) and half bush. The rod may then be drawn out.

5 Return the inner nut to its original position before fitting new bushes and then replace the arm in the reverse order of removal.

6 Tighen the rear nut to 47 lb ft and the arm nuts to 38 lb ft.

7 It is advisable to have the steering geometry checked at a garage with suitable testing equipment after removal and replacement of these control rods.

8 Front suspension anti-roll bar - removal and replacement

All numbers refer to Fig 11.1.

1 The anti-roll bar (60) is mounted at each end to the lower suspension arms in renewable bushes (65, 66) held by a nut and bolt (68, 69).

2 The arm is braced by being clamped to the underbody on two rubber mountings (62).

3 If the clamp bolts and mounting bolts are removed the bar can be taken off.

4 It is important to reassemble the bushes, caps and spacers correctly on reassembly (Fig 11.9).

5 Tighten the mounting bolt nut to the bottom of the thread.

9 Front axle - removal, checking and replacement

1 Sometimes it may be advantageous to remove the front suspension, as a complete assembly, from the car.

The axle crossmember is attached to the underbody side members at two points on each side, one at the top of the spring seat and the other by the bracing arm (Fig 11.5). Rubber mounting bushes are used.

2 With the car jacked up and supported on stands under the body side rails, disconnect the steering column from the steering gear (Section 24). Disconnect the hydraulic brake line unions at the brackets on the engine mounting side rails inside the engine compartment.

3 Support the axle beam in the centre and then undo the nuts from the four mounting bolts - two on each side. Then remove the bolts and lower the axle and draw it out complete with suspension, brakes, wheels and steering gear.

4 The bushes in the body side rails on the front axle brace brackets may be renewed in the same way as bushes in the suspension arms.

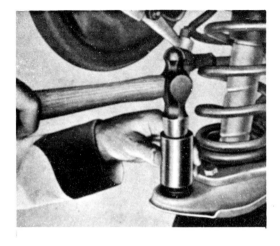

Fig.11.3. Front lower suspension arm ball joint - Driving joint out of arm

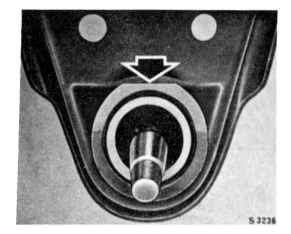

Fig.11.4. Front lower suspension arm ball joint - Location of special washer, concave side upwards

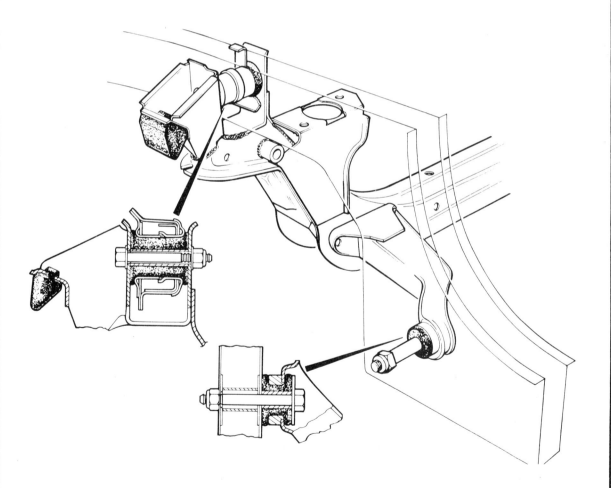

Fig.11.5. Front axle mountings - cross section

194

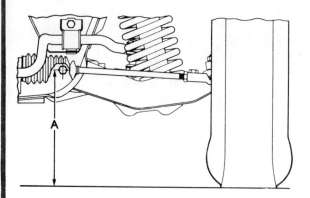

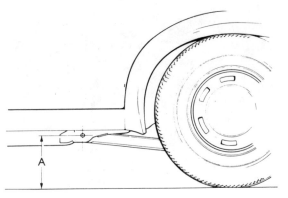

Fig.11.6. Front suspension standing height check

A is the dimension to be measured and checked against specifications

Fig.11.7. Rear suspension standing height check

A is the dimension to be measured and checked against specifications

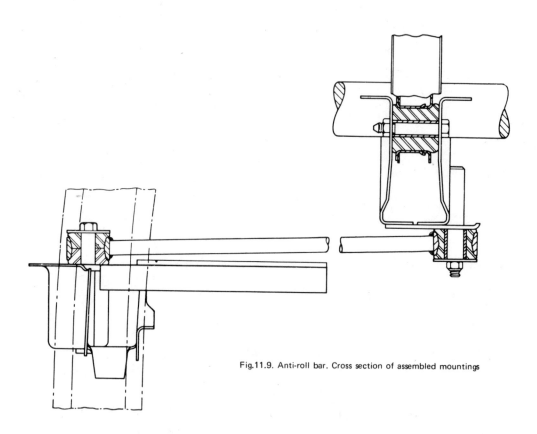

Fig.11.9. Anti-roll bar. Cross section of assembled mountings

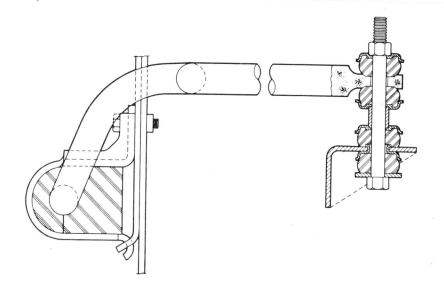

Fig.11.9. Anti-roll bar - cross section.

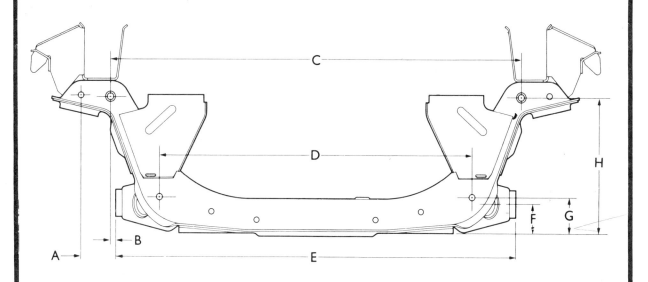

Fig.11.10. Front axle - dimensions

A 2.28 ins   C 31.48 ins   E 30.58 ins   G 2.44 ins
B .46 ins   D 24.00 ins   F 2.00 ins   H 9.70 ins

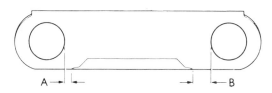

Fig.11.11. Rear suspension upper arm
Dimension 'A' is less than 'B'. A is towards the front

The only difference is that these are not steel jacketed and should be lubricated with soapy water only. The same precaution concerning the lip inside the side frame bush housing must be taken (see Fig 11.5). The bush must be pressed in from the outside.

5 Although it is unlikely that the average owner will have facilities for repair he can check the alignment of his front axle if involved in an accident. The dimensions are given in Fig 11.10.

10 Rear dampers - removal and replacement

1 The rear dampers will need removal if their mounting bushes are worn or if indications are that the unit is no longer performing properly.

2 It is not necessary to raise the car to remove the dampers but if it is raised the axle should be supported as well.

3 To detach the top mounting, remove the rubber plug from the wheel arch inside the boot when the two upper nuts will be accessible. The slotted spindle will need holding firmly whilst the nuts are removed.

4 The lower mounting eye may be disconnected by removing the nut on the mounting pin and pulling it off.

5 Replacement is a reversal of the removal procedure. All bushes are renewable and care should be taken to arrange the bushes and washers correctly as shown in Fig 11.13.

6 Tighten the top securing nuts down to the bottom of the stud threads.

11 Rear springs - removal and replacement

1 Jack up the car and support the body under the rear frame members on stands. Then support the axle on a jack.
   Disconnect the damper lower mounting.

2 Undo the lower spring mounting stud nut which is underneath the longitudinal suspension arm (see Fig 11.13).

3 Lower the jack under the axle until the suspension arm is clear of the spring.

4 Using a socket wrench remove the upper bolt which is in the centre of the upper spring seat and fits into a captive nut in the side member.

5 Lift out the spring complete with the upper mounting seat.

6 New springs, spring seats, rubber insulators and retainers are supplied individually. They are all assembled and held together by the centre bush which is peened over on to the upper seat. Fig 11.12 shows a cross section of the assembly with a special Vauxhall tool used to draw the new bush into position and peen over the top. If other improvised tools are used to carry out this job the main thing to remember is that the upper seat spring retainer must be held tightly together when the bush is being peened over.

7 Note that the upper seat has a dowel peg which locates in a corresponding hole in the side member. This must be correctly positioned when refitting the spring assembly which is otherwise a straightforward reversal of the removal procedure.

12 Rear suspension arms - removal and replacement

1 If the rubber mounting bushes at each end of any of the arms are worn it will be necessary to remove the arms to replace them.

2 The upper arms may be removed simply by undoing the retaining nuts and bolts. Mark the front end.

3 The lower arms can be removed in the same way after the spring has been disconnected at the lower end as described in the previous section.

4 On both upper and lower arms the bush at the front end is softer than the rear and is marked '45'. The rear one is marked '60'. Also the arms only fit one way. The upper one because of the difference in the strengthening flange clearance from the bush aperture (Fig 11.11). The lower one because of the positioning of the spring mounting

Fig.11.13. Rear suspension - components

1	Rear spring assembly	19	Rear bush
2	Spring	20	Mounting bolt
3	Spring seat	21	Nut
4	Retainer	22	Panhard rod
5	Bush	23	Bush
6	Insulator	24	Bush
7	Screw	25	Special washer
8	Lower retainer	26	Special washer
9	Hex. unit	27	Nut
10	Lock washer	28	Bolt
11	Bump strap	29	Damper
12	Upper arm	30	Bush
13	Front bush	31	Retaining cup
14	Rear bush	32	Special unit
15	Mounting bolt	33	Washer
16	Nut	34	Bush
17	Lower arm	35	Washer
18	Front bush	36	Nut

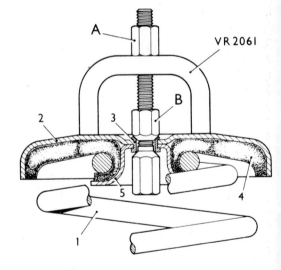

Fig.11.12. Rear spring upper seat - cross section

1	Spring	4	Insulator
2	Upper seat	5	Retainer
3	Bush		

A Special tool clamping unit
B Special tool peening unit

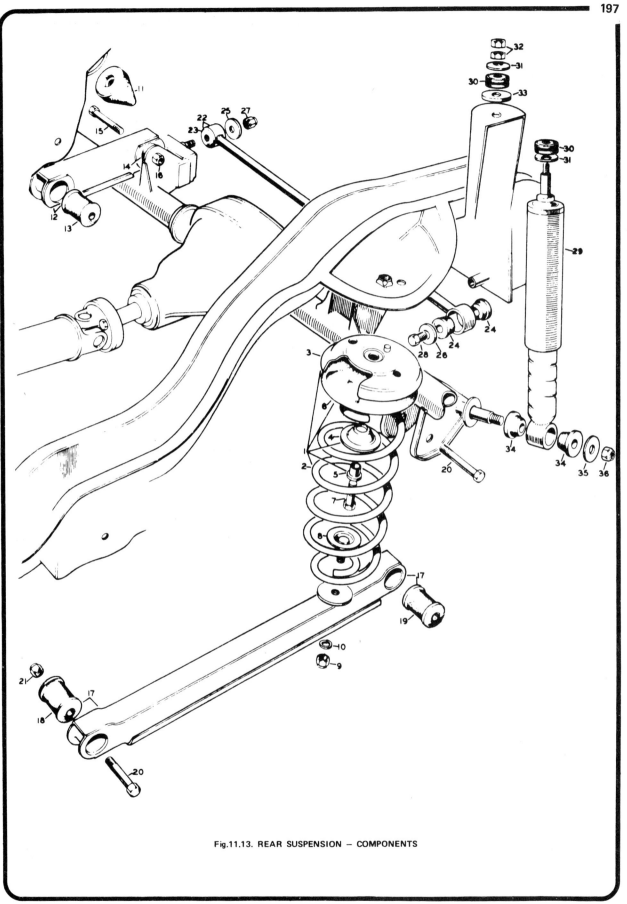

Fig.11.13. REAR SUSPENSION – COMPONENTS

hole. So the bushes must be fitted at the correct ends.

5 Bushes may be pressed in lubricated with liquid soap. Press them in so that they do not snag on the lip inside the bore.

6 When refitting the arms replace the mounting bolts but do not tighten the nuts to their correct torque (38 lb ft) until the weight of the car is resting on the springs.

13 Panhard rod - removal and replacement

1 The transverse Panhard rod is secured to the left hand underbody side member and the right hand upper suspension arm mounting bracket on the rear axle (Fig 11.8).

2 Before trying to remove it jack up the car and support it on stands and then jack up the axle so that the rod is horizontal.

3 The two tapered half bushes at the left end and the press in bush at the other are renewable.

4 When refitting tighten the securing bolts with the rod in the horizontal position to a torque of 24 lb ft.

14 Front wheel hub bearings - inspection and adjustment

1 The steering qualities of the car will deteriorate if the front wheel bearings are maladjusted or worn and can be a cause of rejection under the MOT roadworthiness test.

2 To check the bearings, first jack up the car so that the wheel is clear of the ground. Check that the wheel spins freely with the brakes off.

3 Then grip the edge of the tyre at top and bottom and try and rock it in a vertical plane. If movement can be felt it is normally due to looseness in the bearing but at the same time it should be noted whether there is any sign of lateral movement in either the upper or lower suspension arm ball joints. (If there is they must be renewed as described in Section 6).

4 There should be no detectable movement in the wheel bearings and if there is they should be adjusted. Fig 11.14 gives an exploded view of a front hub with either disc or drum brakes. Figures in the text refer to this drawing.

5 Remove the hub cap from the wheel and then tap the dust cover (29) out of the centre of the hub.

6 Remove the split pin from the nut (28) and, using a tubular spanner, tighten the nut whilst continuing to revolve the wheel. Then slacken the nut off and retighten it using only the tubular spanner without a tommy bar. This will provide the maximum permissible loading on the bearing.

7 The wheel should now spin freely with no indications of movement when rocked vertically. If any roughness is felt on spinning the wheel, the bearings should be removed for further examination.

8 Provided the adjustment is satisfactory fit a new split pin, backing off the nut to line up the hole if necessary. On later models the bearing nut is not slotted but is enclosed in a pressed steel retainer which has eight tags in it to provide more alternative positions for the split pin. This provides for finer adjustment of the wheel bearings. Replace the dust cap and hub cap and lower the wheel to the ground.

15 Front wheel hubs and bearings - removal, inspection and replacement

1 Jack up the car and remove the road wheel.

2 On drum brake models slacken off the brake adjusters as described in Chapter 9. On disc brake models remove the brake caliper as described in Chapter 9.

3 Remove the grease cap and the split pin locking the castellated hub nut.

4 Remove the castellated hub nut and the washer behind it.

5 Withdraw the hub together with the brake drum, or disc, as appropriate.

6 Remove the bolts holding the disc or drum to the hub and separate the two.

7 The outer bearing rollers and cage will come off with the hub. The inner bearing roller cage is held in position by the oil seal so the two must be tapped out together from the inside of the hub.

8 The outer faces of both bearings are a tight fit in the hub and must be drifted out firmly from inside the hub. Take care not to damage the bearing housings.

9 Thoroughly clean the bearings and examine the rollers and races for signs of wear. If in doubt, renew them. Wear can be detected by running perfectly clean, lightly oiled bearings in their races and feeling for traces of roughness. Blue discolouration indicates overheating, but brown discolouration will only be lubricant stain and is not to be taken as an adverse indication.

10 Reassembly of the outer bearing races into the hub is a reversal of the removal procedure. Make sure that the open ends of the tapers of the outer races face outwards from the centre of the hub, also that the housings are clean and that the races are driven completely home. Pack the inner bearing inner race and rollers with grease, and place it in position in the hub.

11 With the inner bearing fit a new seal, which on drum brake models fits over the hub boss and on disc brake types recesses into the hub behind the bearing. The lip of the seal should face to the centre of the hub on the latter.

12 Refit the brake drum or disc to the hub. For disc brakes the bolts should be renewed on later models (they incorporate nylon thread inserts for self-locking purposes). Make sure also that the weather shields are installed for disc brakes to protect the bearings. These shields were modified on later models and must be renewed as a pair.

13 Pack the outer bearing inner race and rollers with the recommended grease, place it in position and refit the complete hub assembly to the spindle. Replace the washer and castellated nut and then adjust the bearings as described in Section 14.

14 Half fill the bearing cover cap with grease before replacement. Do not pack the hub itself in the space between the bearings.

15 Replace the disc caliper as described in Chapter 9.

16 Adjust drum brakes as described in Chapter 9, having first replaced the road wheel.

16 Steering mechanism - inspection

1 The steering mechanism on the Victor is uncomplicated and easy to check. As the statutory test for vehicles more than three years old pays particular attention to it, the owner can save himself a lot of trouble by regular examination, apart from, of course, keeping a check on his own safety.

2 Assuming that the suspension joints and bushes and front wheel bearings have been checked and found in order the steering check involves tracing the amount of lost motion between the rim of steering wheel and the road wheels. If the rim of the steering wheel can be moved more than 1 to 2 inches at its periphery with no sign of movement at either or both of the front wheels it may be assumed that there is wear at some point. If there are signs of lost motion, jack up the car at the front and support it under the front crossmember so that both wheels hang free.

3 Grip each wheel in turn and rock it in the direction it would move when steering. It will be possible to feel any play. Check first for any sign of lateral play in the ball joints which connect the tie rods from the steering gear to the steering arms on the wheel hubs. This is the more common area for wear to occur and if any is apparent the ball joint/s must be renewed. The joints are spring loaded up and down so they can move in this plane, but not without considerable pressure. If the socket moves easily then the joint needs renewal.

4 Having checked the ball joints, next grip the tie rod and get someone to move the steering wheel. Do this with the bonnet open and if there is any play still apparent look first to see whether the coupling in the steering column shaft is causing the trouble. If it is it should be renewed.

5 Finally, if play still exists it must be in the steering gear itself. This is more serious (and expensive!). If either of the rubber boots at each end of the gear housing is damaged, resulting in loss of oil from the

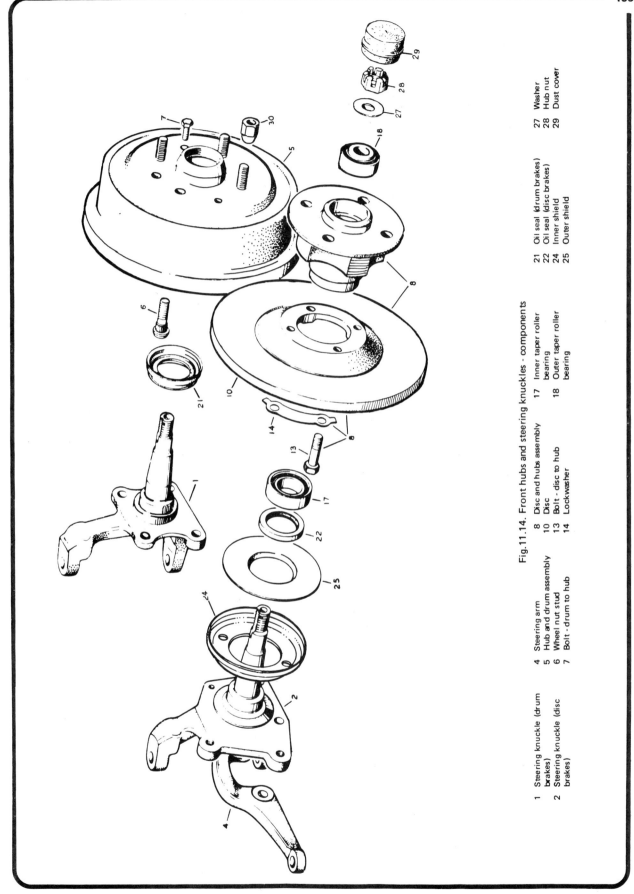

Fig.11.14. Front hubs and steering knuckles - components

1	Steering knuckle (drum brakes)
2	Steering knuckle (disc brakes)
4	Steering arm
5	Hub and drum assembly
6	Wheel nut stud
7	Bolt - drum to hub
8	Disc and hubs assembly
10	Disc
13	Bolt - disc to hub
14	Lockwasher
17	Inner taper roller bearing
18	Outer taper roller bearing
21	Oil seal (drum brakes)
22	Oil seal (disc brakes)
24	Inner shield
25	Outer shield
27	Washer
28	Hub nut
29	Dust cover

unit then various bearings and teeth on the rack and pinion may have been severely worn. In such cases renewal of the complete steering gear assembly may be necessary. Certainly adjustments will be require.

17 Steering gear - examination, adjustment, removal and replacement

1 Assuming that all ball joints and front wheel bearings are in order, it may be necessary to remove and replace, or renovate, the steering gear if there is excessive play between the steering shaft and the steering tie rods. This can be checked by gripping the inner end of both the rods in turn near the rubber boot, and getting someone to rock the steering wheel. If the wheel moves more than $1/16$th of a revolution ($11\frac{1}{4}°$ in either direction) without moving the steering tie rod, then the wear is sufficient to justify overhaul. If the rubber boots have leaked oil they will also need renewal, and, in order to do this and effectively refill the unit with the proper oil, it is easiest in the long run to remove the assembly from the car.

2 To remove the steering gear from the car first disconnect the lower half of the flexible coupling flange from the pinion shaft by extracting the cotter pin from the flange. This item can be a very tight fit and may call for an extraction tool or some form of 'G' clamp. Then disconnect both tie rod outer ball joints from the steering arms as described in Section 18. The three mounting bolts holding the assembly to the front crossmember may then be removed and the unit taken off. Take care of the washers and shims behind each bolt.

3 If it is necessary to replace only the rubber boots and refill the assembly with lubricant, remove both outer ball joints from the tie rods together with the locknuts, having noted their original position carefully. Slacken off the boot retaining clips noting their position in relation to the assembly housing. If the steering arms are dirty clean them thoroughly and slide off the old boots.

4 Refit the clips to new boots and slide them onto the rods. Tighten the clips in position on one boot only. Stand the unit on end, refill the housing with ¼ pint, no more, Castrol Hypoy 90 and then refit the other boot and tighten the clips.

5 It is possible to alleviate some of the play in the gear (between rack and pinion) by checking that the yoke pre-load is correct.

6 Remove the yoke cover plate and remove the shims and spring followed by the yoke.

7 Replace the yoke and cover without the spring or any shims and lightly tighten the bolts.

8 Measure the gap between the cover and the housing with a feeler gauge. The thickness of the shims should be the gap measurement PLUS .0005—.003 inch on Burman units or PLUS .0005—.006 inch on Cam Gear units. Make up the shim packs accordingly. Note that on Cam gears only one gasket is used between the shim pack and the cover whereas on Burman units there is a gasket on each side of every shim. Gasket thickness must be included in the total shim pack dimensions. Adjust the shims required to give a turning torque on the pinion of 12 lb in.

9 Similarly, any sign of end float and slackness in the pinion shaft may be taken up by removing the cover opposite the pinion extension and reducing the thickness of the shims behind the cover accordingly. In this case the shims should be .001—.005 inch LESS than the measured clearance between the cover and housing. The same remarks as regard gaskets apply.

10 It must be emphasised that the adjustments mentioned in this paragraph are not sufficient to compensate for extreme wear. Before making them, therefore, it must be decided whether the wear apparent is beyond adjustment, or sufficient to warrant adjustment anyway.

11 Any play in the tie rod INNER ball joints may be adjusted but involves drilling and re-pinning the joint and this calls for precision work.

12 Replacement of the assembly is a reversal of the procedure as described in paragraph 2. Make sure the assembly is centralised on the steering lock before attaching the pinion shaft to the steering column. Due to some problems of distortion in the steering gear casing later models are fitted with special washers on the outer moun-

ting bolts between the housing and front axle. The centre point is then shimmed between casing and axle to take up any clearance (Fig 11.15). The two outer bolts are then tightened to 19 lb ft and the centre bolt, last, to 9 lb ft.

13 The front wheel toe-in should then be checked with proper equipment.

18 Steering tie rods outer ball joints - removal and replacement

1 The removal of the ball joints is necessary if they are to be renewed, or if the rubber boots on the steering gear are being renewed.

2 It is not necessary to jack the car up but the increase in height above ground level may make it more convenient to do so.

3 Slacken the self-locking nut, completely remove it to clear the threads, and replace it after oiling them until the head of the nut is level with the end of the stud. This will protect the threads in subsequent operations if the same joint is being replaced.

4 If a claw clamp is being used to 'break' the taper of the joint pin from the steering arm, the joint may be disconnected without further ado.

5 If no claw clamp is available and it is necessary to strike the pin out, it is essential to provide a really firm support under the steering arm first. A firm tap with a normal weight hammer is all that is then necessary to move the pin out of the steering arm. Another way is to strike one side of the arm whilst holding the head of another hammer against the opposite side. This tends to 'squeeze' the taper pin out.

6 If the nut now turns the pin when trying to remove it, (despite the precaution taken in paragraph 3) jam the pin back into the arm with the jack to hold it whilst the nut is removed. If difficulty is experienced with a joint being renewed then cut it off.

7 Once the ball joint is clear, slacken the locknut on the rod but leave it at its original position. The joint may then be removed and a new one fitted by screwing it up as far as the locknut. The pin should point upwards and then be fitted into the steering arm.

8 As the nut is self-locking it will be necessary to prevent the pin turning whilst tightening it. This can be done by putting a jack under the joint so that the weight of the wheel rests on the taper.

9 Tighten the locknut on the tie rod.

10 It is advisable to have the front wheel alignment checked as soon as possible.

19 Steering knuckle and steering arm

Neither the steering knuckle (or stub axle as it is sometimes called, from the name of a similar part on a beam front axle) nor steering arm, normally need any attention. It is possible, however, in the case of severe shock or damage to the front suspension and steering, that either or both of them could be bent or distorted. If it is necessary to remove them for checking or renewal proceed as follows:

2 Remove the front hub as described in Section 12.

3 Detach the upper and lower suspension arm ball joints as described in Section 5.

4 Detach the steering arm outer ball joint as described in Section 18.

5 Disconnect the hydraulic brake pipe from the wheel cylinder mounted on the brake backplate (details in Chapter 9).

6 Remove the brake backplate and separate the steering arm from the knuckle by undoing the bolts and nuts joining them together.

7 Reassembly and replacement is a reversal of the procedure. Bleed the brake system when reassembly is complete (see Chapter 9).

20 Steering geometry - checking and adjustment

1 Unless the front axle and suspension has been damaged the castor angle, camber angle and steering pivot angles will not alter, provided, of course, that the suspension ball joints and wishbone fulcrum pin bushes are not worn in any way.

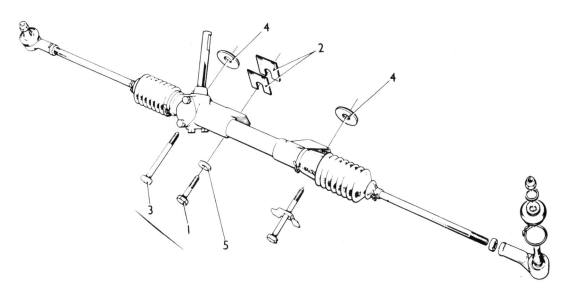

Fig.11.15. Steering mounting details · later modification

1 Centre bolt   3 Outer bolts   4 Concave washer   5 Special washer
2 Shims

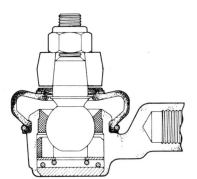

Fig.11.16. Steering tie rod anti ball joint ·
cross section

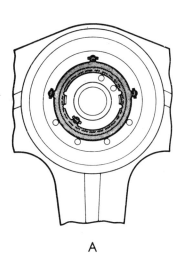
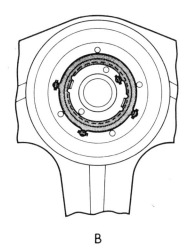
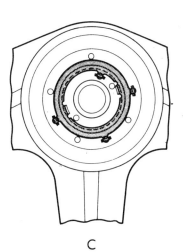

A   B   C

Fig.11.17. Steering wheel · indicator cancelling sleeve positions

A. No steering column lock   B. With steering column lock R.H.D.   C. With steering column lock L.H.D.

2   The toe-in of the front wheels is a measurement which may vary more frequently and could pass unnoticed if, for example, a steering tie rod was bent. When fitting new tie rod ball joints, for example, it will always be necessary to reset the toe-in.

3   Indications of incorrect wheel alignment (toe-in) are uneven tyre wear on the front tyres and erratic steering particularly when turning. To check toe-in accurately needs optical aligning equipment, so get a garage to do it. Ensure that they examine the tie rods for straightness and all ball joints and wheel bearings at the same time, if you have not done so yourself.

21 Steering wheel - removal and replacement

1   The steering wheel is located on splines to the column shaft and secured by a nut.

2   First remove the centre pad by undoing the two screws on the underside of the spoke.

3   Undo the nut with a tubular spanner and then mark the relative position of the wheel to the shaft by making two marks with a centre punch. Then pull the wheel off.

4   The hub incorporates the direction indicator cancelling sleeve which must be prised out if it is being transferred to a new wheel.

5   Replacement is a straightforward reversal of the removal procedure, but make sure that the cancelling sleeve is replaced correctly with the tags in the proper holes (Fig 11.17).

6   If the wheel and shaft was not marked then set the road wheels straight ahead and replace the wheel with main spoke horizontal and dividing spoke pointing down. The combined switch and horn push should not be at a left or right turn position when this is done. On later models there were changes and a retaining nut with a serrated flange was introduced. Also two tapered collar seats were used held in position by a rubber band prior to fitting the steering wheel.

The tightening torque for the new nut is 45 lb ft on all models except the VX 4/90 where it is 38 lb ft.

22 Steering intermediate shaft and coupling - removal and replacement

1   The main steering shaft is connected to the steering box pinion shaft by an intermediate shaft. The upper end of the shaft is connected by a splined universal joint (early models have a cotter pin). The lower end has a flexible coupling, the lower flange being secured to the pinion by a cotter.

2   To remove the shaft and coupling take out both upper and lower cotters and slide the shaft downwards until the upper universal joint is disengaged. Then take the shaft off.

3   If the shaft does not move easily do not strike it in any way as this could damage the collapsible section in the upper column. Twist the section to loosen it if necessary.

4   If the flexible coupling is being put on a new shaft clamp it with a hose clip to stress the rubber before taking it off the shaft (Fig 11.19). This assists installation.

5   New couplings are supplied with a retention band fitted which should be cut off after installation.

6   When refitting the shaft and coupling first set the road wheels and steering wheel in the straight ahead position. Install the upper cotter (or clamp bolt) just to ensure correct axial alignment and then fit the lower one. Tighten them to the correct torque of 7 lb ft for cotter nuts or 14 lb ft for a clamp bolt nut.

23 Steering column lock

1   A steering column lock is fitted to some cars and it is secured by two special bolts with heads that are broken off on installation for security purposes. To remove the lock and switch assembly drill a $1/8$ inch hole into each bolt using a good sharp high speed drill and then extract the bolts with a proper screw extractor. The bolts are

**Fig.11.18. Steering column and intermediate shaft —
Components**

1	Steering column lock	32	Special washer
2	Key	33	Lock washer
3	Lock clamp	34	Nut
4	Breakhead bolt - short	35	Lock washer
5	Breakhead bolt - long	36	Canopy (not column lock)
6	Steering wheel	37	Canopy (with column lock)
7	Nut	38	Support bracket (no column lock)
8	Medallion		
9	Pad	39	Support bracket (with column lock)
10	Plate		
11	Clip	40	Screw pan head No.10
12	Intermediate shaft	41	Screw pan head No.6
13	Coupling	42	Screw flat head No.10
14	Coupling bolt	43	Screw flat head
15	Washer	44	Speed unit No.10
16	Lock nut	45	Mounting gasket
17	Cotter pin	47	Intermediate shaft (splined version)
18	Washer		
19	Nut	48	Bolt
20	Column assembly	49	Washer
21	Column assembly (not 3 speed)	50	Nut
22	Screw	51	Indicator switch housing (with no column lock)
23	Bolt		
24	Anti-vibration nut	52	Indicator switch housing (with column lock)
25	Washer		
26	Grommet	53	Lock plate
27	Bolt	54	Grub screw
28	Washer	55	Flat washer .064 in. thick
29	Upper column bracket	56	Wave washer .018 in. thick
30	Bracket wedge	57	Circlip
31	Bolt	58	Shim - variable from .005 in. to .030 in.

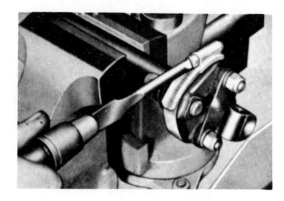

Fig.11.19. Intermediate shaft flexible coupling - fixing box clip to pre-stress rubber section

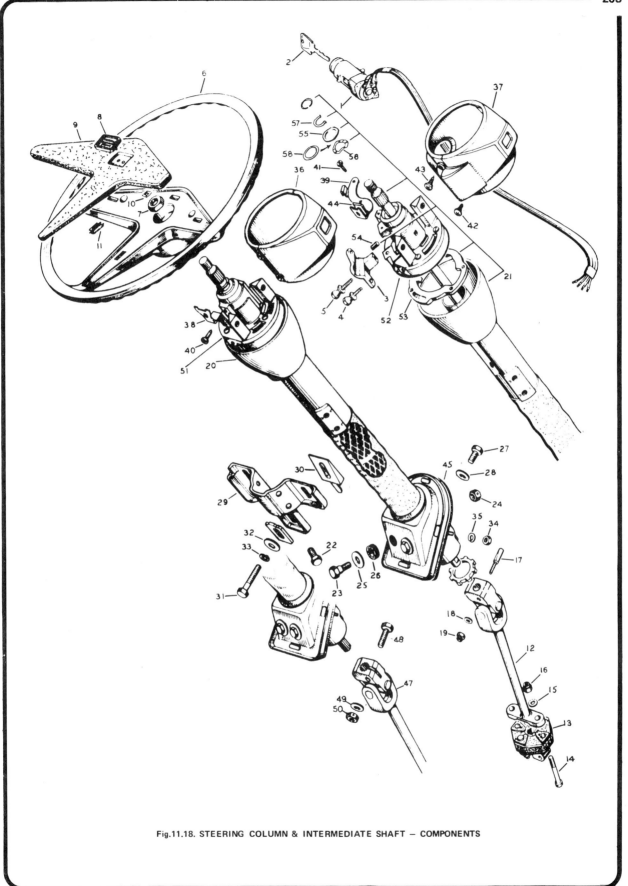

Fig.11.18. STEERING COLUMN & INTERMEDIATE SHAFT — COMPONENTS

very hard so the drill will need sharpening for each one.

2 When fitting the lock special break head bolts should be used once again. Make sure the lock and switch is fully tested before finally breaking the bolt heads off.

24 Steering column - upper mounting bracket and upper bearing - inspection and repair

1 The steering column assembly is designed to collapse under impact to lessen the risk of injury to the driver. The column has a section of expanded metal and the steering shaft is telescopic. The telescoping halves are maintained in their normal position by a plastic substance injected between them which shears on impact. The same applies to the three sections of gear shift tube. It is most important that the assembly and its components are handled with care. Any damage to any of these sections means that the whole column will have to be renewed.

2 The column and mounting bracket may be examined in position. The upper mounting bracket has plastic mounting pads for the three bolts which will shear on impact.

If there are any visible gaps between the bracket and pads then this means that the pads have sheared (Fig 11.20). The column lattice work section will bulge and buckle on impact and this can be confirmed if the overall length of the section has decreased (Fig 11.21).

3 If the steering column upper bearing is loose it can be adjusted in position after the steering wheel has been removed. Pre-load on the double row ball bearing is maintained by a wave washer and shims. Remove the circlip and flat washer and add more shims as necessary to remove any side play (Fig 11.22).

4 If the bearing needs renewal the whole upper housing must be renewed as the bearing is not supplied separately.

5 The upper housing is retained by three screws. It may be drawn off after removing the screws and the bearing circlip washer and shims. If the housing is a bit stiff, do not hammer it or you may damage the columns. It may be necessary to obtain a suitable puller.

25 Steering column assembly - removal and replacement

1 Remove the intermediate shaft as described in Section 22.

2 If a steering column lock is fitted disconnect the battery and cut the wiring harness from the ignition switch just below the upper mounting bracket. These will be reconnected after fitting snap connectors and sleeves. It is much simpler to do this than dismantle the instrument panel and all that goes with it.

3 When steering column gearchange is fitted disconnect the control rod from the change lever and the selector lever from the steering column bracket. Then undo the nuts holding the cover panel to the dash panel (Fig 11.25).

4 Remove the column finisher and wiring cover, disconnect the combined switch horn push wiring at the connector and undo the three upper column mounting bracket bolts to release the whole assembly which can then be lifted out (Fig 11.24). A small packing wedge under the mounting bracket must not be overlooked.

5 Replacement is a reversal of this procedure but it is important to get things assembled and tightened in the proper sequence (Fig 11.23).

6 Locate the cover panel studs at the lower end and then put the top two bolts of the upper mounting bracket in position finger tight.

7 Replace and tighten the lower panel nuts and then tighten the two upper nuts to the correct torque of 17 lb ft.

8 Replace the packing wedge, pushing it home only as far as finger pressure will permit and then replace and tighten the third bracket bolt to the same torque.

9 Reconnect all wires and gear shift linkage.

Fig.11.20. Steering column upper mounting bracket

1 Shear pads   2 Bracket
A = gaps indicating pads have sheared

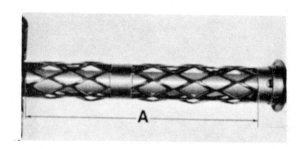

Fig.11.21. Steering column collapsible section

A minimum dimension is 9.7 ins

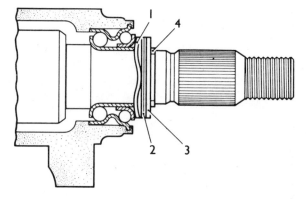

Fig.11.22. Steering column upper bearing - cross section

1 Wave washer   3 Flat washer
2 Shims   4 Circlip

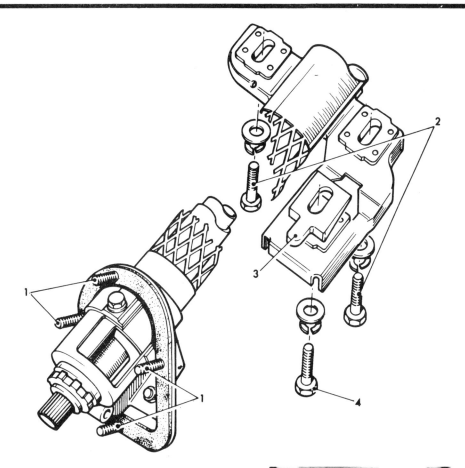

Fig.11.23. Steering column upper mounting and lower mounting bracket details

1	Lower mounting studs	3	Bracket wedge
2	Upper mounting top bolts	4	Upper mounting lower bolt

Fig.11.24. Lifting out steering column assembly complete

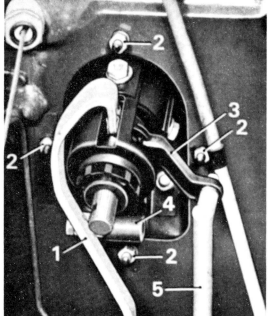

Fig.11.25. Steering column - 3 speed change lever couplings

1	Selector lever	3	Change speed lever
2	Cover panel securing nuts	4	Steering column bracket
		5	Control rod

26 Steering column lower bearing - renewal

1 Remove the steering column assembly as described in Section 24.
2 Remove the column upper bearing housing as described in Section 23.
3 Withdraw the shaft from the gear shift tube and remove the plastic adjusting nut sleeve and spring from the shaft.
4 Remove the five bolts holding the housing, cover panel bracket and column outer jacket together.
5 Tap out the single row ball bearing from inside the housing.
6 Fit a new bearing squarely into the housing fully up to the shoulder of the bracket. Reassemble the housing, cover panel bracket and column jacket, replace the three bolts in the tube and tighten them to 10 lb ft. Then refit and tighten the two bolts holding the bracket to the cover and tighten them the same amount.
7 Fit the spring with a new plastic sleeve and adjuster over the shaft and replace the shaft in the column tube. The adjuster nut should be fully unscrewed.
8 Replace the upper bearing housing and adjust the bearing end float if necessary as described in Section 23.
10 Turn the lower bearing adjusting nut clockwise until it seats on the bearing inner race and the sleeve contacts the shaft flange. Use only finger and thumb pressure. Then fuse the nut and sleeve with a hot iron. The column assembly is then ready for replacement in the car.

27 Wheels and tyres

1 To provide equal, and obtain maximum wear from all the tyres, they should be rotated on the car at intervals of 6000 miles to the following pattern:

    Spare to offside rear;
    Offside rear to nearside front;
    Nearside front to nearside rear;
    Nearside rear to offside front;
    Offside front to spare.

Wheels should be re-balanced when this is done. However, some owners baulk at the prospect of having to buy five new tyres all at once and tend to let two run on and replace a pair only. The new pair should always be fitted to the front wheels, as these are the most important from the safety aspect of steering and braking.
2 Never mix tyres of a radial and crossply construction on the same car, as the basic design differences can cause unusual and, in certain conditions, very dangerous handling and braking characteristics. If an emergency should force the use of two different types, make sure the radials are on the rear wheels and drive particularly carefully. If three of the five wheels are fitted with radial tyres then make sure that no more than two radials are in use on the car (and those at the rear). Rationalise the tyres at the earliest possible opportunity.
3 Wheels are normally not subject to servicing problems, but when tyres are renewed or changed the wheels should be balanced to reduce vibration and wear. If a wheel is suspected of damage - caused by hitting a kerb or pot hole which could distort it out of true, change it and have it checked for balance and true running at the earliest opportunity.
4 When fitting wheels do not overtighten the nuts. The maximum possible manual torque applied by the manufacturers wheel brace is adequate. It also prevents excessive struggle when the same wheel brace has to be used in emergency to remove the wheels.

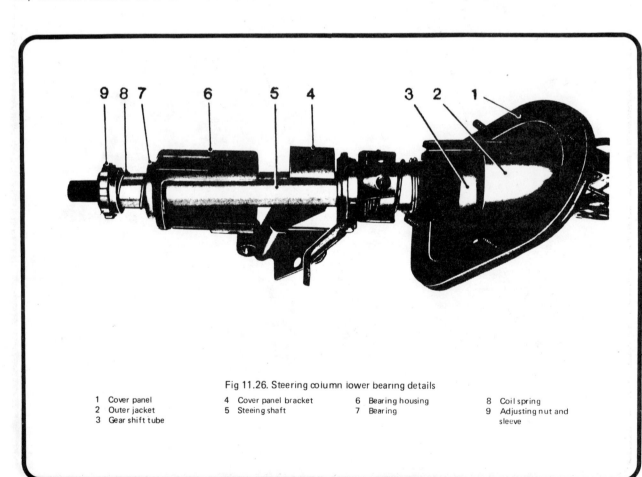

Fig 11.26. Steering column lower bearing details

1 Cover panel	4 Cover panel bracket	6 Bearing housing	8 Coil spring
2 Outer jacket	5 Steeing shaft	7 Bearing	9 Adjusting nut and
3 Gear shift tube			sleeve

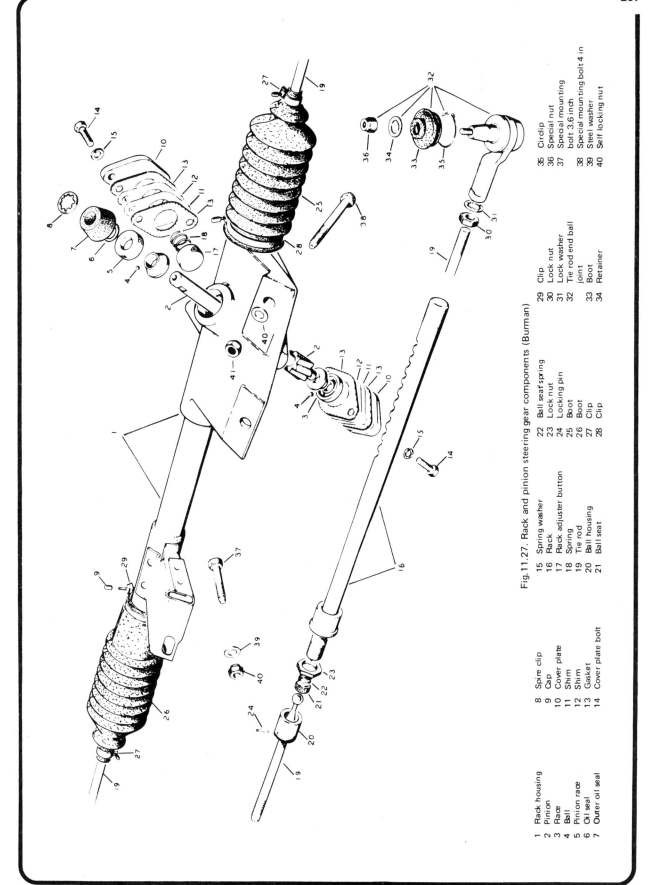

Fig. 11.27. Rack and pinion steering gear components (Burman)

1 Rack housing
2 Pinion
3 Race
4 Ball
5 Pinion race
6 Oil seal
7 Outer oil seal
8 Spire clip
9 Cap
10 Cover plate
11 Shim
12 Shim
13 Gasket
14 Cover plate bolt
15 Spring washer
16 Rack
17 Rack adjuster button
18 Spring
19 Tie rod
20 Ball housing
21 Ball seat
22 Ball seat spring
23 Lock nut
24 Locking pin
25 Boot
26 Boot
27 Clip
28 Clip
29 Clip
30 Lock nut
31 Lock washer
32 Tie rod end ball joint
33 Boot
34 Retainer
35 Circlip
36 Special nut
37 Special mounting bolt 3.6 inch
38 Special mounting bolt 4 in
39 Steel washer
40 Self locking nut

Fault Finding Chart - Suspension, Dampers, Steering

1 Binding brakes
2 Incorrect 'mix' of radial and cross-ply tyres
3 Incorrect tyre pressures
4 Misalignment of the body frame or rear axle

Symptom	Reason/s	Remedy
Steering wheel can be moved considerably before any sign of movement of the wheels is apparent	Wear in the steering linkage, gear and column coupling	Check movement in all joints and steering gear and overhaul and renew as required.
Vehicle difficult to steer in a consistent straight line - wandering	As above	As above.
	Wheel alignment incorrect (indicated by excessive or uneven tyre wear)	Check wheel alignment.
	Front wheel hub bearings loose or worn	Adjust or renew as necessary.
	Worn ball joints on track rods or suspension arms	Renew as necessary.
Steering stiff and heavy	Incorrect wheel alignment (indicated by excessive or uneven tyre wear)	Check wheel alignment.
	Excessive wear or seizure in one or more of the ball joints in the steering linkage or suspension arms	Renew as necessary or grease the suspension unit ball joints.
	Excessive wear in the steering gear unit	Adjust if possible or renew.
Wheel wobble and vibration	Road wheels out of balance	Balance wheels.
	Road wheels buckled	Check for damage.
	Wheel alignment incorrect	Check wheel alignment.
	Wear in the steering linkage, suspension arm ball joints or suspension arm pivot bushes	Check and renew as necessary.
	Broken front spring	Check and renew as necessary.
Excessive pitching and rolling on corners and during braking	Defective dampers and/or broken spring	Check and renew as necessary.

Chapter 12 Bodywork and underframe

Contents

1 General description

The combined bodyshell and underframe is an all welded unitary structure of sheet steel. Openings in it provide for the engine compartment, luggage compartment, doors and front and rear windows. The rear axle is attached to the body by arms bolted directly to it on rubber bushes and a detachable crossmember across the bottom of the engine compartment provides support for the engine and front suspension. A second detachable item is a central crossmember bridging the transmission tunnel which is the rear support of the engine/gearbox unit.

All models including the estate version have four side doors and a heater/ventilator system.

2000 SL models have the same bodyshell but additional trim and more luxurious seating and internal refinements are part of the specification.

2 Maintenance - body exterior

1 The general condition of a car's bodywork is the one thing that significantly affects its value. Maintenance is easy but needs to be regular and particular. Neglect, particularly after minor damage, can lead quickly to a further deterioration and costly repair bills. It is important also to keep watch on those parts of the car not immediately visible, for instance the underside, inside all the wheel arches and the lower part of the engine compartment. The rear of the front wheel arches consists of a detachable panel held by three screws. Make sure that this panel is intact otherwise the aperture behind will fill up with debris. If your car is not fitted with mud flaps at the front, it is strongly recommended that they are installed. Vauxhall agents will supply them made to measure for the car at a very fair price. These protect the door undersills.
2 The basic maintenance routine for the bodywork is washing preferably with a lot of water, from a hose. This will remove all the loose solids which may have stuck to the car. It is important to flush these off in such a way as to prevent grit from scratching the finish. The wheel arches and underbody need washing in the same way to remove any accumulated mud which will retain moisture and tend to encourage rust. Paradoxically enough, the best time to clean the underbody and wheel arches is in wet weather when the mud is thoroughly wet and soft. In very wet weather the underbody is usually cleaned of large accumulations automatically and this is a good time for inspection.
3 Periodically it is a good idea to have the whole of the underside of the car steam cleaned, engine compartment included, so that a thorough inspection can be carried out to see what minor repairs and renovations are necessary. Steam cleaning is available at many garages and is necessary for removal of accumulations of oily grime which sometimes cakes thick in certain areas near the engine, gearbox and back axle. If steam facilities are not available, there are one or two excellent grease solvents available which can be brush applied. The dirt can then be simply hosed off.
4 After washing paintwork, wipe it off with a chamois leather to give an unspotted clear finish. A coat of clear protective wax polish will give added protection against chemical pollutants in the air. If the paintwork sheen has dulled or oxidised, use a cleaner/polisher combination to restore the brilliance of the shine. This requires a little more effort, but is usually caused because regular washing has been neglected. Always check that door and ventilator opening drain holes and pipes are completely clear so that water can drain out. Bright work should be treated the same way as paintwork. Windscreens and windows can be kept clear of the smeary film which often appears if a little ammonia is added to the water. If they are scratched, a good rub with a proprietary metal polish will often clear them. Never use any form of wax or chromium polish on glass.

3 Maintenance - interior

1 Mats and carpets should be brushed or vacuum cleaned regularly to keep them free of grit. If they are badly stained remove them from the car for scrubbing or sponging and make quite sure they are dry before replacement. Seats and interior trim panels can be kept clean by a wipe over with a damp cloth. If they do become stained (which can be more apparent on light coloured upholstery) use a little detergent and a soft nail brush to scour the grime out of the grain of the material. Do not forget to keep the head lining clean in the same way as the upholstery. When using liquid cleaners inside the car do not over wet the surfaces being cleaned. Excessive damp could get into the seams and padded interior causing stains, offensive odours

or even rot. If the inside of the car gets wet accidentally it is worthwhile taking some trouble to dry it out properly, particularly where carpets are involved. Do NOT leave oil or electric heaters inside the car for this purpose.

4 Minor repairs to bodywork

1 A car which does not suffer some minor damage to the bodywork from time to time is the exception rather than the rule. Even presuming the gatepost is never scraped or the door opened against a wall or high kerb, there is always the likelihood of gravel and grit being thrown up and chipping the surface, particularly at the lower edges of the doors and wings.
2 If the damage is merely a paint scrape which has not reached the metal base, delay is not critical, but where bare metal is exposed action must be taken immediately before rust sets in.
3 The average owner will normally keep the following 'first aid' materials available which can give a professional finish for minor jobs:

a) A resin based filler paste.
b) Matched paint either in an aerosol can or 'touch up' tin.
c) Fine cutting paste.
d) Medium and fine grade wet and dry abrasive paper.

4 Where the damage is superficial (ie not down to the bare metal and not dented), fill the scratch or chip with sufficient filler to smooth the area, rub down with paper and apply the matching paint.
5 Where the bodywork is scratched down to the metal, but not dented, clean the metal surface thoroughly and apply a suitable metal primer first, such as red lead. Fill up the scratch as necessary with filler and rub down with wet and dry paper. Apply the matching colour paint.
6 If more than one coat of colour is required rub down each coat with cutting paste before applying the next.
7 If the bodywork is dented, first beat out the dent as near as possible to conform with the original contour. Avoid using steel hammers - use hardwood mallets or similar and always support the back of the panel being beaten with a hardwood or metal 'dolly'. In areas where severe creasing and buckling has occurred it will be virtually impossible to reform the metal to the original shape. In such instances a decision should be made whether or not to cut out the damaged piece or attempt to re-contour over it with filler paste. In large areas where the metal panel is seriously damaged or rusted, the repair is to be considered major and it is often better to replace a panel or sill section with the appropriate part supplied as a spare. When using filler paste in largish quantities, make sure the directions are carefully followed. It is false economy to try and rush the job, as the correct hardening time must be allowed between stages or before finishing. With thick application the filler usually has to be applied in layers - allowing time for each layer to harden. Sometimes the original paint colour will have faded and it will be difficult to obtain an exact colour match. In such instances it is a good scheme to select a complete panel such as a door, or boot lid, and spray the whole panel. Differences will be less apparent where there are obvious divisions between the original and resprayed areas.

5 Major repairs to bodywork

1 Where serious damage has occurred or large areas need renewal due to neglect, it means certainly that completely new sections or panels will need welding in and this is best left to professionals. If the damage is due to impact it will also be necessary to completely check the alignment of the bodyshell structure. Due to the principle of construction, the strength and shape of the whole can be affected by damage to a part. In such instances the services of a Vauxhall agent with specialist checking jigs are essential. If a body is left mis-aligned,

it is first of all dangerous as the car will not handle properly - and secondly, uneven stresses will be imposed on the steering, engine and transmission, causing abnormal wear or complete failure. Tyre wear will also be excessive.

6 Front and rear bumpers - removal and replacement

1 The front bumper is mounted as brackets attached to the frame side rails and at each end to the front wings.
2 The rear bumper is mounted similarly except that the centre brackets fit to the end panel.
3 When removing a bumper take it off by undoing the bolts holding the brackets to the bodywork, then if necessary, detach the brackets from the bumper.
4 Replacement is a reversal of this procedure. It is necessary to use sealing putty (Bostik No 5) round the bolt holes in the rear panels to keep water from entering the luggage compartment.

7 Windscreen and fixed windows - removal and replacement

1 Unlike many vehicles the Victor screens are not secured by a rubber glazing strip but with a special adhesive and caulking strip. It is essential to obtain the proper kit before doing anything else. Leaking screens can be sealed by repeating the final operations of the fixing procedure as described.
2 It must be understood that without the proper adhesive spacers and suction handles for lifting the screen into position attempts by the owner to fit a screen will be doomed to failure.
3 To remove an unbroken screen first prise off the mouldings (see Section 18). Then push a piece of thin steel wire through the adhesive. Fix a wooden handle to each end of the wire and draw it round the edge of the screen, cutting through the adhesive. Do not use a sawing action or the wire will heat up and break. Lift out the screen.
4 The screen and aperture flanges must be thoroughly cleaned of old adhesive using Bostik thinner or any other solvent which is oil free. Any traces of oil will prevent bonding.
5 Stick the spacers into position on the aperture flange (Fig 12.2) and offer up the screen with the suction handles and centralise it laterally. Stick a piece of adhesive tape from body to glass and cut it through. This will act as a reference point. Remove the screen once more.
6 Apply a thin coat of the adhesive primer to the aperture flange and the glass ½ inch wide. Do not let any get on the paintwork.
7 When the adhesive is dry fit the special butyl strip to the aperture flange with a neat joint halfway up one side.
8 Lift the glass into position with the adhesive tape, previously fitted, lined up. Press the screen down firmly and ensure that the glass makes complete contact all the way round.
9 Before fitting the mouldings check that there are no leaks by giving a water test. Leaks can be cured by using a proprietary sealer applied on the outside (Bostik No 5). Trim any material protruding round the glass and apply sealer as shown in Fig 12.3).

The rear window on estate cars is fitted in a similar manner to the rear window quarter glass on saloons.

The spacers have to be adapted to suit the lower rebate, however, and L-shaped spacers positioned as shown in Fig 12.4.

8 Doors - rattles and latch striker adjustment

1 Check first that the door is not loose at the hinges and that the latch is holding it firmly in position. Check also that the door lines up with the aperture in the body.
2 If the hinges are loose or the door is out of alignment it will be necessary to detach it from the hinges (see Section 14).
3 If the latch is holding the door correctly it should be possible to

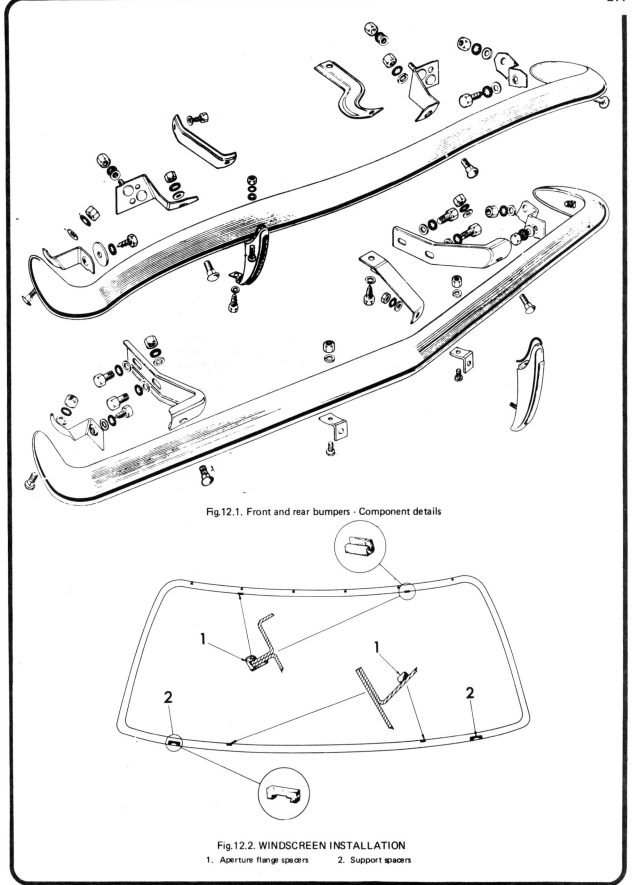

Fig.12.1. Front and rear bumpers - Component details

Fig.12.2. WINDSCREEN INSTALLATION

1. Aperture flange spacers   2. Support spacers

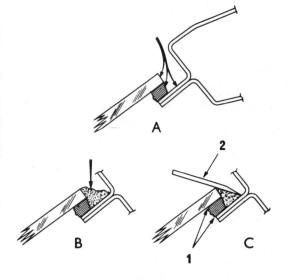

Fig.12.3. WINDSCREEN INSTALLATION AND LEAK SEALING

A Windscreen fixed with butyl strip
B Sealer in position
C Sealer being smoothed off
1 Caulking space
2 Thin bladed tool

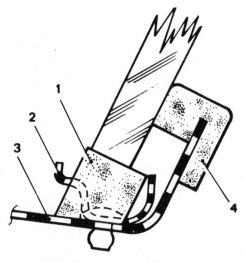

Fig.12.4. ESTATE CAR BACK DOOR WINDOW GLASS
CROSS SECTION OF WINDOW FIXING

1. Spacer adapted to fit moulding retainers
2. Retainers
3. Lower rebate
4. L shaped spacers

Fig.12.5. Door latch striker plate
A = .18 ins.

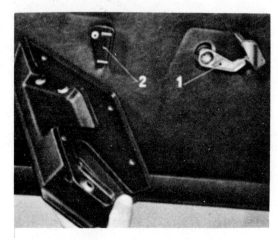

Fig.12.6. DOOR ARM RESTS REMOVAL

1. Latch handle   2. Bracket

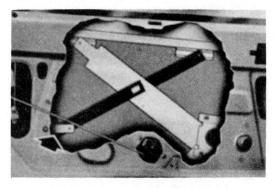

Fig.12.7. Window winder mechanism - front door
lower support channel (arrowed)

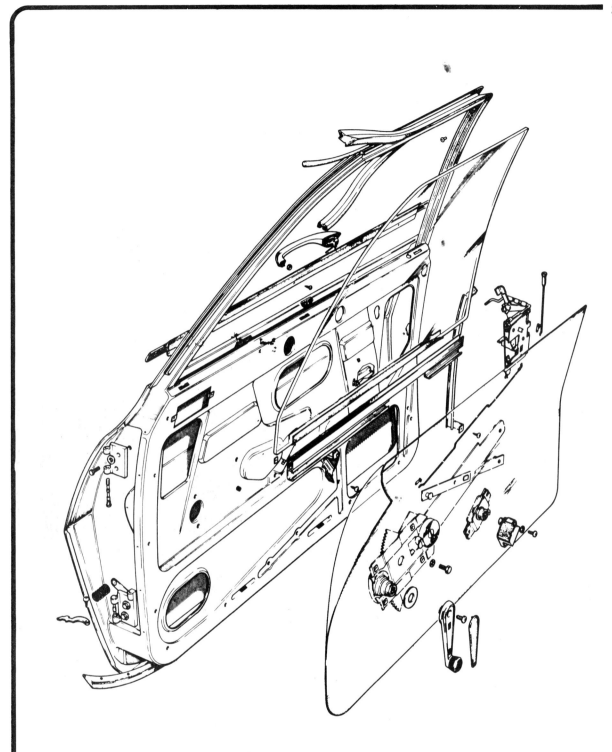

Fig.12.8. Front door - Component details

press the door inwards fractionally against the rubber weatherstrip. If not, adjust the striker plate.

4 Other rattles from the door would be caused by wear or looseness in the window winder, the glass channels and sill strips, or the door handles and remote control arm; all of which are described in the later sections.

5 The striker plate is located by four cross head countersunk screws. These can be slackened to allow vertical or horizontal adjustment. If the door is difficult to latch or is loose when latched, slightly loosen the striker plate fixing screws so that the striker plate will just move.

6 Shut the door carefully and, without touching the release button, move the door so that it is flush with the bodywork. Depress the button, open the door and tighten the fixing screws, making sure that the whole striker plate is square.

7 If there should be further indication of the door latch either hitting the inner recess of the striker or not latching firmly, check the gap between the latch and the inner recess of the striker is correct at .18 inch (4¼ mm) (Fig 12.5). This can be done by sticking a piece of plasticene in the striker recess and closing the door sufficiently to make a mark in it with the latch. If more or less than .18 inch then the packing behind the striker should be reduced or increased. If it cannot be reduced, then the door hinges must be reset. A large gap at the front edge of the door would indicate this latter situation.

8 To remove a striker which may be worn badly, first mark its outline in pencil (assuming it is correctly adjusted) and remove the locating screws. Fit the new striker with the same shims and non-slip packing and, if necessary adjust as described.

9 Doors - interior handles and cover panel trim

1 Arm rests are held by a screw and bracket. Lift the door catch and the screw is under it. Remove the screw and then move the arm rest rearward to disengage it from the bracket (Fig 12.6).

2 Where door pulls are fitted slide the caps off each end to reveal the securing screws.

3 To remove the latch and winder handles lever out the insert which is sprung into the handle and remove the securing screw.

4 The arm rest must be taken off before the latch handle under it can be removed. Do not lose the washers behind the handles.

5 The trim panel is held by clips along the sides and lower edge and by retainer brackets at the top.

6 To remove the trim first remove all the handles, ash tray containers, arm rests and door pullers. Slide a thin stiff blade (such as a putty knife) behind the edge of the trim and run it round next to each fixing clip in turn and prise the clip out of the hole in the door. Do not prise anywhere except next to a clip or the clip will probably tear out of the trim panel.

7 Lift the panel up to disengage the brackets at the top but do not dislodge the rubber retainers into which they fit.

8 To keep water from soaking the door trim panel a polythene sheet is stuck to the door behind it.

As it is difficult to remove the polythene material without ripping it, it is best to think always in terms of renewing it. It is cut to shape - the necessary holes for handles cut in it and then stuck on with a suitable adhesive such as Bostik No 3.

9 Replacement of trim pad and handles is a reverse of the removal procedure. Window winder handles should point downwards when the window is shut and straight type latch handles to the rear.

10 Window winder mechanism

1 To remove the winder mechanism which will be necessary if you wish to take the glass out first remove the inner handles, trim panel and polythene sheet from the top half of the inner door panel.

2 Close the window and wedge it. Undo the nut holding the support channel for the lower balance arm (Fig 12.7).

3 Disengage the upper arms from the channels on the lower edge of the window and then undo the screws holding the winder mechanism

to the door. It can then be taken out. Replacement is a reversal of this procedure. The lower support channel position must be set so that the upper edge of the glass is parallel with the door frame.

11 Door windows - removal and replacement

1 If no quarter lights (ventilator windows) are fitted the procedure is to remove the winder mechanism as described in the previous section. The window can then be tipped and taken out from the top of the door. On rear doors the window support channel is fitted with a roller which runs in an additional vertical guide rail so this must be engaged properly when the time comes to put the window back (Fig 12.10).

2 If quarter lights are fitted remove these first.

3 To remove the quarter lights first remove the two screws which are hidden by the weatherstrip on the front edge of the door. Then undo the screw which holds the vertical dividing strip to the inside of the door panel.

4 Remove the front section of the door outer sealing strip and ease the front section of the glass run channel from the door frame. The glass and division channel can then be lifted out (Fig 12.11).

5 If it is wished to fit a new quarter light glass undo the friction control and support bracket from the bottom edge and then draw it off the upper hinge (Fig 12.12).

6 Looseness in the quarter light friction control can be rectified by adding more plain washers to take up any slack. Assemble the plastic and spring washers correctly (Fig 12.14) and do not reduce the float clearance on the upper hinge to less than .020 inch (.5 mm) (Fig 12.13).

31 Reassembly and replacement is a reversal of these procedures. If a new main glass is to be fitted to a support channel see that the channel is correctly positioned in relation to the front edge of the glass and that the open side of the channel guides face to the inside of the car (Fig 12.16).

8 Once the glass is assembled in the door adjust the lower guide channel on the front door, if necessary, to keep the top of the glass parallel with the frame.

On rear doors the lower guide channel is adjusted in the same way. In addition the vertical guide is also adjusted to ensure that all edges of the glass are fully home in the run channels when the window is closed (Fig 12.15).

12 Front door latches, locks and handles

1 To remove any part of the lock mechanism or handle remove the interior handles and trim panel first. Undo the screws holding the remote control and disconnect the connecting rod (Fig 12.17).

2 Remove the screws holding the glass run channel retainer.

3 The latch screws can then be removed and the latch drawn out together with the locking rod (Fig 12.18).

4 The door handle can be removed after undoing the two securing nuts inside the door. The handle is withdrawn after being twisted round so that the forked ends of the locking lever will come out (Fig 12.19).

5 To remove the push button take out the spring clip from the handle boss (Fig 12.20). The lock can be removed from the push button by pressing down the spring loaded plunger in the end of the lock barrel.

6 Installation of the lock and/or handle is a reversal of this procedure. Fit the lock rod to the bar first. The fork of the handle locking lever should go each side of the bar (Fig 12.21). Replace all anti-rattle clips securely to the ends of the control rods.

13 Rear door latches, locks and handles

1 To remove any part of the lock mechanism or handle the interior handles and trim panel must be removed first.

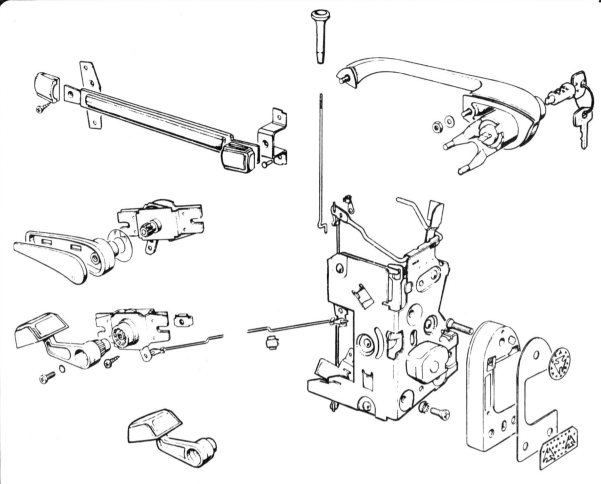

Fig.12.9. Front door lock and remote control - Component details

Fig.12.10. Window winder mechanism - rear door
Vertical guide channel (arrowed)

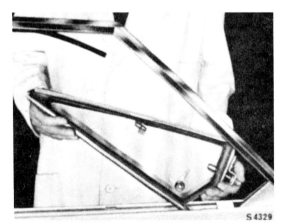

Fig.12.11. Removing front door quarter light

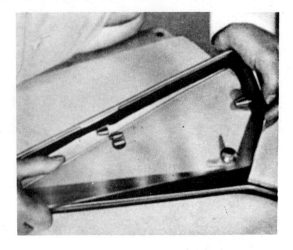

Fig.12.12. Removing quarter light glass from frame

Fig.12.13. Quarter light upper hinge setting

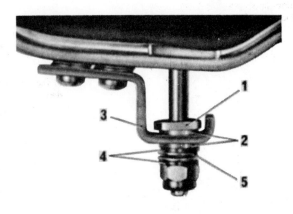

Fig.12.14. Quarter light friction control

Fig.12.15. REAR WINDOW GUIDE CHANNEL AD-
JUSTMENT SCREWS

1. Lower support channel
2. Vertical guide channel

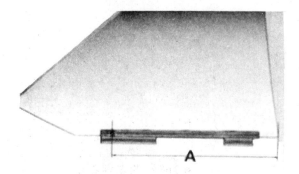

Fig.12.16. Door window support channels giving distance from front edge to front of glass
on front window (A = 4.30 ins) and from guide roller to front edge of glass
on rear window (A = 19.00 ins)

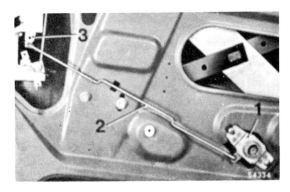

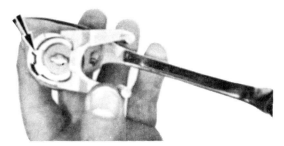

Fig. 12.20. Door handle push button locking ring - arrowed

Fig. 12.17. INTERIOR LATCH HANDLE REMOTE
CONTROLS — FRONT DOOR

1. Remote control
2. Connecting rod
3. Door latch upper plate

Fig. 12.18. Front door lock removal

Fig. 12.21. DOOR HANDLE AND LOCK - RELATIVE POSITIONS

1. Locking rod
2. Locking lever forks
3. Lock bar

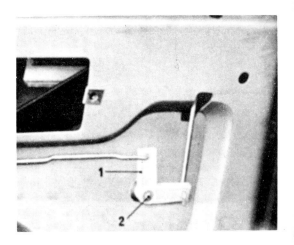

Fig. 12.19. Door outside handle removal

Fig. 12.22. REAR DOOR INTERIOR LATCH HANDLE REMOTE
CONTROL

1. Bell crank lever
2. Pivot pin

2 The control rods can be disconnected after the bell crank lever, pivot pin is punched through the pivot (Fig 12.22).

3 Removal of the lock is the same as for the front door.

4 The handle may be removed without taking the lock out in the same way as for the front door. The push button is retained with a spring circlip and a flanged washer. When replacing the washer the flanged side faces away from the handle.

14 Door hinges and check links

1 Front door hinges are welded to the body and bolted to the door whereas on the rear doors it is the other way round.

2 Door alignment in the aperture should be checked with the door latch striker plates removed so that all the door weight is taken by the hinges.

3 It is possible to adjust the door position by packing plates and movement on the detachable half of the hinge.

4 If door alignment is wrong because of worn hinge pins they can be removed by fitting a forked bar of suitable thickness under the head and driving them out. The heads of the pins face each other.

5 When a door is removed, either by removing the pins or unbolting the hinge flap the door check link must be taken off first. On front doors open the door fully and remove the screw from the end of the link. Then push the end of the spring from over the pip in the hinge plate and pull the link and spring away from the roller (Fig 12.23).

6 On rear doors remove the trim panel inside first. Then remove the rivet from the body pillar and undo the bolts holding it to the door panel (Fig 12.24). Use a new rivet when refitting the link. On later models the bracket is welded to the door panel so holes have to be drilled accordingly to fit the new one which will be bolted on (Fig 12.25).

15 Bonnet and boot lids - hinges and latches

1 The bonnet hinges are adjustable on both halves for fore and aft adjustment and vertical setting of the rear end (Fig 12.27).

2 The height of the front of the bonnet is governed by rubber buffer strips on the underside of the front edge which can be adjusted.

3 The catch engagement is also adjustable by altering the dovetail bolt. It should be set so that there is no perceptible up and down movement when the bonnet is closed and yet so that excessive pressure is not required to snap it into place (Fig 12.28).

4 The bonnet lock cable can be detached from the lock lever after the clip round the cable outer has been released from the edge of the lock unit. The unit itself can be removed by undoing the three nuts underneath (after first removing the radiator grille) (Fig 12.29).

5 The boot lid hinges are slotted on the upper arms which provide for alignment. A torsion bar on the left hand hinge provides a counterbalance to the weight of the lid. This can be renewed only when whole hinge assembly is off the car.

6 The catch striker is in the form of a lock and is adjustable up or down to enable the catch to engage when firm pressure is applied on the lid.

7 The turn button and lock for the boot lid is held in position by a spring locking plate which will release the assembly when moved to one side. The turn button may be dismantled further if necessary (Fig 12.32).

8 The catch unit can be taken out after removing the turn button and securing screws.

16 Estate version - rear door and hinges

1 The back door catch and turn button are similar to those fitted to the saloon boot lid except that the turn button has a catch release plate attached to the catch by a connecting rod (Fig 12.31).

The plate can be disengaged from the connecting rod once the retaining plate has been moved.

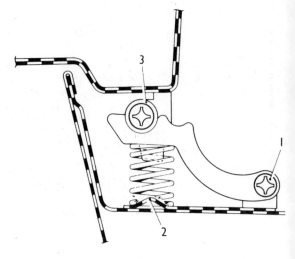

Fig.12.23. FRONT DOOR CHECK LINK DETAILS
1. Screw
2. Hinge plate pip
3. Roller

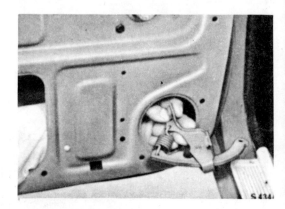

Fig.12.24. Rear door check link. Removal through inner door panel

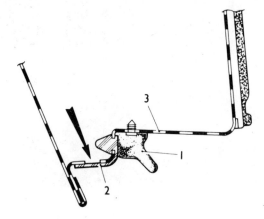

Fig.12.25. WEATHERSTRIP – DOORS
1. Weatherstrip
2. Dust seals
3. Door - underside
Water drain hole - arrowed

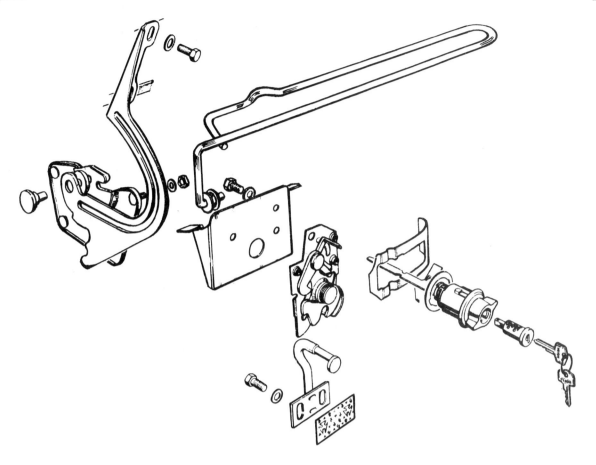

Fig.12.26. Boot lid hinges and catch - Component details

Fig.12.27. Bonnet hinge securing bolts (arrowed) showing adjustment slots in hinge

Fig.12.28. Bonnet catch - adjusting dovetail bolt

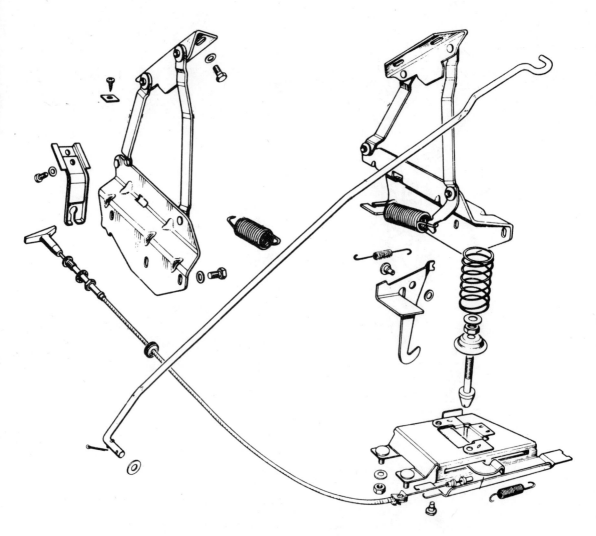

Fig.12.29. Bonnet hinge and catch - Component details

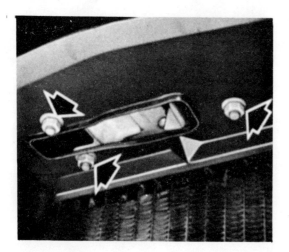

Fig.12.30. Bonnet lock securing bolts (arrowed)

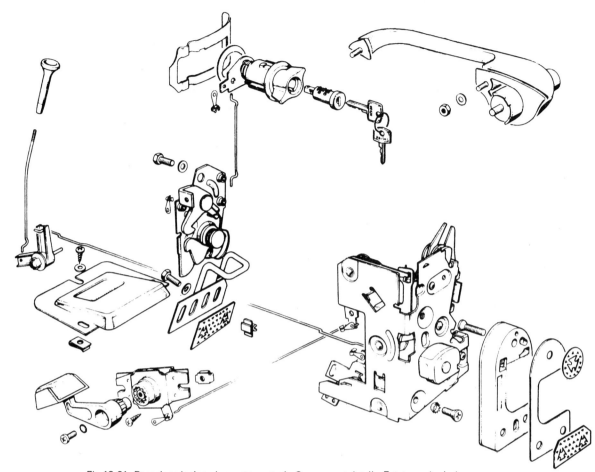

Fig.12.31. Rear door lock and remote control - Component details. Estate car back door
details also included

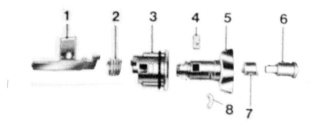

Fig.12.32. BOOT LID TURN BUTTON AND LOCK DETAILS

1. Operating shaft	3. Body	5. Turn button	7. Barrel extension
2. Spring	4. Locking bolt	6. Lock barrel	8. Keep segment

Connect the rod to the end hole on reassembly.

2 The striker is fitted to the body rear end panel. This is mounted with an anti-slip plate and is adjustable.

3 The back door hinges are both fitted with counterbalance torque rods. To remove them the door must be properly supported in the fully open position first. The weatherstrip round the door opening should be pulled off and measures taken to protect the surrounding paintwork (Fig 12.33). The hinge mounting holes are enlarged to permit adjustment of the door position.

17 Weatherstrips

1 The weatherstrips round the doors and boot lid and on the bonnet landing should be examined regularly for correct positioning and damage, and replaced if necessary.

2 The trunk lid strip is a press fit onto the flange and is quite simple to fit. Use adhesive (Bostik No 3) to retain the weatherstrips in position in addition to the fasteners.

3 The door weatherstrips are held in position by fasteners which are a pop fit into holes in the frame. The fastener is fitted into a slot in the weatherstrip. To remove the fasteners from the metalwork a blade with a slot in the end should be fitted round each fastener in turn to lift it out. Replacement is simply a matter of pressing them into the door using adhesive as additional security.

4 If the smooth surface skin is broken or the butt joint at the end of a strip is not properly sealed water will be absorbed and held by the strip which can provide a bodywork rust hazard.

5 Different strips are used for different areas of the car and cross sections are given in Figs 12.34, 12.35, 12.39 and 12.25.

18 Grilles, mouldings and exterior trim

1 The radiator grille can be removed by removing the six screws along the top edge and a stud and nut and a screw at each end (Fig 12.37).

2 All mouldings and trim strips are held by clips and it is most important to remove them properly if they are not to be distorted or the paintwork damaged. Once distorted great difficulty will be experienced in getting them to clip securely again.

3 The upper and lower windscreen mouldings are held by clips pop riveted to the aperture flange. Some early models have clips retained by pegs welded onto the flange.

The windscreen side mouldings are held by pop rivets and these must be drilled out first and the side mouldings removed because they overlap the others.

4 Get a flat blade under the upper or lower moulding next to the glass and rock the blade to ease it away. Do this near a clip.

5 On early models where the clips are held by pegs, loose pegs have to be refitted using a No 4 Pan head self tapping screw (Fig 12.36).

6 When refitting a moulding press it firmly only. If it is bumped it may damage the point.

7 The lower windscreen moulding is removed after the side moulding and scuttle upper panel are removed. If the clips are to be renewed note that all but the end ones have lay tabs which must face forward. The clips must locate in the cut-aways in the flange. When the moulding is in position ease the scuttle panel into position with the plastic finisher strip (Fig 12.38.)

8 Waist mouldings (those running along the window sills) also incorporate a rubber sealing strip between the door and glass (Fig 12.40).

Front door mouldings and strips are held by screws and for the rear door by clips which have to be fitted with a suitable hooked tool (Fig 12.41).

If a new sealing strip is to be fitted to the moulding use soapy water to aid installation.

9 Door centre pillar mouldings are held at the bottom by a pop rivet and the top by a push fit stud and clip. On estate cars a similar piece is attached by two push studs but it is first necessary to remove

Fig.12.33. Estate car. Back door hinge removal

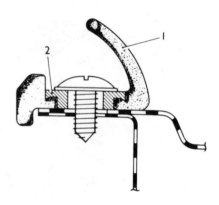

Fig.12.34. WEATHERSTRIP — BONNET LANDING
1. Weatherstrip lip - facing forward
2. Spacers for scuttle panel securing screws

Fig.12.35. Weatherstrip - Estate car back door aperture

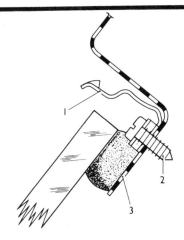

Fig.12.36. CROSS SECTION OF WINDSCREEN UPPER MOULDING
FIXING CLIP RENEWAL (EARLY MODELS)

      1. Clip (special
      2. Screw
      3. Screen aperture flange

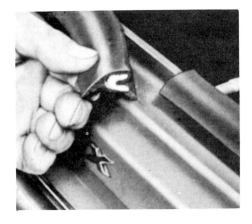

Fig.12.39. Weatherstrips - boot lid aperture

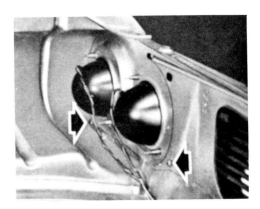

Fig.12.37. Radiator grille end fixing screw and stud and
nut (arrowed)

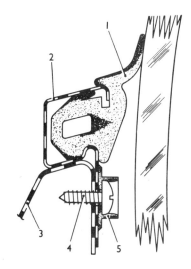

Fig.12.40. WAIST MOULDING AND SEALING STRIP
CROSS SECTION

      1. Sealing strip
      2. Moulding
      3. Outer door panel
      4. Screw (front doors only)
      5. Buffer (anti-scratch for the glass)

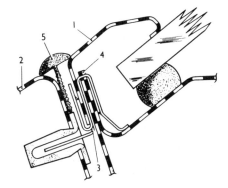

Fig.12.38. CROSS SECTION OF WINDSCREEN LOWER
MOULDING

      1. Moulding
      2. Scuttle panel
      3. Clip with long tab facing forward
      4. Recess in flange
      5. Plastic finisher

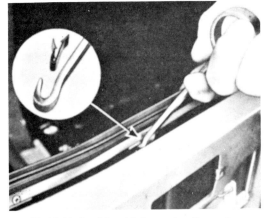

Fig.12.41. Special tool being used to fit rear door
waist moulding clips

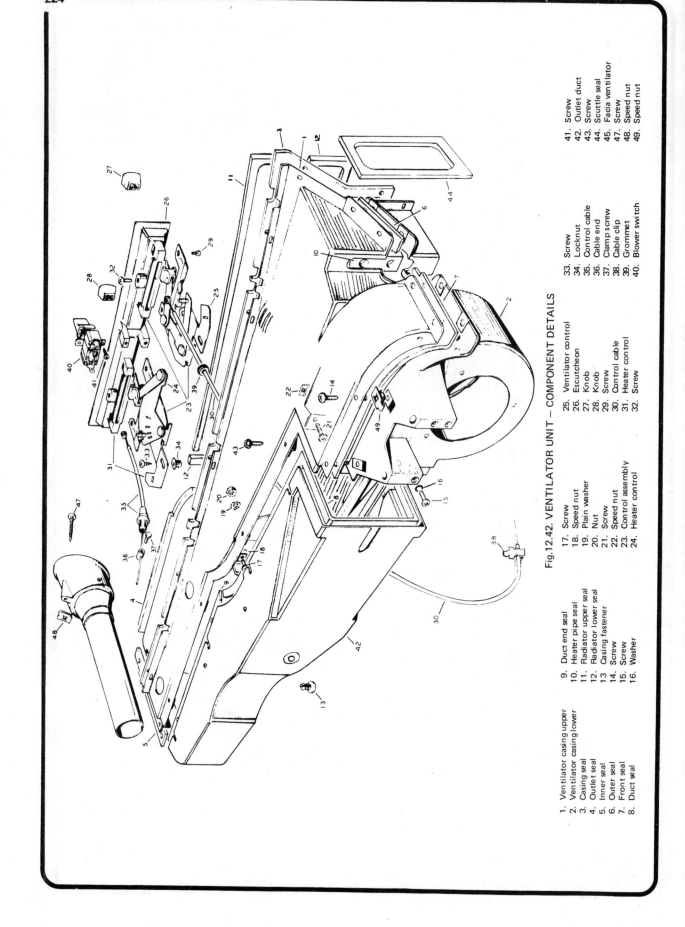

Fig.12.42. VENTILATOR UNIT — COMPONENT DETAILS

1. Ventilator casing upper	9. Duct end seal	17. Screw	25. Ventilator control	33. Screw	41. Screw
2. Ventilator casing lower	10. Heater pipe seal	18. Speed nut	26. Escutcheon	34. Locknut	42. Outlet duct
3. Casing seal	11. Radiator upper seal	19. Plain washer	27. Knob	35. Control cable	43. Screw
4. Outlet seal	12. Radiator lower seal	20. Nut	28. Knob	36. Cable end	44. Scuttle seal
5. Inner seal	13. Casing fastener	21. Screw	29. Screw	37. Clamp screw	45. Facia ventilator
6. Outer seal	14. Screw	22. Speed nut	30. Control cable	38. Cable clip	47. Screw
7. Front seal	15. Screw	23. Control assembly	31. Heater control	39. Grommet	48. Speed nut
8. Duct seal	16. Washer	24. Heater control	32. Screw	40. Blower switch	49. Speed nut

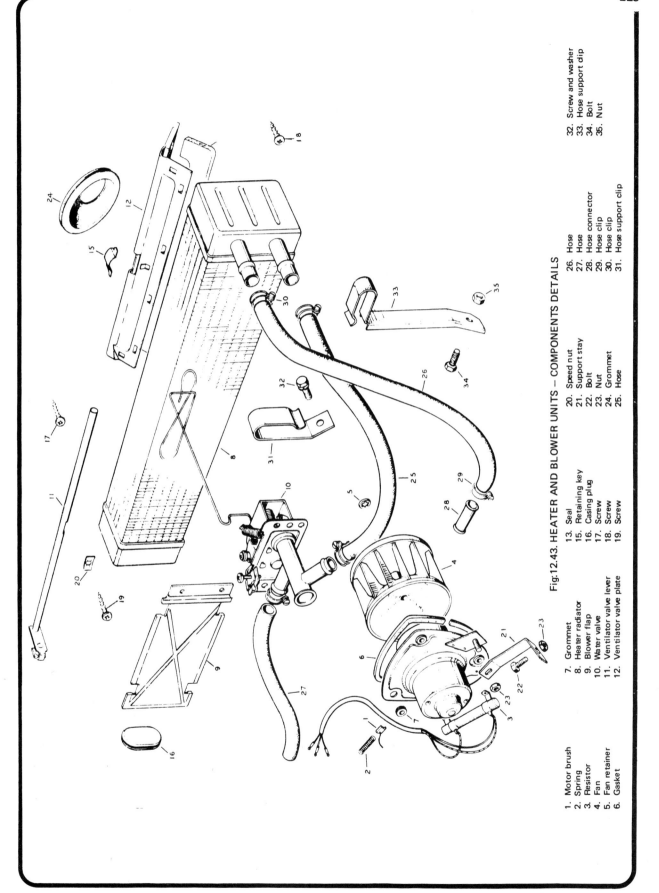

Fig.12.43. HEATER AND BLOWER UNITS – COMPONENTS DETAILS

1. Motor brush
2. Spring
3. Resistor
4. Fan
5. Fan retainer
6. Gasket
7. Grommet
8. Heater radiator
9. Blower flap
10. Water valve
11. Ventilator valve lever
12. Ventilator valve plate
13. Seal
15. Retaining key
16. Casing plug
17. Screw
18. Screw
19. Screw
20. Speed nut
21. Support stay
22. Bolt
23. Nut
24. Grommet
25. Hose
26. Hose
27. Hose
28. Hose connector
29. Hose clip
30. Hose clip
31. Hose support clip
32. Screw and washer
33. Hose support clip
34. Bolt
35. Nut

the rear quarter window upper and lower glass mouldings to get it off (Fig 12.44).

When refitting mouldings using these press studs sealing compound should be put round the base of the studs so that there is no possibility of water getting into the body pillar.

19. Heater and ventilating system - description

All cars are fitted with a through flow ventilator system by which air can enter the car through the scuttle upper panel and exhaust through outlet vents at the rear of the car.

A cable operated distribution valve directs the incoming air to the screen or car interior as selected. In addition, face level air inlets are mounted at each end of the facia which provide a direct jet of fresh air controlled individually at each outlet.

A heater radiator is installed in the main ventilation system which uses hot engine coolant to warm the air entering through the main ventilation system. The flow of water through the valve is operated by a cable and in addition, the valve is controlled thermostatically to avoid the need for continuously adjusting the cable operated control to suit the conditions inside the car. A squirrel cage blower is installed in the ventilation system to boost the air flow when needed. An independent switch is mounted on the facia between the other two controls.

20. Heater controls - adjustment

1 To make sure that the cables are properly attached at the control lever and remove the centre section of the instrument panel when they can be seen.

2 The ventilation flap spindle lever is at the right hand end of the ventilation assembly under the bonnet. Set the dashboard control lever to 'screen' and then slacken the nipple screw at the other end of cable on the flap spindle lever and press the lever against the stop on the casing (Fig 12.46). If the casing cover is removed it is easy to check the flap movement when the control is operated.

3 The water valve control cable is similar with the cable lever in the 'Cold' position see that the valve operating lever is as far back as it will go (Fig 12.47).

4 The controls and switch are easily removed by disconnecting the cables and wires and undoing the screws securing them to the escutcheon (Fig 12.48).

5 When reconnecting the blower switch wires make sure they lead away upwards so as to avoid fouling the cable controls. The centre terminal is uppermost and carries the black wire connection. The left terminal is blue/black and the other (small) terminal green/yellow.

21. Blower unit - removal and replacement

1 Disconnect the wiring harness and remove the screws holding the water valve in position.

2 Carefully lift the water valve out of the way (it is attached to a fragile capilliary tube for the thermostat).

3 Undo the three blower unit mounting screws and take it out (Fig 12.49).

4 If wished the complete ventilator and heater assembly can be removed as a unit. Once all wires, cables and water hoses are disconnected the scuttle mounting screws can be removed and the unit lifted out (Fig 12.50).

22. Seats

1 A front bench seat is mounted to a seat support on four studs which are fitted to the slide. To remove the seat the nuts should be removed and the seat together with the slide unit lifted up and out.

2 The height and rake of the seat can be altered by varying the size

Fig.12.44. Estate car - rear pillar moulding held by push fit studs and spire clips

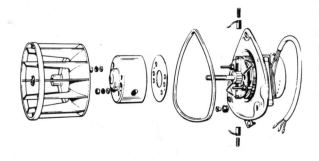

Fig.12.45. Blower unit exploded view

Fig.12.46. Ventilator flap held in 'screen' position (cover removed)

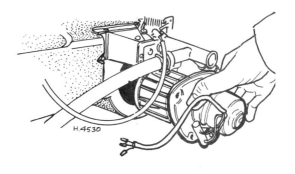

Fig.12.49. Removing blower unit

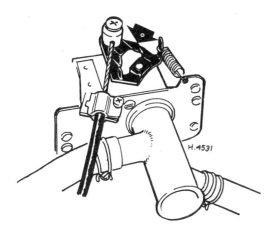

Fig.12.47. Water valve lever (arrowed) in 'cold' position

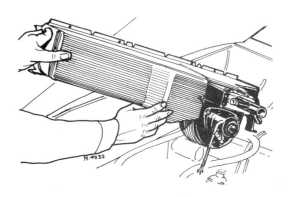

Fig.12.50. Removing complete ventilator/heater assembly

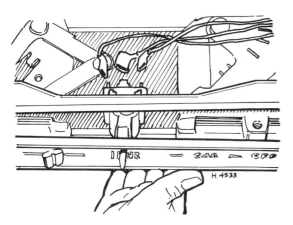

Fig.12.48. Control levers and escutcheon assembly being withdrawn

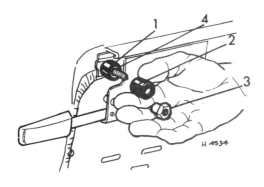

Fig.12.51. SEAT FIXING DETAILS

1. Distance piece
2. Special (additional distance piece)
3. Barrel nut (when additional distance pieces used)
4. Retainer

of the distance pieces fitted over the stud (Fig 12.51).

3 Individual front seats are mounted in the same way and the same sort of adjustment is possible.

4 The rear seat cushion can be removed after undoing the two screws - one each side - which hold it to the floor near the door sill (Fig 12.53).

5 The rear seat squab is held to the floor panel by four metal tabs-visible after the cushion has been removed and by two nuts holding it to the rear shelf panel. These are accessible from inside the boot (Fig 12.54).

6 The rear seat centre arm rest can be taken out after prising off the the finisher panel (it is stuck in place with white glaze tile adhesive!) and undoing the two screws behind (Fig 12.56).

7 On estate cars the rear seat cushion can be removed after first raising the rear edge. Then remove the two screws and retainer plates (Fig 12.57). The seat can then be lifted up and out.

8 The estate car squab and floor panel unit cannot be taken out unless the squab is first separated from the panel. Four metal tags protrude through slots in the bottom edge of the panel. Spring these out and the four retainer plates hooked into the top edge can be disengaged when the squab is lowered.

9 The base panel pivots on two shouldered bolts which can be adjusted so that the floor panel is flat and flush when lowered (Fig 12.58). Access to the catch release mechanism is also possible when squab is removed. The release cables can be adjusted to ensure proper operation of the catches (Fig 12.55).

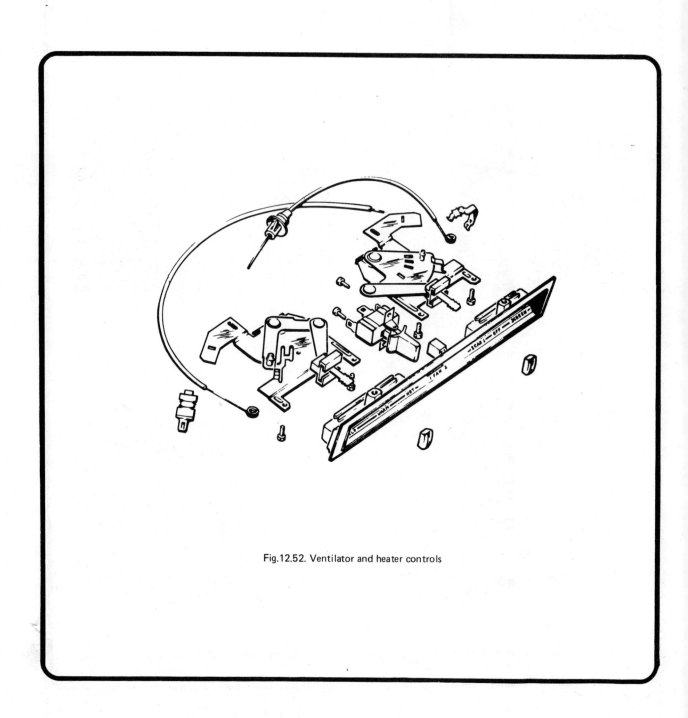

Fig.12.52. Ventilator and heater controls

Fig.12.53. Rear seat cushion fixing screw

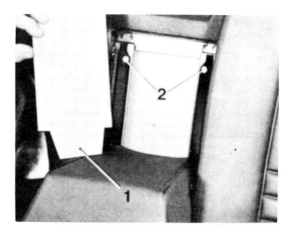

Fig.12.56. REAR SEAT CENTRE ARM REST
1. Trim panel   2. Securing screws

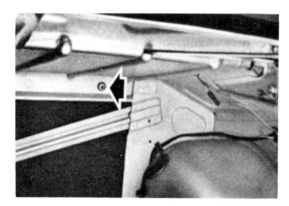

Fig.12.54. **Rear seat squab** retaining nuts (arrowed) inside the **boot**

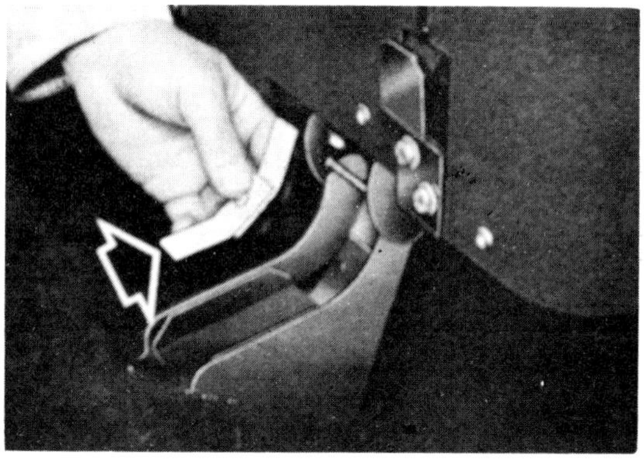

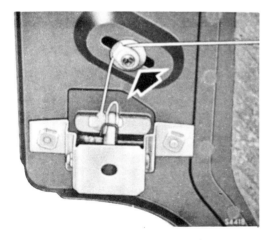

Fig.12.55. Estate car - rear seat catch mechanism - cable adjuster is arrowed

Fig.12.57. Estate car - rear seat cushion retaining plate (arrowed)

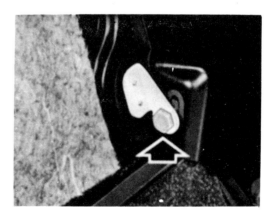

Fig.12.58. Estate car - rear seat base panel pivot bolt (arrowed)

Index

**Printed by
Haynes Publishing Group
Sparkford Yeovil Somerset
England**